The Iron Ship

GREAT BRITAIN

Ewan Corlett

THE IRON SHIP

the history and significance of Brunel's **Great Britain**

Moonraker Press

Dedicated to all who have the courage of their convictions and especially to the memory of the Great Western Steamship Company's 'Building Committee'

Port-e-Vullen and Basingstoke, 1974

This edition is specially produced
for SS *Great Britain* Project

© 1975, 1978, 1980 E. C. B. Corlett
First published 1975 by Moonraker Press
26 St Margaret's Street, Bradford-on-Avon, Wiltshire
SBN 239.00243.1
Design and layout by Anthony Adams
Fourth Impression, 1983
Printed and bound in Great Britain by Butler & Tanner Ltd
Frome and London

Contents

Author's acknowledgements

I have many acknowledgements to make.

To Museums—
Neil Cossons, formerly of Bristol City Museum, for help in locating manuscript lines and contemporary illustrations of the vessel and the Bristol City Museum for continuing and extensive help thereafter; Basil Greenhill and George Naish of the National Maritime Museum and to the Museum, who have been of considerable assistance especially in researching the history of iron ships and in providing some of the illustrations of *Great Britain*; Karl Kortum for his original photographs when surveying the *Great Britain* and for his very considerable help in the early stages of documenting the vessel; Mike Stammers of the City of Liverpool Museum; Basil Bathe of the Science Museum, who helped to clarify the history of the engines of the ship; Marshall Cubbon of the Manx Museum; the British Museum and the Imperial War Museum.

I also want to thank the State Library of Victoria, the Melbourne Public Library and the Wills Memorial Library, University of Bristol, who have supplied a considerable amount of invaluable original information. The Libraries of the Royal Institution of Naval Architects and the Institution of Civil Engineers have also been most helpful.

Many individuals have also helped my research and this book: Paul Johnstone and Ray Sutcliffe of B.B.C. 'Chronicle' have been of considerable assistance, especially at the time of the original survey and the ultimate salvage. I must thank David Moor of Vickers' St. Albans Tank and Vickers Ltd. for tank-test data which is so useful in underpinning the scientific background of the ship. Others, e.g. John Hollingworth, Commander Richard and Graham Farr have all filled in some of the background. Of course I must acknowledge a debt to my colleagues in the *Great Britain* Project who have through their interest in the ship continually helped me to unearth details of her history and construction. The Project Officer, Commander Blake, and his staff have also helped considerably. Others such as Mr. Queenan of the B.I.S.R.A. Corrosion Advice Bureau have helped with research, and my colleagues at Basingstoke and my wife have put up with me during the writing of the book. My wife Edna has also helped with much tedious although interesting research into the history of the ship and the dating of her voyages. 'Lloyd's List' have been of considerable assistance in this direction and the fact that all voyages of the ship can now be documented is due to the Libraries in Melbourne, 'Lloyd's List' and my wife in the main. Most of the drawings are by my own hand but I do want to thank those who traced them—Mrs. Palmer and Mrs. Mills.

Last but not least I must mention my secretary, Mrs. Jacqueline Iversen, without whom this book certainly could not have been brought to completion.

CHAPTER ONE

Background

I'm Queen of the Waters—the ocean world
Has never yet seen a sail unfurled
Like mine o'er its billowing heaving breast
Nor Sea Bird that carried a prouder crest.

Launch of *Great Britain*: Anon 1843

To the casual observer the shipping scene at the end of the first quarter of the nineteenth century bore a close resemblance to that of 50 or even 100 years before. True, here and there small ships with tall, thin smoke-stacks belching black smoke could be seen, but such vessels were curiosities, and the eighteenth-century observer would have felt reasonably at home with the three-decked line battleships, the frigates and the majority of the merchant ships that he could see around him.

Especially was this so with British tonnage. The British Merchant Service, for a variety of reasons, had for long relied upon Protection and had not learned to depend upon its own skill and industry: this situation was a result of a long process of development which had, ironically, encouraged the growth of competition from her prime competitor, the United States of America—the old British colonies.

Up to this time the history of the British Merchant Service was tied to a succession of Navigation Acts, the first of which was promulgated by Richard II in 1381. To encourage shipbuilding and shipping Richard laid down that Englishmen were to freight goods only in English ships. Owing to the prevailing shortage of tonnage, this law was relaxed in 1382 to allow English shippers to use foreign vessels if English were not available. It is interesting to see this pattern repeating itself today in, for example, Latin American countries, and even to some extent with American shipping.

Henry VII was a keen business man and reaffirmed the principle of using English ships for English goods in the Navigation Act of 1489. Henry VIII confirmed this in his Act of 1540 and also required ship-owners to advertise sailing dates and destinations.

The formation of the East India Company in 1600 led ultimately to a vast extension of British trade eastwards and the Navigation Acts of 1650 and 1651 insisted that goods intended for Britain, Ireland and the British colonies in America must be carried in British ships. The only exception was that if the goods originated in Europe they could be carried in ships of the country of origin.

The East India Company flourished and the modern term 'Merchant Service' owes its origin to the Honourable Company which was virtually a civilian navy. Powerful, exclusive and immensely conservative, the East India Company for a long time set the standard against which the rest of British shipping was judged.

Meanwhile, the British colonies in North America were expanding vigorously. By the middle of the eighteenth century some 30 colonies strung along the Eastern Seaboard and the St Lawrence enjoyed a large measure of self-government, and had developed a thriving coastal trade and the beginnings of a sound indigenous shipbuilding industry. Of course their trade was subject to the British Navigation Laws, relaxed slightly in their favour. Smuggling to circumvent these laws was probably one of the main causes of the American War of Independence.

The Navigation Laws thus provided a shield behind which the British Merchant Service developed with no real competition. However, the writing was on the wall and the rise of seafaring competition in North America undoubtedly weakened the Service and, of course, two can play at this game: other countries were discovering the possibilities of retaliation. Indeed the Commercial Treaty of 1786 with France, although ephemeral, was intended to encourage shipping between the two countries and was the direct result of French threats of retaliation. The War of Independence resulted in the complete repudiation of the Navigation Acts by the former British colonists. The natural result was that North American seafarers were excluded from the reserved British trades where they had been serious competitors. This gave some temporary respite to British shipowners, but a more serious cloud was now appearing on the horizon.

It must be realised that at the end of the War of Independence the legislative policies of both countries were bound to have a direct and close influence upon the development of shipping. The exclusion of Britain's most natural competitor resulted in the development of whole trades and of the ships to serve them in a very conservative manner lacking in innovation and energy,while conversely the Americans were forced into an exactly opposite policy. During the Napoleonic Wars the Americans had operated an extensive blockade-running trade, defying all comers—British, French and Spanish—with fast vessels which generally could outsail the blockading ships or the frigates charged with their control. This led to a progressive concentration upon the design of ships for speed.

The tonnage rules of England which were intended to measure the internal capacity of ships for tonnage arbitrarily assumed the depth as half the breadth, resulting in narrow, deep hulls with full ends. The Americans, although originally operating under similar tonnage laws, had soon found it necessary to scrap these in order to produce the type of ship they needed, but it was not until 1835 that the British tonnage regulations were similarly amended and even then they were little used until Moorsom's new rules of 1854 were introduced. The war of 1812 exacerbated the whole situation. Here again the same pattern applied. Fast American naval and merchant vessels were built in quantity as this was the only way to circumvent the vast numerical superiority of the British navy and its possession of an overwhelmingly powerful battle fleet. When peace came there was a dual legacy: of dislike of British maritime competition, and of building highly developed ships to outbid that competition. The first factor resulted in legal retaliation with the introduction of the American Navigation Act of 1817, and the second in the building of packets for the North Atlantic passenger and mail trade which before long did much to run British ships off that trade.

A large-scale emigration to the United States began in the years after Waterloo, and this traffic offered a natural outlet for the energies of American shipbuilders, well supplied as they were with timber and skilled seamen. It continued to develop through a great deal of the nineteenth century, largely owing to the widespread economic disruption and unemployment that had been set in motion by the Napoleonic wars. From 1825 to 1835 between 30,000 and 40,000 immigrants left Europe annually, and a decade later this figure had more than doubled. In the 40 years after Waterloo over four million passengers sailed from Britain alone. Mid-century upheavals in Europe further increased the rate.

The birth of American passenger-shipping on the Atlantic was in 1816, when the Black Ball Line built four 500-ton ships which sailed regularly on the first of the month and were driven across the ocean to a tight schedule. Built of oak and copper-fastened, they mainly traded to Liverpool:

> For once there was a Black Ball ship
> Hurrah for the Black Ball line
> That fourteen knots an hour could slip
> Hurrah for the Black Ball line

This was a new concept and very successful—other American lines soon followed. In 1821 the Red Star Line was formed and shortly after the Swallowtail, Dramatic and Black X Lines entered the service. These American ships were built from home timber and had cotton sails; but iron fastenings and fittings had to be imported from Britain, hemp from Russia and many other articles from foreign countries, so it must not be thought that the great success of this American packet trade was due mainly to the availability of cheap ships. This was not so. Success was due to the concept of 'liner' type sailings on regular dates, the hard driving of faster ships capable of carrying more cargo than those of their competitors, and relentless attention to detail as, for instance, improving blocks and gear. Generally an American packet could be handled by two-thirds the number of men required by a British ship of the same size, and provided a better service.

Competition was keen. In the first nine years of the Black Ball Line the average trip was 23 days eastward and 40 westward, with a record of just under 16 days from New York to Liverpool. Later, these times were much reduced and, for example, the *Fidelia* of the Black Ball fleet made the eastward run in 13 days 7 hrs and westward in 17 days 6 hrs. However, these packets, although sailing on regular dates, could never guarantee their date of arrival even to within wide limits, and this of course was a grave disadvantage for mail and indeed for passengers. They were, furthermore, comparatively small ships and must have been extremely uncomfortable by any reasonable standards. By 1836 some 20 American packets were running on the New York–Liverpool route and some 20 other ships to London and Le Havre. Usually about 170 to 180 ft in length, with breadths of about 36 ft and just over 1,000 tons burthen, they were longer, finer, more heavily rigged and hence faster than the ships of other nations.

In 1824 Britain at last began to relax the system of Navigation Acts, negotiating reciprocal treaties with northern European countries, and shortly after making concessions in favour of American shipping that allowed free entry into British ports. Other forces were at work modifying and improving the background to British shipping. In 1786 a Registry Act was passed which applied to every vessel of 15 tons and over. Such ships were required to carry a Registry Certificate giving their measurement, tonnage, ownership and so on, and to enter the name of the vessel and her Port of Registration on the stern. In 1814 the Indian monopoly of the East India Company was removed and in 1834 the China monopoly followed suit.

The birth of modern iron and steel shipping

Other forces meanwhile were at work in the development of shipping. In 1784 the iron 'puddling' process was invented by Cort, who then proceeded to discover methods for rolling iron plates and bars. Steam-power had begun its invasion of the traditional sources of energy, and not long after Waterloo efficient modern types of steam-engines began to appear and to reach a degree of compactness and economy that would justify fitting them in ships. Mass-production had already been started in isolated pockets such as the Marc Brunel block-making machinery at Portsmouth Dockyard and the boot-making machinery he developed for the British Army.

The paddle wheel was applied to a small canal-ship, the *Charlotte Dundas*, before the Battle of Trafalgar; by Waterloo the first paddle steamer had crossed the English Channel, and by 1827 the same applied to the Atlantic. In 1835 steam tugboats were in commercial use. A year later, in 1836, Smith and Ericsson both filed patents for screw propellers. Thus, all the necessary means were available both for a British counter-attack on American dominance of the Atlantic packet route, and for the technological explosion which has continued to this day. It was at about this point in the mid-1830s that British and American shipping policy began to diverge so widely. The inflow of immigrants into the United States and the drive westward followed by the discovery of the Californian goldfields led to an inward-turning concentration upon land development and upon sailing-ships to carry miners and emigrants to California; but before this happened the Americans were to produce the ultimate development of the sailing merchant ship—the so-called Clipper ship.

The Baltimore brigs and schooners mentioned earlier, which originated in the War of Independence and the war of 1812, were quite unlike the normal sailing merchant-ship, having a great beam well forward, a long fine run and a high bow, but with raked stem, sternpost and masts. They also incorporated a most important feature: long waterlines of slow curvature without the apple-cheeked entry normal at that time. However, the true Clipper form was in no way apparent in the Baltimore Clippers and it was really the China trade which gave rise to the three successive types: the Opium Clippers, the American, and later the British Tea Clippers.

Between 1830 and 1850 the disreputable opium trade led to the building of a number of Clipper Brigs and one or two Ships, some of which were American but most British. As this trade was entirely against the laws and wishes of the Chinese government, and as the ships were also preyed upon by pirates, speed was at a premium and hand-picked crews were needed. The famous British Opium Clipper *Falcon*, built in 1824, was described by one of her officers as having 'a bow round and full above the waterline but sharp as a wedge in her entrance below. Her midship sections gave her a long flat floor which commenced a clean run aft.' The Tea Clipper really originated in the repeal of the East India Company's China monopoly in 1834. Before this time tea and silk were brought to England in slow East Indiamen which were not very different from the ships of 100 years earlier. The introduction of the Tea Clipper is to the credit of the Americans, who began to load in Canton for New York and Boston in the early 1840s. Competition between them soon led to the appearance of the first great Yankee Clipper, the *Rainbow*. This vessel of 700 tons burthen was launched in January 1845, and cost only $30 a ton to build. She had the true Clipper features: a long, sharp entrance with concave waterlines; her maximum breadth well aft but with a clean-lined run. She also had a greater length/breadth ratio than any other ship of the day. *Rainbow* was followed by the great *Sea Witch* which went into service towards the end of 1846 and soon acquired an awesome reputation.

Both these ships attracted much attention and controversy. On the launching of the latter, the *New York Herald* commented:

The splendid ship *Sea Witch* whose peculiar model and sharp bows have for the past few months attracted so much attention was launched yesterday. The *Sea Witch* is for a vessel of her size the prettiest model we have ever seen and much resembles the model of the steamer *Great Britain*, only on a smaller scale. . . .

From there on the Clipper ship developed rapidly, greatly accelerated in the U.S. by the discovery of gold in California. The great builder, Donald McKay, built for all the three great Clipper routes—China, Australia, California—and it was not until 1850 that competitive British tea- and later wool- and emigrant-Clippers made their appearance; *Cutty*

Sark (which we are privileged to have with us today) was launched in 1869. By the time British Clippers appeared on the scene the writing was on the wall, both for nineteenth-century American shipping generally and for the sailing ship in particular.

The British engineer

In the eighteenth century the term 'engineer' was generally applied in a military sense, and the early technical development of industry, steam-engines, canals and so on was by men who had little or no formal training in what we now call engineering. Some were gifted amateurs, others were mechanics of ability and drive; both worked towards a common end. Men such as Watt, Trevithick, Newcomen, Maudslay were all really mechanics who became engineers, forced on by the hothouse atmosphere that was developing in Britain at the beginning of the nineteenth century. They were a new type—pragmatic, forceful, technically practical—paralleled by isolated individuals in other countries, particularly America, but not by a whole new breed of men as in Britain.

At the same time this period saw the birth of the true professional engineer, epitomised perhaps by the two Brunels, Marc Isambard and his son, Isambard Kingdom. Marc, later Sir Marc, was a French naval officer formally trained in the French manner in mathematics and naval construction—a training superior to anything available in its field in Britain in the latter half of the eighteenth century. As a Royalist forced to emigrate by the Revolution, Marc Brunel first tried his hand in the United States where he made rapid progress as a consulting engineer. Approached to design block-making machinery for the British government, he came to Britain in 1803 and designed the celebrated plant, some of which exists to this day. This brilliantly successful technical effort established for him a firm position and was probably the first example of true mass production. Subsequently he applied the same type of approach to the production of army boots, veneer-cutting machinery, the development of circular saws, the design and construction of bridges and the design of shields for tunnelling under the Thames. Sir Marc, like his son, was a man of wide interests, and there is some evidence that in 1820 he was undertaking the tank-testing of model hulls in a circular tank, some of them being self-propelled and even screw-driven. Brunel's famous Triangle engine patent of 1822, described later, is a remarkable technical achievement for the day, and it must be concluded that as a mechanical engineer this man was a genius, superior even to his celebrated son.

Isambard Kingdom inherited technical ability from both sides of his family and was, of course, half-English by birth and totally so by up-bringing. He received a formal education in both Britain and France, and learned his profession at the knee of his celebrated father. Thus, in these two men we see a fusion of the academic, cultivated eighteenth-century French approach to engineering with the pragmatic, thrusting and immensely productive approach typical in Britain at that time.

Isambard Kingdom Brunel was perhaps the greatest of the nineteenth-century engineers—certainly one of the most dynamic and versatile. During his lifetime he built 25 railways in Britain, Italy, India and Ireland; five suspension bridges and 125 other bridges; eight piers and harbour systems; and, of course, the three ocean-going steamships *Great Western*, *Great Britain* and *Great Eastern*. He also invented the railway cargo-container and designed a prefabricated hospital with 1,500 beds which was provided with forced cooling—a primitive form of air-conditioning—and good plumbing. Our interest in him is that he was the first man to embody all the elements of the modern ship in one hull: metal construction, steam-driven screw propeller, and large size deliberately aimed at good economics.

In some ways the last factor is the most important, but it was only made possible by iron construction. Today it is difficult to appreciate the step that Brunel's views represented. As mentioned earlier, the typical American packet was about 170 ft long. Inherently, therefore, its speed was limited by its wave-making resistance to perhaps 14 knots, while its weight-carrying capability per unit volume was small. Brunel was the proponent of the axiom that a ship's power and fuel requirements for a given speed decreased relatively with size. The rapid development of the size of British ships compared with those of other nations was to a considerable extent responsible for Britain's increasing maritime predominance, and was directly the result of the thinking of I. K. Brunel.

These British engineers were steam men, railway men and men of iron. I. K. Brunel was a civil engineer, his father a civil and mechanical engineer; yet both of them felt capable of designing ships, and there is no doubt but that Sir Marc's Triangle engine of 1822 was much in advance of contemporary marine machinery. Such men had no time for tradition in engineering and were impatient of established practices. They saw clearly the way that ships were to develop. Whether they were aware of the shipping position in which the country found itself is not known, but they could supply the tools with which the future could be built. In essence these were size, iron and steam.

Ships would have to be increased in size; the range, payload and economic return of large ships were clearly seen to be altogether superior to those of smaller vessels.

The large wood ships were notoriously weak, and indeed with techniques of the day they were rapidly approaching the technical limit of size. As wooden ships became larger, difficulties with their fastenings increased, and anyway they were unsuited for screw-propulsion because of their lack of rigidity and their characteristic 'hog'.* In terms of cost, too, wooden ships were expensive; indeed, the cost of the hull of a large wooden steamer around 1845 was 40 per cent more than that of an iron ship. Weights too were in favour of iron construction, the iron hulls of the day being only 70 per cent. of the weight of a corresponding wooden ship. With so little weight and space left over by the crude machinery of the day and its coals, this was crucial. The railway engineers, and especially the bridge-builders such as Brunel, knew the strength-to-

* 'Hog' is a tendency for ships to 'droop' at bow and stern.

7

weight efficiency of iron; they also knew its ease of fabrication once the daunting problems of methods of working had been solved.

Steam had become a way of thought in Britain. Faith in it was almost religious and demonstrable progress in reducing the size of engines and of increasing efficiency was made from year to year.

This, then, was the commercial picture in 1835. Britain, with about 2,500,000 tons of shipping, much of it very inferior to that of its prime competitor, the United States, was faced with more or less open competition on all her trade routes. On the Atlantic that competition took the form of fast, efficient American vessels more economic by any standard than that of the bulk of British shipping.

Appearances deceive, however, and beneath the surface and in the minds of gifted men a revolution in ship-design and operation was being conceived. The next decade, from say 1835 to 1845, was to see fantastic changes which started an ever-increasing explosion of marine technology and design that is still with us today and, if anything, is accelerating. The way for Britain to conduct this fight was not with American weapons—sail, wood, canvas—but with the ideas, the tools and the production methods which were developing and which were now about to coalesce into the first modern ship—constructed of metal, thus attaining rigidity, lightness and water-tightness in one step; mechanically driven, thus attaining independence of favourable winds for making a passage; screw-propelled, thus attaining propulsion whose efficiency was not affected by draught and which left the hull clear of encumbrances; of modern proportions and good hull-form. Appropriately, the name of that first modern ship was *Great Britain*.

CHAPTER TWO

The conception
of the 'Mammoth'

By 1835 steam tugs were in use: an American paddler, the *Savannah*, had made a crossing of the Atlantic, but her engines were used only intermittently as auxiliary power; a Nova Scotian-built paddler, *Royal William*, had made the first crossing with paddles working all the way (in 1832);[1] paddle-propulsion had been developed for coastal and inland waters vessels; and ambitious eyes were being cast on the oceans of the world—especially the Atlantic—with a view to steam navigation. The scene was set for the entry of the merchant ship as we know it today.

Isambard Brunel was at this time consulting engineer to the Great Western Railway, having had his plan and layout for the railway adopted in the face of bitter opposition and much inquiry. This, and his work on the Bristol Floating Harbour, gave him a close connection with Bristol. Towards the end of 1835, the directors of the Great Western Railway Company met at Radley's Hotel, Blackfriars, to discuss railway matters. The length of the line from London to Bristol was commented upon and apparently Brunel, perhaps as a joke, remarked that it could be made longer by building a steamboat (to be called *Great Western*) to sail between Bristol and New York.[2] Some of the directors took the idea seriously and formed a committee to examine the suggestion. Thomas Guppy, Captain Claxton, R.N., and William Patterson were appointed to make a tour of British ports in order to collect information. Thus began a remarkable association in shipbuilding of men of diverse interests and backgrounds who nevertheless worked together extremely well for the great benefit of British shipping.

Thomas Guppy was at this time a Bristol merchant. He was nine years older than Brunel and by training an engineer, having started his career with Maudslay, Sons & Field, the marine-engine builders. Fifteen years later he emigrated to Italy where he conducted a mechanical-engineering business. William Patterson was a Bristol shipbuilder and clearly a man of considerable ability—sound perhaps rather than brilliant. He was to build the *Great Western* and to be closely concerned with the *Great Britain*. Captain Claxton was a half-pay naval officer, 16 years older than Brunel. He was Quay Warden when Brunel was involved in the improvement of the docks at Bristol, and thus began a close friendship that lasted until Brunel's death in 1859. Claxton once saved Brunel's life, and he completed his last work, the Clifton suspension bridge. Their relationship was clearly one of mutual respect and affection, and when *Great Britain* was aground in Dundrum Bay, Brunel insisted that Claxton be in charge of the salvage to ensure its correct execution. His attitude to Claxton shows clearly in a letter he wrote in May, 1839, regarding a Maudslay tender for engines:

My dear Claxton, What a state you are in if the *Great Western* is not arrived and how busy you are if she is—yet what I have to say is worth your hearing. . . .[3]

This triumvirate reported to the directors at the beginning of January 1836 and emphasised the economic advantages inherent in large vessels. Brunel inserted a crucial statement regarding the fuel economy of large engines compared with small, and the better resistance and pay-load carrying ability of large ships:

It is well known that the *proportional* consumption of fuel decreases as the dimensions and power of engines are increased and consequently a large engine can be much more economical than a small one. The resistance of vessels on the water does not increase in direct proportion to the tonnage. The tonnage increases with the cubes of their dimensions while the resistance increases at about their squares, so that a vessel of double the tonnage of another capable of containing an engine of twice the power does not really meet with twice the resistance. Speed therefore would be greater with the larger vessel or the proportion of power in the engine and consumption of fuel may be reduced.

The second part of this statement applies to both sailing vessels and steamships, and the whole is a clear enunciation of a law of naval architecture which may have been 'well known' to Brunel but, it should be said, was hotly disputed at the time. In fact his statement relates to the frictional resistance of water against the hull of a ship, and for ships that are relatively slow in relation to their size (such as modern super-tankers) it is fundamental. It shows, therefore, that he was very well aware that if steamships were to succeed they had to be large in order to carry sufficient fuel and payload to make them economically viable.

The report to the committee concluded 'That for the purpose of carrying cargo as well as passengers, the most speedy and certain passage, the greatest economy of power, and the best assurance of a profitable return for the capital investment, would require a vessel of at least 1200 tons'. It was estimated that such a vessel would, if properly designed, regularly make the outward journey in well under 20 days and return in 13. At that time the average outward journey by sailing packet took 36 days, and 24 homeward, although as we have seen these times could be much bettered, though not on a regular basis. It is interesting to compare this forecast with the *Great Western*'s actual performance. The first 34 voyages, in other words from her first up to the end of 1844, were made at an average of 15 days 12 hrs westward and 13 days 9 hrs east: a remarkable confirmation of the predictions made by the committee.

The report was conclusive. The directors—including a certain Robert Bright, later to play a significant part in the history of the *Great Britain*—decided to form the Great Western Steamship Company. Patterson was appointed to superintend the building of the ship, a building committee consisting of Claxton, Guppy and Brunel directing operations. This committee usually met once a week, and the *Great Western* was soon under construction. A celebrated controversy now arose. The British Association for the Advancement of Science held a meeting in Bristol in August, 1836, which was addressed by Dr Dionysius Lardner on the subject of steam navigation on the Atlantic. Lardner had become convinced that resistance was directly proportional to displacement, and that a vessel of twice the overall dimensions of another would require eight times the horsepower for a given speed. In a lecture delivered in Liverpool in December 1835 he had concluded that the best vessels for the voyage would be of approximately 800 tons, 200 nominal horsepower, and stowing 400 tons of coal. The utmost limit such a vessel could steam would be approximately 2,500 miles, and hence he concluded that 'Making a voyage directly from New York to Liverpool was perfectly chimerical, and they might as well talk of making a voyage from New York or Liverpool to the moon'. Lardner was firmly convinced that the Atlantic route should be from Valentia in Ireland to St Johns in Newfoundland, a distance of 1,900 miles. At the meeting in Bristol Lardner asserted confidently that it would be impossible for *Great Western* to succeed in crossing the Atlantic and that it could only be accomplished by taking on relays of coals.[4]

Brunel, whose correct views have been stated above, took part in the discussion and criticised Lardner's calculations, but without effect. This meeting was of far-reaching significance as the citizens of Bristol were so impressed by Lardner's claims that the share capital of the company was much under-subscribed and the original intention of building several consorts for *Great Western* had to be shelved. So, although Brunel was entirely correct in his estimates, Lardner effectively ruined the chances of the Great Western Steamship Company to become the great line of the Atlantic, and thus provided Samuel Cunard with the opportunity.

Great Western was launched on 19 July 1837, and on 18 August sailed for London to take her engines on board, though her crankshaft had been forged locally and was carried as cargo. While she was sailing back to Bristol to make a departure for New York, the felt lagging on the boiler ignited and the ship was beached. Claxton was below in the engine-room when an unconscious Brunel fell on him from the deck above. Claxton carried him from the bilge-water in which he was lying to the deck, undoubtedly saving his life. The ship—the first steamship specially designed for the Atlantic route—sailed on 8 April 1838 for New York and arrived on Monday, 23 April, with a quarter of her bunkers still full. She sailed on her return voyage on 7 May and arrived in Bristol on the twenty-first, although nearly a day had been lost through a mechanical breakdown. Thus began the Atlantic ferry service, and the committee charged with the design and construction of the ship must have felt well satisfied with a difficult job brilliantly carried out. To quote the Managing Director, 'The *Great Western* [was] the first ship regularly laid down, equipped and sent to sea, for the purpose of establishing a steam line between America and England.' The race was on and Britain was winning, as a shipping writer was to note in 1840: 'Two years have now

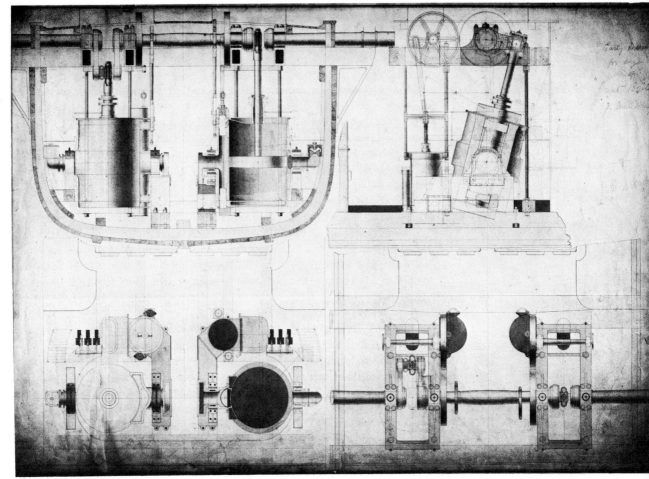

1 First set of oscillating engines proposed by Maudslay, Son & Field

elapsed since the Atlantic has been crossed by English Steamers and as yet not a single American one is afloat. This is passing strange . . . and the carrying trade of which the Americans used to think so much is fast getting into our hands.' This achievement was clearly of great promise to The Great Western Shipping Company and to Britain, but, as with all Atlantic liners since, it was soon found that there was a crying need for a consort.[5] Indeed, as soon as it was obvious that the *Great Western* was a success, the directors began to consider providing one. In the Bristol newspaper of 29 September 1838 (during *Great Western*'s fourth voyage) it was announced that

the Great Western Steamship Company are about to build another vessel of equal size to the *Great Western*; she will be called the *City of New York*. A large cargo of African oak timber has been purchased for this and further ships.

The directors, however, later came to the conclusion that 'Steamships of larger dimensions would offer better chances of remuneration'.

The early history of the steamship *Great Britain* is so beset with changes that perhaps one may be forgiven for labelling the various ships in modern fashion. The plans for the *Great Britain* (the *City of New York*) may be labelled GB1; it was to be of the same dimensions as *Great Western*, i.e. 236 ft from the forepart of the figurehead to the after part of the taffrail, and 205 ft on the keel. Breadth was to be 35 ft 4 in., depth of hold 23 ft 2 in., draught about 16 ft 8 in., and displacement approximately 2,300 tons. Size soon started to increase. The directors 'guided by the suggestion of that superior man', as Claxton declared,[6] were clearly doing their sums, and the larger ship envisaged was disclosed by Captain Claxton in a letter of November 1838. It was to have a keel of 254 ft in length, and a breadth around 40 ft, with a depth of hold of about 23 ft.[7]

From tender drawings by Maudslay, Son & Field (now in the Science Museum) for engines for this ship an idea of the preliminary design of GB2 can be determined. Fig. 1 shows the vessel to be of wood construction, with vertical-wall sides like those of the *Great Western*, a moderate rise of floor, and fitted with oscillating engines. The breadth scales at 38·5 ft. The old builders' measurements from the Tonnage Laws of 1773 which were used by builders for contract purposes until 1854 (when the Moorsom Law was passed—although an Act of 1835 had in fact promulgated a new Tonnage Law that was rarely used) were based on the 'length of keel'. Claxton quotes the length of keel of GB2, and since we know the breadth at that stage to have been 38 ft 6 in. we can calculate the overall length at 228 ft, or thereabouts.*

In November 1838, Brunel wrote to Claxton about the power of the new ship:

It is assumed that the midship section and general resistance of the new vessel will be the same as that of the *Great Western* but that the speed must be increased in the ratio of 10·6 to 12 [knots]. It is assumed also that an increase of speed from 7 to 9¼ requiring the power to be doubled or at about the square root of the fifth power the increase of speed from 10·6 to 12 miles therefore requires an increase of cylinder of 73 to 85 in. diameter and it is proposed to cut off the steam always at the fifth notch at about five-twelfths of a stroke and this will require an increase in cylinders to 87·5 say 88 in.

The boilers to be of sufficient capacity to supply these cylinders working at the fifth notch and with the pistons travelling at the rate of 220 ft per minute.

Query, would it not be better to have the cylinders somewhat smaller say 84 in. and the pistons to travel at an average rate of 240 ft.?

The cylinder diameter of 73½ in. referred to *Great Western*, so Brunel was working from this ship to the new one. In the light of modern knowledge his conclusion was not far wrong and would have formed a reasonably accurate guide. The final screw-machinery as built was designed for a piston speed of 216 ft per minute.

In January 1839 the first iron proposal was described, again by Captain Claxton in a letter, with a length of keel of 260 ft, a breadth at paddle-shaft of about 41 ft and a depth of 24 ft, incorporating 88-in. trunk piston engines. This ship, GB3, would have had an overall length of about 295 ft.

The size of the ship seems to have increased continually through this

* The old builders' law defines the length of keel as the length along the keel from the sternpost to a perpendicular dropped from the forepart of the stem minus ⅗ of the extreme breadth over plank. The tonnage was derived from the formula (L × B²)/188.

13

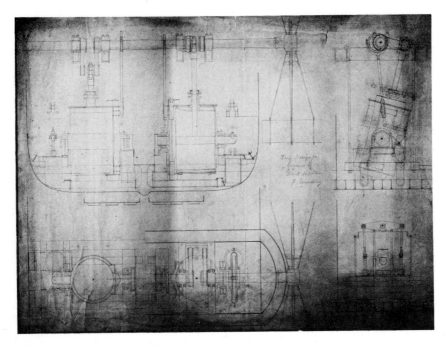

2 Maudslay's second set of oscillating engines for iron GB.4

period. GB1, 2 and 3 had tonnages by the old 'Builders' Rule' of approximately 1,340, 2,000 and 2,430 tons respectively, and by April 1839 the dimensions had increased again, when tenders for engines with cylinders of 100 in. in diameter and 7 ft stroke were invited. It may be surmised that the ship was still of normal shape, as Fig. 2. shows a tender by Maudslay probably for this machinery. Here again a wall-sided midships section is used with a curved plate keel. Twin oscillating cylinders are shown in a hull of approximately 49 ft breadth and 29 ft depth.

The final form of *Great Britain* must have been under development at this time, because fabrication of the iron keel began on 19 July 1839.[8] This presumably was the reason why—sometime between April and June—Brunel asked Messrs Maudslay and a Mr Humphreys to prepare designs for cylinders of 120 in. in diameter. Maudslay's, however, wished to put forward their new patent for twin-cylinder engines (presumably of Vee type) and Brunel induced the directors to postpone their decision on the choice of engines on two occasions. Humphreys' estimate was appreciably less than that of Maudslay's, who were favoured by Brunel. Messrs Hall's, the licensees of Humphreys for his patent, recommended that as much new plant would be required in their works to construct these engines the Great Western Company should undertake the construction themselves.

Brunel reported in June 1839 to the Board that he had no doubts that both the Humphreys and Maudslay engines were excellently adapted to their particular case and stated that the choice would depend upon other circumstances than the construction of the engines.[9] He considered that

14

the prime factors were the relative costs and the advantages of forming an establishment, which would become necessary anyway for the repair and maintenance of the company's engines, compared with the responsibility and experience in all details of an established manufacturer to which he attached very great value.

Maudslay's tender was for four 75-in. cylinders which he calculated to be equal to a pair of ordinary engines of about 106 in.* On the assumption that the machinery would be fitted on board in London, he assessed Maudslay's estimate at £40,000; whereas if the engines were to be fitted on board in Bristol, and allowing for freight, insurance, etc., he estimated a cost of approximately £43,150. He felt, however, that the cylinder bore should be increased to 77¾ in. which would be equivalent to Humphreys' pair of 110-in. cylinders, and on a true comparative basis he estimated Maudslay's quotation at £45,500 compared with Humphreys' of £30,700. But he was not happy about the latter:

I cannot help expressing the fears I entertain that Mr Humphreys is over sanguine and that the cost would greatly exceed the sum named. . . . The items seem to me to be moderate prices only for each article named and I see no allowance for those alterations, damages and waste of parts and a variety of other contingencies which in a piece of machinery of this magnitude and novelty is certain to amount to a very large sum. . . .

In his estimate of the fittings of smaller parts I think also he has greatly underrated them. . . . I cannot but come to the conclusion . . . that the first outlay will be fully as large or probably larger by adopting the plan and making our own engines than by employing a manufacturer. . . .

Brunel did recognise that by building themselves the Company would gain valuable tools and shops and much experience, but his fear was that the risk of the undertaking would be too great for a newly formed establishment:

The making of the vessel itself is no mean effort and to superadd the construction of the largest pair of engines and boilers yet made and upon a new plan is calculating very much upon every effort being successful and particularly upon the continued assistance of those who hitherto attended to the subject; as it must be well known to the Directors that if Mr Guppy for instance should be prevented from giving his time as he has hitherto done or that Mr Humphreys should from illness or other cause leave us the manufactory would be brought to a stand and the loss would be serious. . . .

He considered that the question should not revolve upon cost. His finely-reasoned argument concluded by giving the advantages of manufacturing the engines at Bristol, but added that they were

fully counterbalanced by that of the experience in all the details which is brought into operation in an old established manufactory and a great relief from responsibility and risk obtained by contracting from the whole work.

This was calm and sane advice from a man who was certainly not impetuous. The Brunel connection with Maudslay's was of long standing. The original models of the elder Brunel's block-making machinery were constructed by Maudslay in 1803 as was the plant itself. The pumping-machinery in the Thames tunnel construction had also been built by Maudslay's, and clearly Isambard felt he could and should rely on them.

* At the time a cylinder was called an engine, so four cylinders would be four 'engines'.

Nevertheless, the directors decided to make the machinery themselves, to erect it and fit it in the ship.

We know the arrangement of Humphreys' type of engine from the much smaller set fitted in the packet *Dartford*. Essentially the patent consisted of an inverted trunk engine with a perforated piston. The connecting-rod penetrated the piston as shown and the hole and cross-pin were sealed by a steam-tight domed cover. A recess in the cylinder bottom accepted this dome at bottom of stroke. Attached to the piston was a hollow skirt of rectangular general cross-section, but radiused in the plane of the connecting-rod, which was located by a steam-tight gland-bearing at the top of the cylinder. The piston and skirt then formed a dual unit which moved up and down in a true vertical. Thus the need for a cross-head did not arise and the cylinder assembly was not unlike that of a modern car-engine. Slide-valves and eccentric rod, air-pump and hot-well were all quite conventional. The main virtue of the engines was their low overall height, surely not very important to the new ship. The disadvantages were numerous—complexity and inaccessibility, a grave danger of hydraulic lock, and lubrication difficulties with the piston cross-pin bearing.

Francis Humphreys was appointed Engineer-in-Charge by the company, but almost immediately found that the 30 in.-diameter intermediate paddle-shaft was beyond the capacity of existing forge hammers. Now Humphreys was already in contact with James Nasmyth, the engineer, over the supply of machine-tools for the construction of the engines,[10] and, in fact, much of the machinery for the works at Bristol was eventually supplied by Nasmyth. When, in November 1839, Humphreys found that the largest forges in the country could not undertake so large a forging, he wrote to Nasmyth describing the difficulty, even asking him if he thought that he (Humphreys) dare use cast iron. In his autobiography Nasmyth wrote that this letter set him a-thinking.[11] Existing hammers could not encompass the shaft and at the same time give a reasonable power of blow. These tilt- or trip-hammers consisted of a lever with a heavy hammer at one end, a fulcrum and a means of either depressing the other end or lifting the hammer with a cam shaft, suddenly releasing it and allowing the hammer to strike a blow on the workpiece. The principle was indeed very little different from the hand hammer much increased in scale. Naturally, however, owing to the limited movement of the cam the stroke was not large and the hammer could become 'gagged'.

On the same day that Nasmyth received Humphreys' letter he sketched out the basis of the steam hammer. Here there was a massive anvil on which to rest the work, a block of iron constituting the hammer, and an inverted steam cylinder to whose piston rod the hammer block was attached. To quote Nasmyth, 'all that was then required to produce a most effective hammer was simply to admit steam of sufficient pressure into the cylinder so as to act on the underside of the piston and thus to raise the hammer block attached to the end of the piston rod. . . .' He made a delightful drawing of the device. Of particular interest are

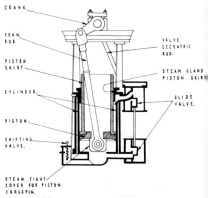

3 Humphreys type engine

the little sketches in the bottom right-hand corner showing the principle of the trip-hammer, and James Nasmyth himself about to behead it!

This brilliant invention, which was to form one of the foundations of Victorian heavy industry, was immediately communicated by Nasmyth to Humphreys, who submitted it to Brunel as Engineer-in-Chief of the ship, and to Guppy, the manager of construction, both of whom approved it. Nasmyth gave permission for any forge proprietor who might feel so disposed to adopt it, but the arrival in Bristol of the screw steamship *Archimedes* and the subsequent adoption of the screw for *Great Britain* cut the ground from beneath the paddle engines and Humphreys with them. This development will be dealt with later, but suffice to say here that the large engines which Humphreys had designed and which were well advanced in construction were cancelled, to his great regret and mortification for he had pinned his ambitions and hopes upon their successful performance. The poor man was then instructed to prepare fresh designs of engines especially suited to a screw-propulsion but, according to Nasmyth, 'being a man of most sensitive and sanguine constitution of mind' he fell ill with a brain fever which killed him.

A word is appropriate here as to the situation at Bristol. The ship was by now known as the *Mammoth*—as indeed she might be, her final dimensions being 322 ft long overall, the length on keel, according to the old builders' measurements, 274 ft, and with an overall breadth of 50 ft 6 in. The length on keel of 274 ft is also given in the original Registry Certificate of 1845. There is some ambiguity regarding the tonnage measurements of *Great Britain*. The overall length ex-bowsprit was 322 ft and on the old Builders' Measurement this gives a length on keel of 274 ft—indeed this is the length shown in the original Registry Certificate no. 3 of 1845. In the Register the breadth is shown as 48 ft 2 in. and this must have been the mean breadth used for calculation under the 'New Measurement' Rules introduced in 1836. This was a volumetric method of measuring tonnage. The tonnage by the old measurement is quoted by Guppy and Claxton as 3,443 tons, while the length on keel quoted by them is 289 ft. This does not agree with the registered length, but the Register dimensions in Certificate no. 3 refer to the calculation under the New Measurement Rules where it can be shown that the volume under deck, minus the volume of the engine-room, when divided by 100 gives in fact approximately the right tonnage—viz, just over 1,000 gross registered tons. Returning to the old Builders' Measurement, the length was taken on a straight line along the rabbet of the keel of the ship from the back of the main stern post (rudder post in Great Britain) to a perpendicular line from the fore part of the main stem under the bowsprit. For raked posts an allowance of 4 in. of reduction of length for every 1 ft of draft was made. The length above was 295 ft, the draught about 18 ft, so the length on keel would be 295 minus 6, i.e. 289 ft, which agrees with Guppy and Claxton (See Appendix One.) Calculated on this length, the tonnage would be 3,490, not far off the figure they quote; be that as it may, the ship was large—and very large for Bristol. Bristol Harbour consists of what is known as the

Floating Harbour forming the City Docks, leading via locks at Hotwells into the Cumberland Basin which in turn exits through locks into the River Avon. This had been the original course of the river, which between 1802 and 1808 was converted into this Harbour by William Jessop, who diverted the Avon's flow through a newly constructed watercourse, the New Cut. At the time *Great Britain* was building the locks between the Floating Harbour and Cumberland Basin were approximately 44 ft wide and the single lock between the Cumberland Basin and the Avon 45 ft wide.

The gates between the Cumberland Basin and the Floating Harbour really constitute a regulator for the level of the Floating Harbour. A spring tide will rise above the normal level of the Floating Harbour and the gates between that and the Cumberland Basin prevent flow into the Harbour. This is necessary because, if the level in the Harbour is allowed to rise too high, flooding takes place in Bristol and hence the Cumberland Basin is used as a kind of reservoir. When the level of the Avon reaches that of the Basin, the gates between it and the Harbour are closed and ships can be brought into the Basin from the Avon. When the level falls to that of the Harbour on the ebb tide the locks into the Avon are closed, the stop gates to the Harbour are opened and ships held in the Basin proceed into the Floating Harbour. This interesting system still works as it did when originally commissioned. Brunel improved and straightened parts of the Floating Harbour, but fundamentally it is as it was originally. All this had a very distinct bearing upon the design of the *Great Britain*. First the length of the ship was affected by the River Avon itself, because the Horseshoe Bend imposed, and still imposes, limitations upon the lengths of ships traversing it. *Great Britain* was built to the limit of length possible for navigation at the time. She is still nearly at a length to require special permission to transit the River. Additionally the locks clearly imposed severe restraints.

The arrangement of the ship was to include cabins in the wings of centreline public spaces at two deck-levels, and this led naturally to an

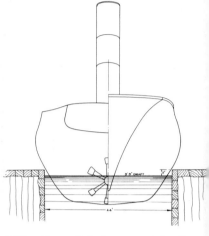

4 The *Great Britain* was a tight fit in a 44-ft lock

5 Comparative cross-sections of GB.3, *Great Western*, the *Great Britain* as built and H.M.S. *Victory*. It can be seen that both the *Great Western* and GB.3 without their paddles were a comfortable fit in the dock entrance at Bristol

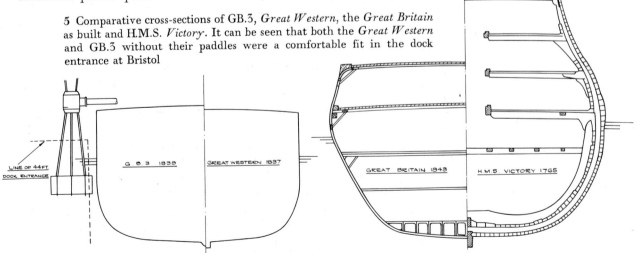

extreme breadth of the vessel of about 50 ft. The quart was fitted into the pint pot by the expedient of designing the midship section such that when the ship was very light she could pass through the 44-ft gates between the Floating Harbour and the Cumberland Basin where it was intended to fit the machinery. The ship floating at a draft of about $9\frac{3}{4}$ ft, quite empty, would clear a 44 ft coping 2 ft above water level. This was the reason for the peculiar and apparently archaic midship section adopted for the ship. The original GB1 to GB4 designs were wall-sided and quite conventional even by modern standards. The peculiar and archaic shape of GB5 was solely the result of a desire to accommodate passenger capacity at the upper levels with a narrowed form at the level of the dock coping-stones. It is instructive to compare the midships sections of the *Great Western*, GB2, GB4 and the ship as built. Fig. 5 shows these together with the midship section of H.M.S. *Victory*.

As regards the lock from the Cumberland Basin into the Avon, there appears to be some confusion as to the exact course of events. Guppy states:

When the *Great Britain* was commenced, the City of Bristol had taken up the subject of widening the dock gates to the port with other improvements so warmly that no doubt was entertained that before she should be completed there would be no difficulty in going out. . . . Accordingly she was designed 5 ft 6 in. wider than the existing locks. Various causes led to the abandonment for a time of these improvements and the ship when ready for sea was not only discovered to be a prisoner but likely to continue so, in consequence of the personal liability, which it was assumed that the Dock Company might incur, if by permitting any disturbance of their works not provided for by Act of Parliament, any injurious consequences should ensure to the Port.[12]

There is evidence that a plan by Brunel to widen this lock from 45 ft to 54 ft had not been approved by the Dock Company some time earlier—of course at this breadth there would have been no difficulty whatsoever.

As the ship was so large, it was decided to build her in a dry dock—a very modern feature—this being a shallow dock not suited to completed vessels but specifically intended for building hulls. This dock, built on the opposite side of the Floating Harbour from the gas works, was for many years known as the Great Western Dock; later known as the Wapping Dry Dock, it has now returned to its original name.

Captain Claxton was put in charge of the construction of the dock, a responsibility that appeared to worry him. A letter of encouragement from Brunel in 1839 points out that ' *of course* the bottom of the dock is likely to rise due to water pressure, they always do!'[13] He counselled Claxton not to worry about it but simply press on with the work.

As will be seen later, this dock was a very close fit for the ship as built. The completed works at the Wapping Wharf, including the Dock, cost just over £53,000; a large sum at that time. The works, finished in late 1839, were lit by gas and constituted the first shipyard in the world specifically designed for the construction of iron ships.

The position, then, at the end of 1839 was as follows: the shipbuilding works were complete; the ship itself had been through five major changes of design, culminating in an iron monster called the *Mammoth*, more than twice as large as the next largest ship in the world, to be propelled by paddles driven by twin-cylinder trunk engines to be constructed on Humphreys' designs in the Great Western Steamship Company's own works. Humphreys, the Engineer-in-Charge, was well advanced with the construction of machinery; the steam hammer had been invented in order to forge the ship's crankshaft, and it was hoped that the ship would be in service in the spring of 1841 (letter from Brunel to Claxton—21 November 1838). It was probable that this date was already over-optimistic, in view of the decision to adopt iron, but nevertheless the scene was now set for the construction of the ship.

It is convenient at this point to review the state of the art reached in 1839–40 by the major factors that affected *Great Britain*—the progress and practice of iron shipbuilding, the development of the screw propeller and the evolution of the marine steam-engine. Indeed, it is relevant to summarise the history of iron shipbuilding after the building of *Great Britain*, which had so much influence on future progress.

	GB1	GB2	GB3	GB4		GB5	GB6
	Sept. 1838	Nov. 1838	Jan. 1839	April 1839	June 1839	July 1839	Registered Dimensions
Length overall (ft.)	236	288	295			322	Not relevant
Length between perpendiculars (ft.)	212					285	,,
Length of keel (ft.)	205	254	260			274 (289)	274
Breadth	35′ 4″	38′ 6″	41′	49′		50′ 6″	48′ 2″
Depth	23′ 2″	23′	24′	29′		32′ 6″	31′ 6″
Draft	16′ 8″					16′/18′	Not relevant
Tonnage by Old Rule (Builders) (tons)	1,340	2,000	2,430			3,443	3,443 (under 1836 Rule 1,016 tons)
Displacement (tons)	2,300					2,980/3,618 tons	Not relevant
	Wood	Wood Paddle Two Cyl. (1) Osc. 85½″ dia. (2) Trunk 88″ dia.	Iron Paddle Two Cyl. Trunk 88″ cut-off at $\frac{5}{12}$ stroke	Iron Paddle Two Cyl. Osc. 100″ dia. Stroke 84″ Invited tenders	Iron Paddle Humphreys' Two Cyl. Trunk 110″ × 96″ stroke Maudslay Four Cyl. 75″	Iron Paddle Two Cyl. 110″ × 96″ stroke	Iron Screw Four Cyl. 88″ × 72″ stroke

CHAPTER THREE

The rise and progress of iron shipbuilding

Today, when steel production is measured in tens of millions of tons, it is difficult to realise what a revolution occurred in industry when, in 1784, Henry Cort invented first the puddling process for producing wrought iron and then later in the same year grooved rolls capable of producing plate and bar iron. Up to that time British wrought iron had been inferior in quality, mainly because of the relatively poor ores which were available; in any case iron was produced in very small quantities, virtually by hand. The only plates available were hammered from small ingots by trip hammers, a process invented in 1725. Naturally these plates were very small (8 ft long), of poor quality and uneven thickness. As a result practicable engineering plates and sections were simply not available so that, for example, when James Watt was experimenting with his steam-engine, he was forced to use hammered iron, or copper plates, or cast-iron sections for his boilers. Cort's introduction of puddling and then of the grooved roll for expressing slag from the bloom or block of semi-molten metal and for producing bars was absolutely necessary before metal shipbuilding materials could become commercially available.[1]

The result of this revolutionary innovation was that British industry was thereafter able to produce malleable iron of a quality and at a cost that completely replaced imports and led eventually to the establishment of Britain as the dominant industrial power of the middle of the nineteenth century. Iron production rose steadily—150,000 tons in 1800, 258,000 tons in 1806, 450,000 tons in 1823, 700,000 tons in 1828, a million tons in 1835, and half as much again in 1840.

The first real application of iron plates came quite soon after Cort's invention with the construction, in 1786, of Haystack boilers for generating steam for the atmospheric engines of the Northumberland and Durham collieries and the mines of Cornwall. Wrought iron during the period we are considering was made in quantity only by the puddling process. In making ductile malleable iron from pig it is essential to remove the excess carbon, which is present to the extent of about 4 per cent., and to reduce the amounts of silicon, manganese, sulphur and phosphorus in the metal. This is done, of course, by oxidation. Later, the production of steel depended upon devices such as the Bessemer converter, where air was blown through the mix and by burning off these constituents simultaneously raised its temperature; but in the puddling process oxidation was achieved by melting in a furnace lined with iron oxide refractories.

Pure iron does not melt until a temperature of over 1,539°C is reached and, as an open grate with forced draught will only produce about 1,400°C it is clear that this will not produce a completely liquid melt of nearly pure iron. Pig iron, with its 4 per cent. or thereabouts of carbon, melts at about 1,250°C, so that it will melt completely in such a furnace but, as oxidation proceeds, the mix must stiffen up and eventually when nearly all the carbon has disappeared a doughy product much mixed with slag is produced. The puddling furnace was characterised by having a chamber beneath the chimney in which the charge was heated before being put on the hearth. The hearth had an iron bottom and the charge was kept in the pasty condition until the carbon had been removed. When the pig iron was melted, the puddler would lower the damper on the furnace which would bring the bath up to the boil and slag would come to the surface, being lighter than the metal. This would be skimmed off over the sill plate of the furnace and removed. As oxidation proceeded, boil over would gradually cease and the puddling process itself would start. Puddling was a very difficult and trying task which involved working over the furnace for half-an-hour or more. It consisted of dividing the white hot metal charge into four by pushing a rod through it and then turning and moving each of the four pieces around in the furnace until it had reached a suitable state of malleability. Each of these pieces weighing about 100 lb. was removed separately and compressed by what was known as a 'shindling' hammer to remove excess slag. It was then formed into a suitable shape for further re-heating and rolling, more slag being expressed by Cort's grooved rolls. The larger puddled iron plates and bars were made from a pile of these small pieces welded together under the hammer or between the rolls.

Most of the British irons were made from clay ironstone and what was known as spathic ore, as Britain is more endowed with these types of ore than with the higher-grade red haematite and iron peroxide ores which are magnetic. The spathic ores produced a cold-blast pig iron containing about $1\frac{1}{4}$ per cent. of silicon, $\frac{1}{2}$ per cent. of phosphorus and somewhere between 3 and 4 per cent of carbon. There were various distinct types of wrought-iron plate—from Yorkshire, Derbyshire, Shropshire and Staffordshire in particular—and these gave surprising variations in strength both along and across the grain. Unlike steel, the slag inclusions which had been rolled out into platelets gave distinctly different properties for the plate in different planes. For example, tests carried out around 1850 showed the breaking strength in tons per square inch of Yorkshire plates along the grain to vary between $22\frac{3}{4}$ and $25\frac{3}{4}$. Across the fibre, curiously enough, these same plates gave 26 and $27\frac{1}{2}$ respectively. Derbyshire plates were lower at 21·7 and 18·7, while Shropshire plates were nearly 23 tons per square inch along the grain and 22 across. Staffordshire plates were the lowest of all at about $19\frac{1}{2}$ and 21 respectively. It can be seen that Yorkshire plates generally were the strongest and the famous Lowmoor brand was the best known of these. The weakness of wrought-

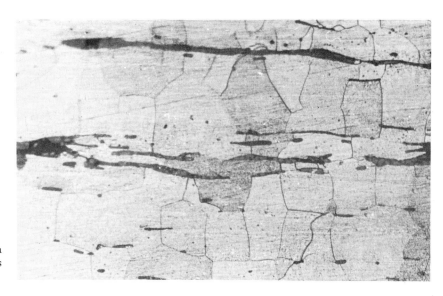

6 Microphotograph of metal from the *Great Britain* along and across the plane. Magnification × 120

iron plate was, of course, at right-angles to the surface of the plate itself. The slag lamination much affected the strength, and even sound material could be laminated and fractured by quite minor repeated blows on its surface.

There were many rather bitter complaints about the quality of iron used for shipbuilding from 1830 onwards. For example, Fairbairn remarked:

. . . Plates of ordinary manufacture or such as are used in shipbuilding, seldom exceed in tenacity 20 tons to the square inch. Unfortunately many of them are under that standard and no plate should be allowed on any account to enter into the construction of a seagoing vessel under a tensile strain of 20 to 22 tons per square inch.[2]

In a paper read at the first meetings of the Institution of Naval Architects, founded in 1860, he went on to say that

Twenty to Thirty shillings to a ton will make all the difference between good plates and worthless ones and no plate should be used which will not stand an average tensile strength of 20 tons per square inch.

Anyway, up to the invention of the Bessemer converter in 1856, the bulk of the malleable iron produced for shipbuilding was made by this puddling process. It was of very low carbon content. For example, the analysis of a specimen from the *Great Britain* herself is as follows:

Carbon	0·03 per cent
Sulphur	0·10 per cent. plus
Phosphorus	0·15 per cent. plus
Silicon	1·60 per cent approx.
Manganese	0·02 per cent. ,,
Iron	98·1 per cent

Fig. 6 is a micro-photograph of this specimen and shows the laminae of slag included in the iron.

The only evidence to date of the origin of the iron used in the *Great Britain* comes from a reference made at a meeting of the Institution of Naval Architects in 1871.* John Grantham wrote an historical paper on the *Richard Cobden* iron sailing ship and read it at the April meeting of the Institution. The *Richard Cobden* was built in Bristol in 1844 in the same yard as the *Great Britain* and by Guppy. She was quite a small ship 136 ft long and 27 ft broad, and was of apparently excellent constructional design, materials and workmanship. She gave such good service that Grantham wrote his paper 27 years later. In the discussion on that paper William F. Sim, the managing owner of the *Richard Cobden*, made a number of interesting remarks. He pointed out that she was designed by Thomas Guppy, but he also made the categoric statement that

The whole of the iron of the *Richard Cobden* as well as the *Great Britain* was made by the Coalbrookdale Iron Company in Shropshire, one of the oldest iron companies in the world It was entirely from the clay band ironstone and before cinders were used.

Iron vessels

Probably the first iron vessels ever built were the canal barges of the Birmingham area. A local newspaper, dated 28 July 1787, reported:

A few days ago, a boat built of English iron by J. Wilkinson, Esq. of Bradley Forge, came up our canal to this town loaded with 22 tons and 15 cwt. of its own metal. It is nearly of equal dimensions with other boats employed upon the canal being 70 ft long and 6 ft $8\frac{1}{2}$ in. wide. The thickness of the plates with which it is made is about $\frac{5}{16}$th of an inch and it is put together with rivets like copper or fire engine boilers, but the stem and sternposts are wood and the gunwale lined with the same. Her weight is about 8 tons. She will carry in deep water upwards of 32 tons and draws 8 or 9 in. of water when light.[3]

The boat was built at Willey in Shropshire and was thus constructed only three years after the invention of rolling iron plates. As might be expected, the project had met with much scepticism. John Wilkinson wrote to a friend: 'Yesterday week my iron boat was launched: It answers all my expectations and has convinced the unbelievers who were 999 in every 1,000'.

Other barges of this type were constructed for use on the canals and on the Severn, and in 1809 the well known engineer Trevithick took out a patent for several marine inventions involving the use of wrought-iron plates in 'ships of war, East Indiamen and other large vessels'. His patent covered for the decks as well as for sides of such ships to be constructed of wrought-iron plates riveted or joined by screws. This patent even proposed to make 'masts, bowsprits, yards and booms of wrought iron, out of plates riveted or screwed together in hollow or tubular forms. These masts being hollow tubes the upper mast may be made to slide into the lower mast.'

The Royal Navy was given an opportunity to enter the metal-ship age only five years after the Battle of Trafalgar. Sir Samuel Bentham, who had been concerned with Marc Brunel in the block-making machin-

* 'On the *Richard Cobden* Sailing Ship': John Grantham, *Trans. I.N.A.* April 1871.

24

ery at Portsmouth, proposed to the Admiralty the introduction of iron as a shipbuilding material, probably in view of the increasing scarcity of timber. The Admiralty turned a deaf ear—or perhaps one should say a blind eye? In fairness, one must quote Nelson's reaction to Bell's steamship when he saw it on the Clyde in 1800: 'Gentlemen, if you do not take advantage of this invention, you may rely upon it—others will.' Probably he would have said much the same of iron.

The first iron vessel to float in salt water seems to have been a small pleasure-boat launched on the Mersey by Thomas Jevons of Liverpool in 1815. The boat was not built there, however, but near Birmingham by Joshua Horton of Tipton. The development of iron ships began in Scotland at an early date. An iron boat called the *Vulcan* was built in 1818 by Thomas Wilson at Faskine, some six miles from Glasgow, and put on the Forth & Clyde Canal. This craft was 61 ft long, 11 ft broad and drew 4 ft 6 in. of water; it was carvel built, the plates being flush and had bulkheads fitted with diagonal stiffeners—the frames were made from flat bar-iron 24 in. apart. It seems that the plates were 2 ft broad and ran vertically. They butted on each frame which therefore acted as a butt strap. This boat apparently remained in existence until 1865.

Thus, by 1820 some experience of iron boats—generally for canals—had been built up in the various shipbuilding areas of Britain. A significant event was now to take place. Charles Manby, FRS, the son of Aaron Manby, and for many years Secretary to the Institution of Civil Engineers, took out a patent on iron steamboats. With his friend Captain, later Admiral, Sir Charles Napier he formed a society whose first ship, the *Aaron Manby*, was completed in 1821. Intended for work on the Seine, the ship was sent to London in parts and assembled in dock. After loading a cargo of linseed and iron castings, and with Captain Napier in charge and Charles Manby as Chief Engineer, she sailed direct from London to Le Havre and thence to Paris without unloading. She thus became the first and only steam vessel to sail direct from London to Paris, until about 1850. The *Aaron Manby* was the start of steam/iron navigation, and seems to have been quite successful, for from 1821 to 1830 her hull required no repairs although she was repeatedly aground, often loaded, in tidal ports.

The father of the celebrated iron shipbuilder, John Grantham, was responsible for the second iron steam vessel, also built by the Horsley Company, between 1823 and 1825. This vessel sailed to Ireland and went into service on the River Shannon. Thirty years later she was still afloat and working. The next iron steam vessel was built in Leeds, of all places, by a William Gravitt in 1829, and was distinguished by the installation of a horizontal, tubular locomotive boiler. The paddle-shaft was placed in front of the smokebox on which the plummer blocks were bolted.

That year also saw the building of the first iron vessels on the Mersey, when William Laird & Sons launched a 60-ft boat, 13 ft in breadth, followed by two more of similar size. In 1831 they built the *Elburkah*, which went out with McGregor Laird in 1832 with the Niger expedition and was thus the first iron vessel ever to make an ocean voyage. 70 ft in length, 13 ft in breadth, and of 15 nominal horsepower, she drew only 3 ft 6 in. of water and confounded the prophets of doom as to the dangers of going to sea with so light a draft. She made two ascents of the Niger and was entirely successful. Iron vessels now began to follow thick and fast. To quote Fairbairn:

In the early stages of this important manufacture many difficulties had to be encountered and it was only those who were the first to undertake the designs and labour of these constructions who were calculated to ensure success and competent to carry out the responsible duties consequent upon such undertakings.

Worthy sentiments and quite true; it must have been a very difficult period. The established shipbuilders and shipwrights and the Admiralty were all violently opposed to iron as a shipbuilding material, as witness John Grantham, writing in 1842:

Many, therefore, still view the subject (iron shipbuilding) with distrust and regard it as one of the visionary schemes of this wonder working age which will soon be relinquished and forgotten.[4]

This period also saw the invention of the longitudinal system of framing used in the bottom of the *Great Britain* and later extensively in the *Great Eastern*. Here the frames or 'ribs', instead of being at right angles to the keel, lie parallel to it and hence contribute in the longitudinal strength of the ship, whereas they do not in the transverse system. A Mr Wheelwright of London in 1838 published an illustrated pamphlet describing the longitudinal system, but there is no record that he put it to practical application. The pamphlet is in the library of the Institution of Civil Engineers.

Half-a-dozen other iron ships should be mentioned among the many constructed during the decade 1830–40. The first is a little ship called the *Garry Owen*, built by Laird's at Birkenhead in 1834, which worked on the Lower Shannon until 1866 when, upon being sold for coastal service in Africa, she was found to be in excellent condition. Only 130 ft long and 21 ft 6 in. wide, this was the first iron steamship to introduce transverse watertight bulkheads. In iron, this was the invention of Charles Wye Williams, the founder and manager of the City of Dublin Steam Packet Company who later in 1837 strongly urged their adoption in a paper he presented to the British Association. Watertight bulkheads for wooden ships had first been introduced by Captain Shanks in 1790, in a sailing vessel called the *Trial*.

Another vessel worthy of mention was also built by Laird's, in 1837. This ship, the *Rainbow*, was a Channel packet displacing 580 tons. It belonged to the General Steam Navigation Company and was employed in the Le Havre and London trade carrying goods and passengers. Her significance is that, as we shall see later, she was a reason for iron being adopted for the construction of the *Great Britain*. She was also quite large, being 198 ft long overall, 25 ft wide, but under 13 ft in depth of hold.

The ship-rigged sailing vessel *Ironside* of 264 tons was launched in October 1838 at Liverpool by Messrs Jackson & Gordon. This ship was important in that according to contemporary accounts she was classed by the Committee of Lloyd's in November 1838, the first iron ship ever guaranteed 'fit for the safe conveyance of dry and perishable cargoes'. According to Lloyd's Register's own official history the honour belongs to the *Sirius* built in 1837. Built of angle- and plate-iron *Ironside* made her maiden voyage to Rio de Janeiro and back without any damage to her cargo. This voyage was also notable as being the first oceanic test of Airey's compass correction for iron ships. It was a complete success.

The other three ships were all built by Laird's in 1839. The first iron steamship for the Royal Navy was intended for the Dover station, it was appropriately named *Dover*, and perhaps marked the beginning of the modern Navy. The *Nemesis* and the *Phlegethon* for the Honourable East India Company, of 660 and 570 tons respectively, had the distinction of being the first vessels to engage in naval action, taking part as they did in the Chinese war of 1842.

The decision to build *Great Britain* of iron was also taken at the end of 1838, and it can be seen, therefore, that for iron shipbuilding the second half of the 'thirties was of the greatest possible significance: the first watertight iron bulkheads, the first iron ship for the Navy, the first iron ships classed by Lloyd's, proof that compasses on iron ships could be corrected, the decision to build the first 'modern ship'—all decided upon within a space of five years.

Iron and the 'Mammoth'

In late 1838 the largest vessels yet built of iron were the steamer *Royal Sovereign*, built by Totton McGregor to ply between Glasgow and Liverpool, and the *Rainbow*, mentioned earlier. *Royal Sovereign*, completed in that year, was 178 ft in length and had a tonnage of 446, with 220 nominal horsepower installed; *Rainbow* was a little larger. As the *Great Britain* was to be over 300 ft in length, something like $2\frac{1}{2}$ times the breadth of the *Royal Sovereign*, and eight times the loaded weight, the increase in scale was enormous.

In October 1838, the technical committee—Brunel, Claxton and Guppy—had started thinking theoretically of using iron for the ship. They communicated their views to the directors, who instructed them to conduct searching practical inquiries.[5] The *Rainbow* called at Bristol in October 1838 and provided a golden opportunity for personal investigation. Claxton, then managing director of the Great Western Steamship Company, made a number of passages in her and in other iron ships, accompanied by Patterson—examining their seagoing qualities, considering the effect of the metal upon the compasses, investigating subsidiary but important aspects such as rusting, fouling and so on. It soon became clear to them that iron 'would afford greater strength, greater buoyancy and more capacity at less expense than wood'. Claxton, for example, pointed out that in capacity alone the *Great Britain* would gain more than 600 tons. He gave a rather graphic illustration of this:

Suppose all the angle irons or ribs the shelves etc. were all rolled out flat and added to the thickness of the plates forming her sides, when an average thickness of 2 ft of timber would be replaced by an average thickness of $2\frac{1}{2}$ in. of iron, with far better ties, a more compact framework and greater strength, than wood can under any circumstances give.[6]

To substantiate Claxton's claim it can be shown that the volume thus saved would amount to 24,000 cu. ft—600 measurement tons of 40 cu ft.

A detailed report was prepared for discussion,[7] with Brunel pointing out the above advantages and further ones such as freedom from dry rot, vermin and 'the stench and unhealthy consequences of bilge water'. It was concluded by the triumvirate that the compasses could be easily adjusted; that with care oxidation could be guarded against and that the expenditure of keeping the iron hull in order would be much less than with one of wood; that lightning strikes, which frequently caused serious accidents with wood-built ships, would be avoided; and that—a very important factor—finer lines were attainable with equal strength, thereby giving greater speed. They also concluded that the ship would be less liable to damage if stranded and that the only real disadvantage was that of fouling. However, 'a steamer always rapidly progressing at sea and whose ports will be in high northern latitudes. . . . would have nothing to fear even on this point'. On this crucial subject of fouling they were over-optimistic, as we shall see later.

Brunel's own views were entirely in agreement with Claxton, Patterson and Guppy, and he personally recommended the directors to build the ship of iron. They agreed, authorised Claxton, Guppy and Brunel to act as the Building Committee, and requested Brunel to draw up plans for construction of the ship at the yard owned by the Company. At the time this decision was taken to use iron for the great new ship, it is apparent that Brunel and his colleagues knew very little about some practical details of shipbuilding in iron. In a letter dated 17 November 1838 to John Grantham he asked, 'Will you have the goodness to let me know who makes the best and largest plates adapted for boat building and who makes the angle irons?'[8] Grantham was, perhaps, one of the most likely sources of such information, although in his books he does not mention giving Brunel advice and assistance. In the end the Committee carried out their own testing of joints and rivets at the Works to help fill this gap.

The resulting design, GB5, was approved and, as mentioned in the previous chapter, iron fabrication started in July 1839. Claxton rightly points out that at the time this decision was taken nothing had been published regarding the construction of iron ships and that the directors had nothing to guide them other than their confidence in their advisers, the facts that the latter had deduced and their reasoning from these facts. The directors must surely share the credit for a bold and brilliantly successful decision. The result of their decision lies today in the Great Western Dock in Bristol, having survived more than 130 years since the start of fabrication.

CHAPTER FOUR

The practice of iron shipbuilding

7 Flush-butted shell plating

8 Clinker-laid shell plating

When *Great Britain* was laid down in 1839, iron shipbuilding was primitive and in a state of flux. Methods of construction were being tried on a more or less *ad hoc* basis. Nevertheless the builders were practical men who well understood the nature of most of the loads coming upon a ship's structure, and the remarkable service record of these first iron ships speaks well for the ability of their designers.

One major disadvantage was the small size of the plates. Even when the *Great Eastern* was built one and a half decades later the largest plates that could economically be rolled were 10 ft long by about 2 ft 9 in. wide and $\frac{3}{4}$ in. thick. This, of course, necessitated an enormous amount of work in riveting the plates together, though a consideration of the primitive nature of the available handling equipment makes the handicap appear less serious.[1]

The oldest method of plating the shell was that used on the sides of the *Dover*, mentioned earlier as being built for the Admiralty. The edges of the strakes of plating butted one against the other and the joints thus formed were strapped internally; usually the butts of these internal straps were in turn strapped although sometimes they were thinned down and overlapped. The end joints or butts of the plates were also flush-jointed and secured by internal butt straps. Liners or pads had to be provided at each frame between the seam butt straps. In some places the vertical butt straps ran between the horizontal seam strips but in others they were joggled over them. This method gave very good support to the side of the ship, the edges of plating bearing one upon the other as, for instance, when the ship was docked, but it was heavy and expensive.

The second method of plating, shown in Fig. 8, is in fact that adopted for *Great Britain*. This was the 'clinker' method where plates of adjacent strakes lapped over each other and were riveted together. It is, of course, very similar to wood clinker building. Normally tapered liners were fitted between the plates and the frames, but in poor practice plate washers replaced these liners. The tapered liners were expensive and there was the imagined disadvantage of having vertical loads borne by the rivets in shear. The advantages, however were several. The edges of the plates required far less care and precision in fitting than in the flush method and the amount of riveting was much reduced. Additionally it was excellent for repair work as any plate could be lifted out quite easily after the rivets had been removed. The two systems were sometimes combined, as in the *Dover* which had the clinker system from the keel to the turn of the bilge and flush plating on the sides where it was considered there would be considerable vertical loads.

Fig. 9 shows the bow of *Great Britain* in the spring of 1972 after salvage and after the wood sheathing fitted in 1882 had been removed. The shift of butts was usually as shown in Fig. 10. Fig. 11 shows the actual arrangement of butts on *Great Britain*. As her plates are especially short (6 ft as against the 8 ft of later ships), butts occur approximately every third frame and not every fourth. Contemporary shipbuilders remarked that the fitting of the joints and butts of these early ships was generally rough and usually by hammering down the projecting parts and then caulking. It was complained that some Scottish shipbuilders did not even do this but drove in strips of iron and caulked the edges to them, at any rate above the waterline. John Grantham repaired a ship built this way at Aberdeen in 1838, the 550-ton *John Garrow*, after a single voyage to the East. His comments were: 'The outside seams were very large and were filled in with wood and iron cement and it was necessary that these joints had to be cleared out and caulked in the usual manner.' Furthermore, 'the spaces between the plates and the frames ought to have been filled with wedge shaped liners instead of cement as they were'. Dupuy de Lôme after a tour of British shipyards stated that this bad practice was general in Glasgow and Greenock. In fairness to Guppy, Patterson and Brunel, the *Great Britain* is built meticulously with tapered liners, beautifully fitted plates, has never been caulked but has had a remarkable record of watertightness. Of course she was not built as a competitive job but more or less as a 'one off' by men finding out as they went, and one suspects that nothing but the best was even considered as being good enough.

Scott Russell and J. R. Napier introduced the so-called 'in and out' system very commonly used until the advent of welding in the middle of this century. Here each alternate strake is worked directly on to the frames and the intermediate strakes lie on top of them with a flat liner below the outer or raised strakes. This method was soon generally adopted, as liners were required for only half the strakes and were of uniform thickness instead of being wedge-shaped. When joggling* machines of sufficient power to bend frames became common the method was further adapted to that which became standard for iron and steel ships right up to the advent of welding, namely joggled frames. An exception was the practice of some continental builders who joggled the seams of plating instead.

In 1852 another method was produced by a shipbuilder called Seaton in which all the plates were worked directly on to the frames with no liners and with flush longitudinal joints covered by external straps. This system, anticipated by the top strakes of the *Great Britain*, returned to the supposed advantage of taking vertical loads directly on the plate edges but doubled the number of rivets of previous systems. A very similar method was used on the early ironclads such as *Warrior*

9 Clinker plating on the bow of *Great Britain* taken 129 years after the plating was riveted together. The ship is shown under restoration in 1972

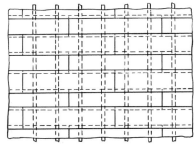

10 The way butts between plates were shifted from strake to strake

* Joggling is a term applied to kinking a plate or angle.

30

11 *Great Britain* conformed closely with the standard system of shifting butts

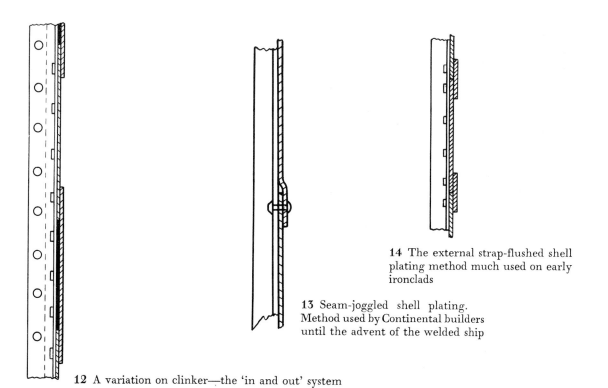

14 The external strap-flushed shell plating method much used on early ironclads

13 Seam-joggled shell plating. Method used by Continental builders until the advent of the welded ship

12 A variation on clinker—the 'in and out' system

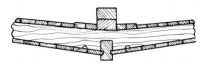

15 Typical wooden ship keel construction

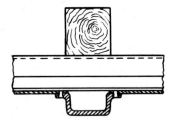

16 Iron construction embodying little change from wood methods

17 An early patented iron keel

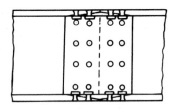

18 The keel construction of the steamship *Dover*—an expensive and cumbersome method

19 One of the last of the iron 'wood' keels

where the skin plating in way of the armour was worked flush with external edge strips and shelves upon which to bed the armour. In ironclads later than *Warrior* the skin plating in way of the armour was often worked flush, made up of two thicknesses, and hence with no need for straps. Away from the armour these ironclads were flush plated with edge strips worked inside. However, to avoid the use of liners, all the plates were riveted directly to the frames and the seam straps worked intercostally in short lengths between the frames. A rather weird system was proposed by a Mr Daft, perhaps appropriately named, where longitudinal strips of plating or straps were worked inside the plates to take the edge riveting but the plates were separated at both seams and butts so as to form grooves. These grooves were filled with teak and then zinc sheathing was put on the outside of the hull for anti-fouling. A lengthy description of a development of this system appears in the 1886 *Transactions of the Institution of Naval Architects*.

Turning to some of the details of the earlier iron ships, perhaps one of the most interesting is the construction of keels. A wood ship, of course, has a keel with rabbets cut in it for the planking with the floors running across it and a keelson on top. The early iron ships attempted to copy this form of construction. Fig. 16 shows an obvious attempt to achieve this, while Fig. 17 is a variation upon the same theme which was patented by the Oak Farm Iron Company when sufficiently large rolls became available. A great objection to these systems was that the internal straps joining lengths together formed an obstruction to the flow of bilge water in them, and our friend the *Dover*, which had such a keel, used internal flush-riveted scarphs, an exensive and tricky form of construction.

Still trying to retain the wood type keel, some builders built a complete external keel where two angle bars and a shallow gutter plate were riveted together by single riveted straps. A ship employing this system was the ill-fated troopship *Birkenhead*, wrecked with much loss of life off the Cape of Good Hope, which incidentally was one of the ships to tow *Great Britain* off what was nearly her grave on Dundrum Beach. The design was soon abandoned in favour of a shallow curved keel, and a further variation was to run the plating right through underneath, across the centreline of the ship, and to attach the plate externally. All these arrangements were deficient. Apart from producing a discontinuity in the shell plating they were peculiarly liable to corrosion and the collection of mud, grease and so on. They also failed to give adequate vertical strength. A system introducing a vertical centreline keel the depth of the floors was certainly an improvement but very expensive and soon followed by even more expensive variations.

The two simplest keels were the plain bar and the flush plate keel. The former was a rectangular iron bar on which the floors rested with an intercostal centreline plate keel and a keelson above. The shell plating was riveted to the external keel but was not attached solidly to the intercostal keel and in some variations the latter was moved sideways so as to lap the bar keel and be riveted to it. Around 1850 Lloyd's showed a similar arrangement in their Rules where either a single or double

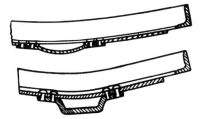

20 External iron keels

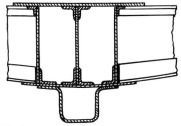

21 An attempt to incorporate longitudinal strength in the keel

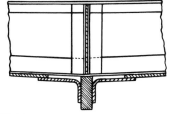

22 The straightforward bar keel much used later in small vessels

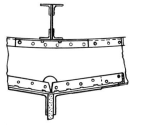

23 The bar keel combined by Lloyds with 'wood' construction in iron

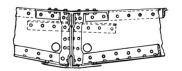

24 The modern keel at last, flush externally, fitted to ships with open floors

keelson rode on top of the floors. This was really a return to the wooden form of construction and did not provide adequate protection against tripping of the floors. (The floors are the transverse members in the bottom, extending into the frames or 'ribs', and tripping is a term applied to the sideways collapse of these members.) The other type of keel was flush or internal and eventually became universal practice both for merchant and naval ships. Generally the flush plate keel lapped over the two adjacent or garboard strakes and was connected by plate angles to a vertical keel which in turn was connected to a top member. If there was an inner bottom, the top member was connected to it in the same way as the bottom one was to the shell plating. The keel ran continuously through the length of the ship with the floors riveted on either side of it.

Some ships had a false keel of timber bolted outside the hull, and indeed this very feature was applied to the *Great Britain* nine years after her launch. Grantham comments upon the idea:

The plan of bolting on a false keel of timber to an iron vessel cannot be too highly deprecated. It nearly caused the loss of the *Iron Duke* which striking heavily upon a sand bank tore away the false keel and breaking off the bolts by which it was fastened water entered by the holds.[2]

One must comment that it has lasted 120 years on the *Great Britain*.

Naval practice was slightly different. The *Warrior*'s keel and keelson plates consisted of a continuous centre plate connected below to the two keel plates by angle irons and above by two smaller irons to a flat keelson plate on top of the floors. The external plate keel forms a doubling or strap to the garboard plates and the whole arrangement is very strong and compact. It is almost identical to that adopted in the *Great Britain* twenty years earlier. Finally, with longitudinally framed iron ships exemplified by the *Great Eastern*, a vertical keel was employed with a single flat keel plate and a similar plate on the inner shell. This of course is a very simple and economical arrangement.

Bilge keels were not commonly fitted to early iron ships. The *Great Britain* has them, but they are really for docking. Fitted 9 ft each side of the centreline these keels extend over about 110 ft of the length of the ship, are $1\frac{1}{4}$ in. thick, aligned vertically and riveted to the shell with angle irons 5 in. wide and one in. thick. As originally built the bottoms of these keels were level across a line with the centreline flush keel and they are most convenient for docking—indeed the ship has been docked upon them since her salvage. Such keels were often used in France to reduce leeway on ships, but not as rolling chocks, and it is probably not until the mathematical study of rolling by Froude that their importance as roll damping devices was appreciated.

The stem and stern posts of these early iron ships varied as widely in type as their keels until designers found their feet. The *Birkenhead* mentioned earlier had a hollow iron stem formed from $\frac{3}{4}$-in. iron plates. This was obviously an extremely expensive and difficult method and anyway the heavy working probably did not do the iron much good. Before long it became common practice to use heavy forgings or some-

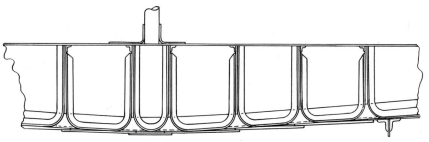

25 The bottom and keel construction of
Great Britain, thoroughly modern in concept

times plates scarfed together and one of the first applications of this method may be seen on the *Great Britain*. The stem is 12 in. deep at the forefoot and 5 in. thick. 8 ft up from the bottom it has become 16 in. by 2½ in. and thereafter diminishes to a width of 12 in. and a thickness of 1½ in. The basic stem is 18 ft long, hammer-welded into one piece— a massive and beautiful forging and all done with trip hammers. Much the same practice was adopted with sternposts. The early paddlers had, of course, sailing ship type rudders trailing directly from the after end of the deadwood. Our two friends the *Dover* and the *Birkenhead* had hollow iron fairings riveted to a fabricated post as shown in Figs. 28 and 29. This soon gave way to solid bars on to which the plating was lapped and riveted as with stems, and this is the system adopted in the case of the *Great Britain* up to the top of the propeller aperture at the 16 ft water-line. Once again this ship preceded standard practice.

The framing of the ships was generally fair without joggles or bends and, as we have seen, the plating was arranged to allow this. As one might expect the small plates and the internal butt straps led to difficulties. We have very few of the early iron ships to examine but the classic one, *Great Britain*, when measured shows that very few frame or 'rib' spacings agree with the nominal measurements. They are all at sixes and sevens, a typical set of measurements being as follows: 17, 22, 16·5, 21 and 18 in.—these are all nominally 18 in. Fig. 11 shows the inside of the shell; one can see that in order to avoid the butt straps the frames had to be of uneven spacing unless they were exact multiples of the plate lengths (which they were not).

Before 1850 it was not general practice to apply what is known as a reverse bar to a frame. *Great Britain* only had reverse bars in the region of the main engine where there were also intermediate frames. The modern method of bracketing deck beams and frames together had not yet been developed and it was common practice to cut the end of a deck beam, bend the toe of the beam down to form a bracket and then insert a triangular piece of plate and fire-weld it there. This is in fact good practice but very expensive. Fig. 31 shows the junction between a deck beam, a side frame and a longitudinal or box stringer in the 'tween decks. This may be compared with Fig. 11, where a similar arrangement can be seen. The box stringer or longitudinal member was introduced into the

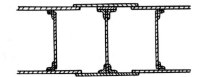

26 The simple and effective keel construction of *Great Eastern*

27 An early iron stem-piece, that of the *Birkenhead*

28 Fabricated sternpost of *Birkenhead*

29 Fabricated sternpost of *Dover*

Great Britain around 1866. This invention by a Mr Leslie, of the subsequently famous firm Hawthorn Leslie's, was incorporated in Lloyd's requirements shortly afterwards. The original 'tween deck stringers on the *Great Britain* were of heavy timber but this iron box is obviously a much more efficient arrangement. It is far from clear how the box stringer was riveted together. Some arrangement must have been made for backing up the rivets with a dolly that could be pulled along inside, but even so it is difficult to imagine how the final closing run of rivets could be worked. A curious feature of such stringers was that they were sometimes used as ventilating ducts.

Early iron ships were notably weak at deck level. These ships, typified by the *Great Britain*, carried the angle iron of the upper deck beams down two or three feet of the vessel's side in a curve; in some cases there was also a curved deck plate or stringer which in turn was joined to the top of the side of the ship. The triangular space thus created was sometimes plated in, a construction of considerable strength. When it was not, while strong enough for vertical loads, it did not afford enough strength transversely to prevent the ship 'racking' or 'lozenging' sideways when the bottom was pushed one way and the deck the other. The main defect, however, of the early decks was that the deck itself was of wood, laid on the iron beams and secured with diagonal iron straps but nevertheless fundamentally weak.

A ship may be regarded as analogous to a girder or 'I' beam commonly used in bridges and buildings. Such a beam has top and bottom flanges and if the middle is bent downwards the bottom flange is in tension and the top one compressed. When a ship is supported by a wave at the bow and stern she will be bent downwards amidships by her own weight, whereas when there is a trough at bow and stern and a crest amidships she will bend the other way. As wood is more easily stretched than iron a wooden deck (or top flange) of a ship will give less resistance to these pressures and place more strain on the iron sides of the ship than would an iron deck. Thus the use of iron decks would greatly have improved the structural efficiency of the early iron ships; the additional weight could have been compensated for by reducing the thickness elsewhere.

Perhaps the first man to speak out for iron decks was John Grantham, tentatively in 1842 and loudly in 1858.[3] Their chief advocate became Sir William Fairbairn, who was associated with Stephenson in the building of the Britannia tubular bridge over the Menai Straits. He wrote a paper on the subject for the inaugural meetings of the Institution of Naval Architects and in 1865 pointed out that many ships were decidedly defective in their distribution of material.[4] He drew the analogy between an 'I' beam and a ship with iron weather and 'tween decks and an iron bottom. *Great Britain* was built differently, with iron stringers or shelves 3 ft wide and $\frac{1}{2}$ in. thick at her three deck levels, and diagonal iron straps underneath the wood of the decks. The relative efficiencies of the all-iron ship and the *Great Britain*, treated as beams of the same weight and depth, would be approximately 100:99.

Having carried out tests, Fairbairn pointed out that an iron structure

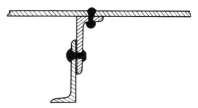

30 The method of strengthening a frame by a reverse bar

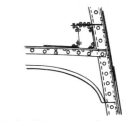

31 Mr Leslie's patent box stringer as fitted later to the *Great Britain*

* Fairbairn was a scientific engineer and did a great deal of work on the basic characteristics of iron plates, particularly investigating the effect of their thickness upon mechanical properties. He found that 'density and tenacity increased and diminished together'. This is hardly surprising as the only reason why density should decrease would be by virtue of slag inclusions.

broke with 300,000 changes of load, each equivalent to one-third the static breaking strength of the metal in it. He went on:

Time is an element in the endurance of [iron] structures when subjected to severe strains affecting their ultimate powers of resistance. It is difficult to determine or pronounce what is the correct measure of safety . . . but we have sufficient data to be assured that every disturbance however minute in the molecular construction of bodies finally tends to destruction and it is only a question of time when rupture ensures. We may however be assured that a ship is practically safe when the strains repeated in the same direction do not exceed the Government rule of 5 tons per sq. in. upon the wrought iron plates of which it is composed.[5]

In practice, however, strains were never repeated in the same direction, but alternately one way and the other as the ship rode over crests and troughs of waves. The legal limit of stress of 5 tons per sq. in. of cross-section would, he said,

acting alternately in opposite directions at least injure if it did not fracture the material after a great number of alterations. Such a number might not take place during the continuance of a single storm but the destructive effect goes on accumulating in the course of years. Hence it is highly desirable that iron ships should be built much stronger than they are at present.

He urged strongly that all decks, while they might be sheathed with wood for convenience, should be built of iron for strength.

Brunel had in fact anticipated Fairbairn by having an extremely strong and effective iron deck built for the *Great Eastern*, in whose structure there is little to criticise even by modern standards. But 10 years after the *Great Eastern* was completed iron-plated decks were still by no means universal. When they were fitted, the methods of plating were generally similar to those of shell-plating, clinker-laid plating symmetrical about the centreline of the ship being much favoured.

Sailing ships, whether of iron or wood, were generally built without bulkheads and the practice of using them was introduced in Europe with the iron steamship. Watertight bulkheads had been used for centuries by the Chinese and this was freely acknowledged but, apart from a few warships, it was not until the time of Charles Wye Williams that they were introduced to merchant ships. By the late 1850s iron watertight bulkheads were a legal requirement of the Board of Trade and this process of invention, development, regulation and enforcement, applied with vigour during the nineteenth century, helped to give Britain her commanding technical lead in shipping.

Great Britain had five water-tight bulkheads, but four was perhaps the most common number. Aft of the stem there was what was known as the forepeak bulkhead which in effect was a protection against collision. In the *Great Britain* it is 10 per cent of the ship's length aft of the waterline ending position meeting the modern legal requirement that it should be not less than 5 per cent. of the length of the ship aft of the forward perpendicular through the waterline. Natural positions for bulkheads are at the forward and aft ends of the engine room, while a bulkhead analogous

34 How shell plating split through butts—note severed butts in way of the crack in the *Great Britain*

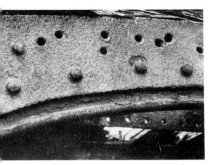

32 An upper 'tweendecks web-frame in the *Great Britain* (1968) showing the 'nibbled' edge to the plate

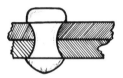

33 Scott Russell's diagram showing how rivets should be countersunk for strength

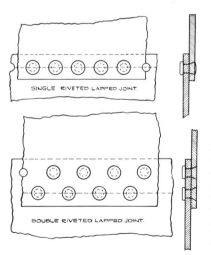

35 Typical early iron rivet-joints as drawn by John Grantham

to the forepeak bulkhead would be fitted right aft, primarily as protection against damage due to a breaking propeller.

A very bad practice was introduced into some of these early iron ships, including the *Great Britain*. Their bulkheads ran only to the deck below the weather deck; in the event of flooding this gave poor protection, as water could flow over the top of the bulkhead into the next compartment. That this is not a theoretical point is shown by the fate of the great Italian liner *Andrea Doria* whose loss in our own times was due to this very cause. Fairbairn in the 1850s was one of the leading advocates of carrying bulkheads well up and spacing them suitably to prevent water lapping over them in the event of bilging, but others were still pressing the same point in 1882. Modern legal requirements for tanks forward of the forepeak bulkheads are that any valves, such as those to pumping systems, must be inside the tanks and controlled by spindles reaching right up to the weather or bulkhead deck. The fact that this is precisely what was done in *Great Britain* illustrates the Committee's careful attention to logical, practical detail.

We have seen how the main elements of an early iron steamer were constructed. It remains to look into how the components were joined together and protected from oxidation and corrosion, and to discuss that great bugbear of the early iron steamers: fouling.

In the very early iron steamers large plate holes were drilled, as may be seen from the curved edges of the plates in the *Great Britain* which have been cut by drilling holes, lapping one into the other. Quite early on, punching was introduced and this was an improvement because of its tendency to produce a slightly conical hole, giving the rivets a degree of countersink. Where deep countersinking was required the plates were un-doubtedly drilled. John Scott Russell, the builder of the *Great Eastern*, was a great advocate of the conical rivet hole. A diagram, Fig. 33, was supplied by him in the discussion of a paper, accompanied by these remarks:

. . . I think it most advisable that the rivet as it goes through the two plates, should be of this form. It then has this manifest advantage that when the head is gone the rivet remains and the ship is watertight.[6]

As seen earlier there was some controversy as to the desirability of allowing the weight of the side of a ship to come in shear upon the rivets in the plating. The idea was that the sliding of one plate over the other would neatly behead the rivets, chopping them off at the junction between the plates. However, as was remarked at the time, it was well known to practical men that the plates themselves almost invariably gave way first, tearing in the parts weakened by the holes formed to receive the rivets. We have visual proof that this was so from the split in the starboard side of the *Great Britain* repaired during her recent salvage. As the split ran down the ship's side through a plate it continued down through the butt strap below, which neatly parted along the line of holes—the rivets themselves did not give way. (Fig. 34 shows the crack just after salvage.) Brunel and the Building Committee made extensive tests of clinker and flush joints and found that clinker was 20 per cent. stronger. These tests are the reason for adopting clinker construction in the *Great Britain*. They also concluded that there would be a weight saving of about 100 tons—no mean advantage.

The practice of using double riveting added greatly to the strength of these joints, largely because of the considerable frictional area developed between the plates in way of the wide riveted seam. When the Britannia Bridge over the Menai Straits was being constructed, experiments were made to demonstrate this. Three plates were riveted together, the two outside ones with circular holes in which rivets fitted exactly, and the central one with an oval hole which fitted tightly sideways but not lengthwise. The plates were pulled longitudinally until the centre plate began to slide. The force required was found to be considerable and, of course, would have been greater if the joints had been double-riveted.[7] This view gave the early iron shipbuilders considerable confidence and it was claimed that by good and judicious riveting the friction could be nearly sufficient to counterbalance the weakening of the plates from the punching of the holes. Fig. 35 is taken from Grantham's 1842 book *Iron Shipbuilding* in which he makes a strong plea for the double-riveted joint. In the *Great Britain* all seams were double- with butt straps single-riveted; for one plate to move relative to another, thus tearing the butt strap, it would first have to move its seams with the plate above and below. That the seams were the most important structural joint was well recognised by the Building Committee.

The quality of any riveted ship depends upon the riveting itself. Good-quality construction used countersunk rivets with the great advantage that, as corrosion proceeded, the plates were held firmly together until the rivet had nearly completely wasted away. On the outside of the *Great Britain* only a very mild countersink is used and it is probable that the rivet holes were punched. The plates lying flat to the frames would be put temporarily in position with bolts and then faired up to the shape of the ship; if much shaping was required they were machine-bent. The holes required for the rivets were then marked off and punched, and the plates again clamped temporarily on to the ship. The outer plates were also put up temporarily, and a wood plug which had been dipped in white lead was pushed through the rivet holes in the inner plates, thus marking the rivet positions in the outer ones. The holes were then punched from the inside, giving the correct outward taper. A gang of four riveters would drive between 100 and 140 rivets in a 10-hour day.[8] The clamped plates could now be riveted in position on the frames. This whole process if carefully carried out would produce a very sound and fair structure, though it can be imagined that careless workmanship could produce an abomination, as indeed was not infrequently the case.

After riveting up, the process of caulking was carried out. This was done by two men, one holding a chisel and the other striking it with a hammer, making a slight indentation along the seam where one plate met another. This distorted the edge of the top plate forcing it hard against the lower one. Rivets themselves do not appear to have been caulked in these early days although the practice later became common with steel ships. *Great Britain* does not appear ever to have been caulked. She never leaked, so her shell plating must have been fitted with great care and accuracy, even perhaps to the extent of manual filing down of any burrs or irregularities on the frame surfaces and the laps.

Iron rusts, and the antagonists of iron shipbuilding in the early days pointed this out forcibly, forecasting short lives for iron ships. They were wrong as soon became apparent. Oxidation takes place at the same rate on thick and thin plates and $\frac{1}{2}$-in. plate, therefore, lasts at least twice as long as $\frac{1}{4}$-in. plate. The opposite applies with wood as it is difficult to season large thicknesses of wood. It was found that different considerations applied to the different areas of an iron ship. Below the waterline, for example, oxidation took place very slowly, and examination of ships that had been in service for some time even led some to suppose 'that coating in that quarter is superfluous'. Good white lead was regarded as the best underwater protection, though the majority of builders used red lead.[9] The success of this method of protecting the underwater body of the ship is dramatically illustrated by the *Great Britain*. We are nearly into the fourth quarter of the twentieth century and the bottom plating of this ship is still in remarkably good condition with sharp plate edges and much of the original thickness left, although it has been underwater continuously since 1843, much of the time without adequate protection. (*See* Fig. 9.) Another distinct area was that at the waterline, particularly forward, where the bow wave broke, and aft in way of the wake of the propeller. In both these areas the water was heavily aerated and hence there were ideal conditions for oxidation. Undoubtedly the worst wastage took place here and this is so in the *Great Britain*'s hull. Lloyd's were insistent that plating in this area be of adequate thickness—rightly so, although there were those who disagreed strongly. White lead was also used for protection in this area, with pitch as a standard topcoat.

Internally in the upper levels the environment was reasonably kind to the plating although this was not necessarily so in the boiler area where the heat and alternate wetting and drying made the life of the upper topside plating rather a hard one. In the bottom of the ship, however, conditions were tough. If there was bilge water present, turbulence as the ship rolled tended to erode the plating, partly by pure mechanical action but probably more by a combination of corrosion and erosion, the rust formed being worn away, exposing a new surface which rapidly rusted again. It was soon found, however, that it was sufficient to paint the inside of the hull with pitch or asphalt or even limewash. Under boilers there were conditions of combined heat, bilge water and lack of access which boded ill for the life of the plating. However, John Grantham and Laird found in 1842, when taking the boiler out of Laird's iron vessel *Cleveland* after five years in service in salt water, that the plating under and around the boiler was in remarkably good condition. It had been pitched when built and this was apparently enough to preserve it even here. Perhaps the worst wastage in a metal ship occurred where water dripped on to a surface from, say, a scupper; this may be observed today in the *Great Britain*. Such water is heavily oxygenated and also contains dissolved chemicals from the atmosphere. The mechanical action of the drip tends to remove the paint film or at any rate penetrate it, and quite heavy localised corrosion and penetration of the plate can result. However, this does not happen in a short time and, while we do not know the life intended for the early iron vessels, it soon became apparent that they had nothing much to fear from any aspect of corrosion. Indeed, during an experimental inquiry into the strength of iron in 1840 a Mr Mullet opined as the results of his experiments that a $\frac{1}{4}$-in. plate would last 100 years in salt water—how right he was.

An early opinion of the longevity of these vessels was given by John Grantham in 1858: 'The *Garry Owen* built about 1834 is in excellent condition on the Lower Shannon . . . The *Rainbow* of 1837 is to be seen in the Thames doing her work well.'[10] These were early days. Anybody in doubt now as to their durability needs only visit Bristol or consider ships such as the *Euterpe (Star of India)*, *Huascar*, and *Warrior*, all of which, perhaps with the exception of *Huascar*, have led hard lives and been little cared for much of the time.

Wrought iron does not seem to rust in the same way as steel. First, it rusts in sheets as might be expected from its laminar nature. Secondly, it seems to produce more voluminous scale for a given conversion of metal to oxide, and, third, much of the scale seems to remain attached to the iron, affording the base metal a considerable amount of protection. When *Great Britain* was floated in Sparrow Cove in 1970 complete sheets of scale fell off the bottom, leaving a clean and almost smooth surface. These bottom plates, after pressure water cleaning, show that wastage has been quite small considering their age.

The two real bugbears of early iron ships were compass deviations and fouling. Iron vessels had, of course, been used on canals and rivers for some time before they ever went to sea, but it was only at sea that the effect of the iron hull on the compass became important. This was a splendid hobby-horse for the sceptics, and when *Great Britain* went ashore in Dundrum Bay in 1846 the loss was immediately attributed by some to compass deviation. Three ships we have already met—*Rainbow*, *Garry Owen* and *Ironside*—figure in the story of the compass. In 1835 the Admiralty directed a Captain Johnson to carry out some investigations with the *Garry Owen* on the Shannon to see if corrections would be possible and to find the best position in the ship for a compass. Johnson published a memoir in the *Philosophical Transactions* showing that during construction an iron ship became in effect a large permanent magnet causing a serious disturbance to the general polar direction in which the needle pointed. He also concluded that correction was difficult. The Astronomer Royal, Professor Airey, who was consulted two years later settled this quite vital question once and for all.

Professor Airey carried out very careful experiments on the *Rainbow* at Deptford and on the *Ironside* at Liverpool and published a paper on them, culminating in a mathematical analysis, in the *Transactions* of the Royal Society for 1839. This showed that the magnetism of an iron ship in any place could be represented by an equivalent permanent magnet combined with the magnetic field arising from the earth's induction on a horizontal bar of soft iron. Consequently, he concluded that the effect of an iron ship upon a compass could easily be neutralised. The compasses of the *Rainbow* were compensated in this way in July 1838, and those of the *Ironside* two months afterwards. Professor Airey published a method of adjusting the compass in an iron ship showing how the elaborate calculations used in these two ships could be avoided. The method is essentially that used today although by comparison crude and incomplete. Nevertheless, in the case of the *Rainbow* Airey reduced the deviation of the compass at the steering position from 100° before compensation to a maximum of 1° after it!

All ships could be covered by Airey's procedure:

On completion of the ship and knowing the exact position in which the compass was to be placed, a point on the deck was taken immediately below it. Through this point two lines were described, one parallel to the keel and one at right-angles to it. Two or three powerful magnets about 2 ft long, in boxes full with tallow and finally nailed to the deck, and one or two boxes about 7 in. × 3 in. × 3 in. filled with small iron chains were needed. The ship was moored in a wet dock, held so that she could be aligned with the cardinal points of the compass. Starting pointing North any deviation of the compass needle was corrected by placing one of the magnets on the deck at right-angles to the meridian and moving it till the needle was correct. The ship's head was then turned through 90° and the needle corrected by a magnet in the box on the fore and aft line. . . .

The complete and elaborate procedure was described by Professor Airy and, to quote a contemporary account:

When these corrections are made with great nicety the compass should be free from any practical error—but it is recommended that the ship should always be swung round afterwards and the deviations if any noted on each or on each alternate point of the compass for use of the captain in navigating the ship.

This method was quite accurate enough to prevent accidents such as the one that struck down the *Great Britain* in 1846.

The problem of fouling was not so easily solved. The *Great Britain* Building Committee was very sanguine on the subject but clearly had little or no evidence on which to base its optimistic views. Most of the ships that had been built to date were small and were used around the tidal waters of Great Britain. Any fouling that occurred was easily scraped off. But a ship of some size, even by today's standards, presented problems: it could not with impunity be allowed to dry out on tidal berths and anyway was too big to clean in the time available. Writing in 1842, Grantham did not seem particularly worried by the problem either, but later versions of his book on *Iron Shipbuilding* told a very different story. In 1868 he wrote:

The old enemy to iron—the adhesion of animal and vegetable matter to the outer shell popularly termed fouling—has remained unsubdued. For 30 years at least every nerve has been strained to remove the evil. Science has exhausted its resources and practical men have availed themselves of every suggestion that promised a remedy but very slight progress has been made.[11]

Wooden ships had long been able to overcome this problem, by the same means which they used to combat the destructive activities of the Teredo and Gribble worms. The Romans sheathed their ships with lead, and copper sheathing had become standard practice in the eighteenth century. Copper oxidises in salt water and as the oxide is not adherent the fouling attached to the copper is simply removed mechanically with the oxide. The oxides of iron, however, do not behave in this way in salt water and, if the iron is painted, however smoothly, the various marine growths, common barnacles, the shellfish bolanus, zoophytes and grasses can all gain a footing without difficulty.

The subject continued to increase in importance for 25 years or more after the *Great Britain* was completed. A Mr Lamport, in a paper for the Institution of Naval Architects in 1864, wrote: 'I took up the Shipping Gazette the other day and looked at all the ships overdue for China . . . they were all over six months on a voyage, two to three months more than they ought to be. Out of the seven, six are of iron.' In 1870, the Peninsular & Oriental Steamship Company was spending some £70,000 a year in keeping the bottoms of their vessels clean and free from fouling, while six of the iron-plated ships of the French Imperial Navy in the 14 months up to March 1866 spent an average of 55 days each in dock being cleaned. A Mr Mallett, at the Royal United Services Institution's meeting in 1862, pointed out that if a 'clean ship of the enemy caught one of ours that happened to be foul, ours was at a disadvantage nothing can make up for'. Lord Clarence Page remarked that most of our iron-clads 'were almost as foul as lawyers' wigs'. The Southampton pilots found that during the spring and summer seasons they had to lay their iron pilot vessels on shore once a fortnight to scrub off weeds and growth, and others had the same experience. Warships were a particular worry. The *Achilles*, an iron frigate covered before her launch with an anti-fouling composition developed by the Admiralty, was so foul by the time she ran trials that her speed was three knots below that she achieved after being cleaned. This particular anti-fouling composition developed by Mr Hays, the Admiralty chemist, actually seems to have been a magnificent manure for marine growths.

The standard anti-fouling was red lead and tallow but the experimental approach seems to have been to use oxides or sulphates of some suitable metal, mixing them with grease or some other vehicle and then smearing or plastering this over the whole underwater surface of the vessel. Young remarked in 1867 that 'an increasing zoological and chemical knowledge cannot fail to show poisoning is an absurdity'.[12] He gave a marvellous list of preparations that had been tried and in some cases patented; it reads like a witch's brew: 'Silicates, quicksilver, plumbago, gutta percha, asphalt, shellac, guano and cow dung'; compounds of 'clay, bats, sawdust, hair, glue, oil, logwood, soot, etc. mixed'; 'baryta, litharge, arsenious acid, asphaltum oxide, calcium and creosote'. A splendid one was 'grease from boiled bones, kitchen stuff and butter without salt mixed with poisonous matters'. Our friend Mr Daft made the following remarks on the subject: 'To ensure a hull from fouling it is absolutely necessary that

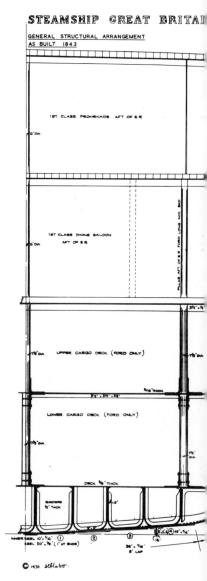

STEAMSHIP GREAT BRITAIN

GENERAL STRUCTURAL ARRANGEMENT
AS BUILT 1843

it should be composed of or sheathed with a metal that will by galvanic action peel or flake off as zinc, copper or yellow metal. Paints and compositions are utterly worthless in this respect.'

Grantham made an interesting forecast in 1842. He found that the *John Garrow*, with which he was concerned, had returned from India heavily fouled with shells but that these did not adhere to the rivets.

The cause of the shells not adhering to the rivets is probably to be traced to a slight galvanic shock which they received from them and it has been suggested that a galvanic battery might be employed by which oxidation would be prevented and the bottom kept free from shells.[13]

This was an inspired bit of crystal-gazing: cathodic protection is widely used today and effective against electrolytic corrosion and to some extent against fouling by shells.

Enough has been said to show that this was a very serious problem. It is questionable whether it was ever finally solved during the lifetime of the iron ship and certainly the witch's-brew approach was rather like trying to shoot bats on a dark night without a torch. It is quite possible that the popularity of composite ships such as the *Cutty Sark* with iron frames and a wood skin which could be coppered was to a considerable extent due to this very problem. Certainly two sailing clippers, one of iron and one of copper-sheathed wood, would be ill-matched on a long voyage, the composite ship having the distinct advantage.

We are now ready to consider in further detail the actual construction of *Great Britain* and how this compared with the practice of the day.[14]

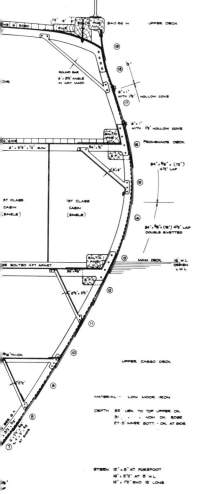

36 The amidships structure of *Great Britain*

CHAPTER FIVE

The shape and structure of 'Mammoth'

During 1839 the lines were drawn, the structural design of the *Mammoth* settled upon and construction started.

The lines of the ship were drawn in 1839 by William Patterson but were probably much influenced by the design committee generally and Brunel in particular. The midship section shape was of course determined by the exit from Bristol Docks, but the bow lines were fine with hollow, or concave, waterlines, and the stern was very fine indeed with a long run, the flow being fundamentally on what are known as buttocks, that is upwards along the longitudinal sections of the ship. Brunel was interested in wave patterns round ships, and Sir Marc had conducted experiments of his own: 'I had a circular canal made in which the various models could be made to operate with great precision. The screw was one of the means.' So the lines of the ship were probably a co-operative effort, and certainly they were advanced for the day. When first drawn the lines were for paddles but, as Brunel remarked in his 'screw' report, they were easily adaptable to screw propulsion. The *Great Britain* was the first large ship to be built with what came to be known as 'Clipper Lines', in other words with a fine hollow entrance and a fine run aft—the first of the great Tea Clippers, *Rainbow*, was not launched in New York until January 1845. Appendix 1 gives technical particulars of this hull form which as tank tested in 1970 proved to be quite efficient, suffering only from the peculiar midship section shape and, when propelled by a screw, from the unduly blunt waterline endings at the sternpost at about the 15 ft waterline level. In the light of the knowledge of the day, the lines reflect great credit upon Patterson and Brunel.

The ship was to be based on a strong platform 3 ft 3 in. deep on the centreline. The top of this is flat and because of the rise of the bottom (deadrise) athwartships the platform narrows down towards the bilges. It is very similar to a modern double bottom but is not watertight, the $\frac{3}{8}$ in. thick top being simply a deck. Fig. 36 is a composite structural cross-section of the ship as built, incorporating the forward cargo decks and the after spaces. On each side of the centreline there are fitted five solid longitudinal girders $\frac{1}{2}$ in. thick and there is thus no centreline vertical keel.

The frames of the ship run right down under the platform to the centreline and the longitudinal girders thus sit on top of the frames. The girders are attached to the shell plating by smithed angle bars, and to the platform deck by fore and aft angle bars, like the others with 3 in. × 3 in. leg lengths. This forms an extremely strong bottom structure. There is a flat plate keel 10 in. wide and $\frac{11}{16}$ in. thick and an outer keel 20 in. wide and $\frac{7}{8}$ in. thick. The bottom plating is clinker, the seams facing outwards until the turn of the bilge when strake No. 5 is reached. Nine feet from the centreline are the two docking keels made of $1\frac{1}{4}$-in. plate riveted to the ship by 5 in. × 5 in. angle bars $\frac{1}{2}$ in. thick. This bottom plating was originally $\frac{11}{16}$ in. thick but the bilge plating and the whole of the side up to the top strake was $\frac{5}{8}$ in.— $\frac{1}{16}$ in. less. As can be seen, the frames or ribs were formed from 6 in. × $3\frac{1}{2}$ in. angle, $\frac{5}{8}$ in. thick.

Up the ship's side the clinker strakes face downwards and are laid thus up to strake No. 16, just below the white band round the hull. This band was marked at top and bottom by an iron strap; the plating is flush from the bottom of this band up. There is thus a combination of two types of plating in the side shell (*See* Chap. IV.) At each deck level there is an iron stringer 36 in. wide and $\frac{1}{2}$ in. or $\frac{5}{8}$ in. thick. The one at the weather deck is curved to fit the shape of the deck beams. (*See* Fig. 32.) These stringers were reinforced by massive wood ones at each level.

The bottom platform runs level right through the ship and of course becomes very narrow and shallow right at the stem. Figs. 38 and 39 show sections through the forward and aft ends of the ship as built and it can be seen that there were four decks:—the lower cargo deck, the lower and upper 'tween decks, and the weather deck. The cargo deck forward is still in place although its plating has been much wasted away—it is flat with no camber and the deck beams run out to the ship's side with forged feet for riveting their ends and with angle iron struts instead of brackets. There are wood pillars $7\frac{1}{2}$ in. in diameter throughout this space as can be seen today. Aft there was no lower cargo deck, but a flat below the shaft formed the top of the fresh water tanks which carried the ship's stock of potable water. The top of these tanks is about 6 ft 6 in. above the bottom of the keel and the space above was not used for passengers or cargo but contained the large intermediate propeller shaft, a wrought iron thin wall tube 32 in. in diameter. There was no metal shaft tunnel or longitudinal tubular space enclosing the shaft and hence there must have been a wooden protection built around the shaft so as to render the space usable. As originally built there was no access from the weather deck to this space so that it is probable that it was used only for passengers' luggage, which would have been lowered into the space through a trap in the lower 'tween deck or dining-saloon level.

The lower 'tween deck was also flat with no camber across the ship. The beams were heavier than those of the cargo deck, being much the same as the frames, and the toes of these were again forged out to make a riveting foot on to the frames. Again, $2\frac{1}{2}$-in. angle iron struts were used instead of brackets. This deck was planked transversely with 5-in. pine. The design required the ship to be as wide as possible just above this level[1] which was almost coincident with the design draught of 16 ft. As the ship would clearly take berthing loads on her sides owing to the

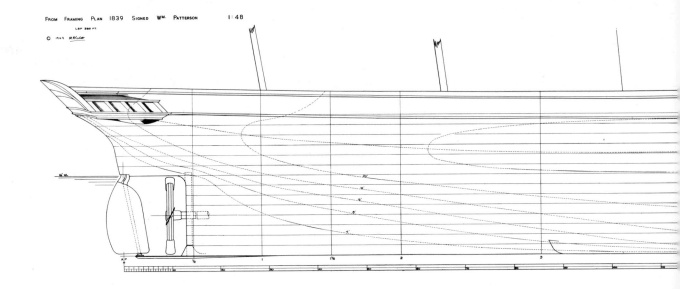

From Framing Plan 1839 Signed Wm. Patterson   1:48
LBP 288 FT.
© 1969 W. Blake

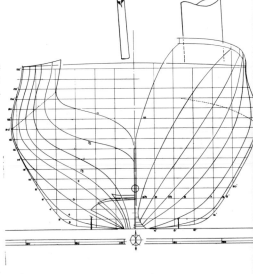

37 The lines of the *Great Britain.* The lines have been redrawn to incorporate known changes in construction and to eliminate distortion in the original paper

bulge in them, Brunel felt that she should have as much athwartships strength as possible at this level; hence the unique feature of transverse planking.

Above this is the dining-saloon deck, stretching both forward and aft of the engine room with cabins extending to the ship's side. The clear height available from the top of the planking to the deck beams was 7 ft 6 in.; the next deck up was similarly arranged. As in the deck below, there was a heavy Baltic Pine stringer along the ship's side supplying longitudinal strength and tying all the side frames together. The upper 'tween deck was used for first- and second-class promenades and for cabins outboard of this. It was planked with 4-in. pine, laid longitudinally as was conventional. The weather deck above is again formed with 6 in. × 3 in. deck beams but this time with camber, increasing rapidly at the extreme sides of the ship, the beam being smithed down to make downward-facing lugs which are riveted to the side frames. Again there was

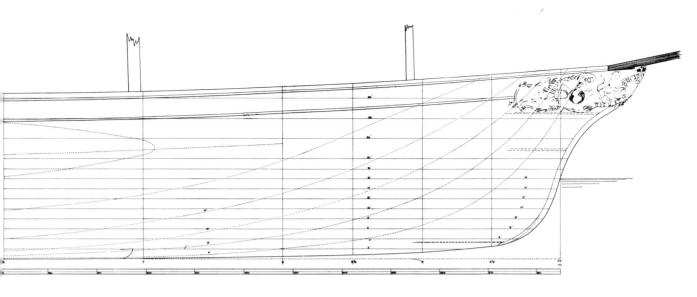

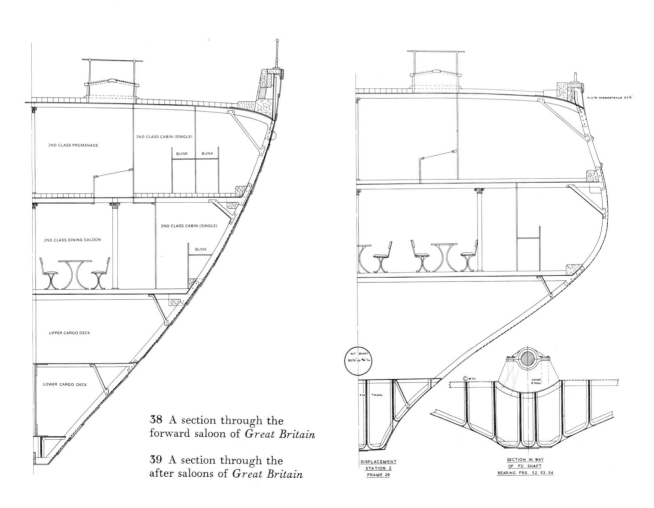

2ND CLASS PROMENADE

2ND CLASS CABIN (SINGLE)

BUNK   BUNK

2ND CLASS DINING SALOON

2ND CLASS CABIN (SINGLE)

BUNK

UPPER CARGO DECK

LOWER CARGO DECK

PLATE SHEERSTRAKE 2×½″

INT. SHAFT
30'6″ UP ½ TH

1870

WOOD STOOL

FW. TANK

DISPLACEMENT
STATION 2
FRAME 29

SECTION IN WAY
OF FD. SHAFT
BEARING FRS. 52.53.54

38 A section through the
forward saloon of *Great Britain*

39 A section through the
after saloons of *Great Britain*

originally no bracket between the frame and the deck beam. Round bar struts were used as can be seen today, although these were replaced by heavy 6 in. × 3½ in. angle struts in the region of the machinery.

At weather-deck level the ship's side plating was ½ in. thick, and a very heavy pine gunwale and deck-edge stringer 2 ft wide and 340 sq. in. in cross-section was incorporated to give strength to the top corner or gunwale of the ship. This is in fact a crucial area; the *Great Britain* would have been much stronger if the curved stringer plate about 4 ft wide had been extended right across the whole of this deck. The deck was planked with 3-in. red pine as shown. The ship was built with no appreciable sheer on her weather deck; to avoid an unpleasant appearance sheer was therefore incorporated in the heavy wood and iron gunwale structure. Just forward of amidships this begins to deepen and eventually becomes a full-height bulwark at the break of the forecastle. The same pattern is repeated on the forecastle.

The decks were supported by heavy pillars in the lower or cargo decks, extending up through the dining-saloons. They were not continued in the promenades as the bulkheads in these spaces were arranged approximately in line with the pillars and hence picked up the vertical loads.

The keel has already been described. The keel plates, ⅞ in. in thickness, were fire-welded into lengths of 50 or 60 ft and these were then joined by scarphs 18 in. long and riveted all over. The keel, being a dished plate, gradually came up at the bow to envelop the stem, the dimensions of which have been given before. The frames are generally 6 in. × 3½ in. angles, ⅝ in. thick; their variable spacings have been mentioned in the previous chapter. In the area of the engines the frames up to the lower 'tween decks are doubled by 6 in. × 3½ in. angles reversed, i.e. with similar angles riveted to their inner edges. There are also nine additional intermediate double frames in the area of the original main engines. These frames are of course formed to the peculiar transverse shape of the ship and their smithing must have been a tricky job. They were formed on heavy cast-iron slabs with holes in them, and dogged down and bent hot around formers, as indeed was the practice until comparatively recently. Records exist of the supply of these heavy bending slabs— massive objects in their day. Aft, the sternpost extends to just above the 16-ft waterline. It is 14 in. fore and aft and 3 in. wide, formed from a heavy flat bar at top and bottom which was fire-welded to a boss to take the propeller shaft. The plating aft was taken in a curve round the sternpost, above the propeller.

Above this level the stern runs aft over the propeller aperture and is formed into radiused endings at the foot of the counter. This is well shown in Fig. 40, a photograph taken when the ship was a wreck in the Falklands. A forging was incorporated a couple of feet forward of the extreme end of the stern at this level, on to which the rudder post was bolted, and plating around it was carried up in a trunk shape, taking the recess for the stock well above any possible water level. Two heavy knees are formed from plating and a reverse angle on the top, running forward from the area of the top of the sternpost bracketing it in a fore and aft

40 The rounded plating at the bottom of the counter of *Great Britain*. Photograph taken in 1968 during the salvage survey

41 The curious bulge in the top-sides at the stern in way of the original fake quarter-galleries. Taken in 1968 during salvage survey

direction; the shaft ran between them. A horizontal shelf runs across from these knees, preventing them from tripping or falling over under load.

Well outboard of these, some 15 ft from the centreline, a further pair of long plate knees, extending over eight frame spacings, run forward from the bulkhead. At the time of building, the bulkhead was considered an aid to safety, but since it only ran up to lower-'tween-deck level (which was just about water level) it would have afforded no real help to the ship if, for instance, a propeller blade had come loose and penetrated the plating above the bottom aperture. The second pair of knees, running forward from this perpendicular to the shellplating and continuing through the hold as plate stringers, were intended to make the afterpeak bulkhead structure rigid. This heavy, 'wood-type' structure, experimental in an iron ship, is somewhat difficult to justify, since the thrust of the screw would not be transmitted to the bulkhead but went up the shaft line to the thrust bearing. It is not surprising that this part of the ship, being stronger than was strictly necessary, has given no trouble.

At the stern above this level the structure is perfectly straightforward with a square transom with windows just above the upper-'tween-deck level, and the plating below that taken round in an ever-increasing radius, thus forming rather an attractively shaped counter. The clinker construction is peculiarly adapted to this shape, each shape being a section of the surface of a cone and the overlapping allowing some tolerance on fitting. The ship was fitted with false galleries on the port and starboard quarters. These were made of wood with four windows each side, a cornucopia at the after end running up the corner of the transom and a gilded swan drooping over the top of the windows. This decoration was applied on top of the shell plating which, curiously, is curved both horizontally and transversely into a bulge to take the decoration. Even the frames in the after cabin are curved out to fit this bulge. This was an expensive idiosyncrasy. The internal structure of the ship in this area has been much altered, of course, the new stern and rudder post and the trunk for lifting the propeller having been fitted in 1857.

Right forward the forepeak bulkhead extends from the keel to the forecastle level. Up to the 9-ft level the space forward of it forms a water-tank; above this there is a store and then two levels of accommodation for crew and a higher one for officers. The hawse pipes were at the 22-ft level, very far forward, with the stem bisecting what was in effect a common opening. The two hawse pipes bifurcated 3 ft inside the hawse and then led upwards to the break of the forecastle on the weather deck where the inboard ends of the hawse pipes are 5 ft apart. These hawses can be seen in Fig. 9, a photograph taken during the reconstruction of the ship in 1972.

All decks in the forecastle are without sheer, showing Brunel's intensely practical outlook on ship design. The top of the forepeak tank is level with the lower cargo deck, and the lower accommodation level with the dining saloon deck, but the decks above diverge in level from those aft. Even the forecastle head is without sheer. The space below, which was used for officers' accommodation, has an iron bulkhead across its forward end, 24 ft from the break of forecastle. Forward of this were the officers' heads. The beams of the whole of the forecastle are 6 in. × 3 in. angles, spaced 26 in. apart. Fig. 47 shows all this in a longitudinal inboard profile of the ship. Through the forecastle area at weather deck level the stringer plates of the weather deck are continued forward as a heavy stringer with a face bar on the inboard side. Similarly, the deck below the upper 'tween deck is carried forward in the first tier of seamen's accommodation as a heavy stringer running right through the stem and bracketed to it. Below this, the deck levels of the forecastle coincide with those of the after structure and there was no need for these arrangements of stringers. The partners for No. 1 mast* run down forward of the break of the forecastle. In the upper forecastle a shelf is run across the ship joining the port and starboard stringer shelves and this is bracketed to the forecastle bulkhead and mast partners formed in it. These are continued downwards through each deck, and a lower stub for No. 1 mast was tenoned on to the top of the forepeak ballast tank.

The total weight of iron used in the hull amounted to 1,040 tons and the total weight of wood in the decks, fittings, bulkheads, etc. 370 tons.

Modern development of ship construction was forecast in a letter Brunel wrote to Guppy in August 1843:

I have been thinking a great deal of your plans for iron shipbuilding and have come to a conclusion which I believe agrees with your ideas. I will state mine. At bottom and at top I would give *longitudinal* strength and stiffness gaining the latter by the former so that all metal used should add to the longitudinal tie while in the neutral axis and along the sides to resist swells from seas. I would have vertical strength by ribs and shelf pieces thus:— the black lines being sections and longitudinal pieces and dotted lines vertical and transverse diagonal plates throwing the metal as much as possible into the outside bottom plates and getting the strength inside by form, that is depth of beams, etc. the former being liable to injury from blows etc. the latter being protected.[2]

It is clear that Brunel must have been thinking of longitudinal construction long before the *Great Eastern* was built, and these basic ideas are typical of modern cargo liner structures.

Even in the light of today's knowledge the *Great Britain*'s structural arrangements appear fairly good: the disposition of material in the shell is sensible, the bottom structure expensive but efficient, the pillaring good and the deck beams probably adequate. Criticism would be mainly of the quite inadequate bracketing arrangements between the frames and the deck beams at the upper deck levels, and above all of the lack of a metal deck right across the ship at weather deck level. Possibly also the ship would have been better with one less longitudinal girder; a central one could well have been arranged as a vertical keel plate directly on the centreline under the centre row of pillars.

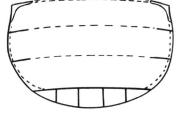

42 How Brunel thought longitudinal material should be disposed in a ship

* Officially the six masts were known as Fore, Main and then 1, 2, 3, 4; unofficially as Monday, Tuesday, Wednesday, Thursday, Friday and Saturday masts. However, for greater convenience they will be referred to here as Nos. 1–6, starting at the bow.

CHAPTER SIX

The birth of commercial screw-propulsion

The history of the screw propeller starts with that of the iron ship and is really dominated by two names: Captain Ericsson and Francis Pettitt Smith. However, using the screw to propel ships was a very old idea and had been used with manual drive in the eighteenth century. By the early part of the nineteenth century an American named Stevens was conducting experiments with a specially built boat on the Hudson River, and in 1820 Sir Marc Brunel conducted model experiments in a circular tank or canal on various types of hulls including some self-propelled by screws. Altogether between 15 and 20 experiments preceded the practical application of the screw, including that carried out in 1825 by an inventor named Jacob Perkins, who actually tried an 8-ft diameter contra-rotating surface propeller in a canal boat, with some success.

In May 1836 Francis Pettitt Smith, a farmer from Hendon, took out a patent for a screw propeller, and in July of the same year Captain Ericsson took out another for his propeller. The outstanding feature of Smith's invention was the placing of the screw described 'in a recess or open space formed in that part of the after part of the vessel commonly called the deadrising or deadwood of the run'. Indeed, he limited his claim to this point, though his designs were quite efficient in other respects. Propellers had previously been positioned aft of the rudder or to one side of it, but never immediately in front of it. Smith's position has several advantages. The propeller is able to pick up the so-called 'wake' of the hull. This is water which has been slowed down by friction with the hull and acts to increase the efficiency of the screw. The screw also generates a solid, fast-moving stream of water which is directed on to the rudder and greatly improves the steering capabilities of the ship. The rudder itself tends to take twist out of the race of the propeller, slightly improving its efficiency. This is also a very advantageous position as regards shafting and the ability to transmit power to the propeller. The main disadvantage is its closeness to the hull as there is a certain loss of thrust caused by the propeller sucking the hull back into it as well as thrusting the whole ship forward. This must be countered by moving the propeller well aft of the sternpost and by making the endings of the hull waterlines sharp in the vicinity of the propeller. This was not done very well in the *Great Britain* 'conversion' as we shall see later. Smith originally specified a screw of not more than one thread and of more than one convolution, but in a disclaimer in April 1838 he limited his claim to a single-threaded screw

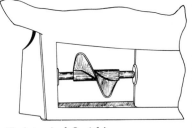

43 A typical Smith's screw installation

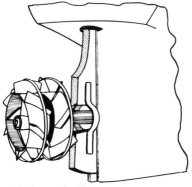

44 An early Ericsson's
screw arrangement

of one, or a double-threaded screw of half a convolution. Later this half shrank to one-sixth, and *Great Britain*'s third screw exactly conformed to this latter practice.

Captain John Ericsson, at one time an officer in the Swedish army, had developed a screw which was very sophisticated and hence more complicated in design and placing than Smith's. To use Ericsson's own words, this propeller consisted of

two thin broad hoops or short cylinders made to revolve in contrary direction round a common cylinder, each cylinder or hoop kept moving with a different velocity from the other, each hoop or cylinder being also situated entirely under the water at the stern of the boat and furnished each with a series of short spiral planes or plates—the plates of each series standing at an angle the exact converse of the angle given to those of the other series and kept revolving by the power of the steam engine.

Each Ericsson screw consisted of an inner and an outer propeller. A three-bladed helical screw was attached at its rim to a plate cylinder and between this cylinder and a further outer cylinder were about eight blades, forming an auxiliary outer propeller. The original arrangement was contra-rotating: two propellers of opposite pitch, placed one behind the other, rotated in opposite directions. A hollow shaft carried the forward propeller and the shaft for the after one revolved inside it. Though this type of double propeller was fairly efficient, Ericsson's designs soon showed preference for a single screw placed before the rudder in the stern, in the manner of Smith.

Both inventors started with small models, Smith on his farm pond with a 2-ft steamer and Ericsson with a similar-sized model which steamed round a pole in a circular tank—steam being supplied from the pole. Both then proceeded to pilot plant experiments. On 20 September 1837 the first trial of the Smith experimental launch was carried out on the City and Paddington Canal. This little ship was 34 ft long, 6 ft 5 in. broad and drew 4 ft of water. She was fitted with a screw of 2 ft diameter and 2 ft 5 in. pitch which initially consisted of two complete turns of a single blade on a long axis. On this preliminary trial part of the blade broke off and the boat's performance improved noticeably. The next day she left Gravesend and made the Nore light in two hrs 14 mins, Herne Bay in four hrs 25 mins, and Margate seven hrs after sailing. A couple of days later she left for Ramsgate, Dover and Folkestone where she spent some days making a series of experiments. Coming back she had a very rough passage from Ramsgate to Margate but, although the weather was such that it was thought that a steamer of this size with paddles could not weather the Foreland, this boat, little better than a launch, reached Margate in safety in two hrs 10 mins. When she arrived back at Blackwall she had covered 400 miles at an average speed of seven knots. In the Thames she towed the *Great Western* into the East India Dock at $2\frac{1}{2}$ knots—this may have been Isambard Brunel's first contact with screw propulsion.

Captain Ericsson's first experiment was also on the Thames. His boat was a little bigger—45 ft long, $8\frac{1}{2}$ ft broad, drawing 6 ft of water—and was fitted with a contra-rotating double screw, each propeller being just over 5 ft in diameter. Being a military man, he approached the Navy who carried out a technical trial, saw that it was obviously successful and promptly took no further interest in it on the grounds of potentially poor steering. This little boat towed a 650-ton ship at 4½ knots in these experiments and demonstrated a static pull of nearly one ton but, her propeller being aft of the rudder, there was probably something in what the Admiralty said. Ericsson's screw in Smith's location would have been most effective. Ericsson then built a twin-propeller canal boat, the *Novelty*, to operate on the Manchester Ship Canal. The American Consul at Liverpool knew of these experiments—indeed, the experimental boat was called the *Francis B. Ogden* after him—and drew the attention of a Captain Stockton of the U.S. Navy to Ericsson.

Stockton was responsible for the construction of a further Ericsson boat, the new towboat *R. F. Stockton*, 70 ft long, 10 ft beam, launched in Liverpool in July 1838. Fitted with direct acting engines designed by Ericsson she was very successful. The propeller was 6 ft 4 in. in diameter and 2 ft 9 in. long. The forward section ran at 44 rpm and the after at 49. In January 1839 she towed four loaded coal barges weighing nearly 100 tons each, lashed alongside, up the Thames at 5½ mph. Smith, who was present on these trials, suggested deleting the after wheel; this was done, producing an improvement. In April, the *R. F. Stockton* sailed, without using her screw, to America, followed by Ericsson who saw his propeller immediately applied to the steam frigate *Princeton*.

All was not lost to Britain, as Smith proceeded with his experiments and interested Messrs Rennie in the subject. The Screw Propeller Company was formed and constructed the famous *Archimedes*, 125 ft long overall, 21 ft 10 in. in breadth, and drawing 9 ft 6 in. of water. *Archimedes* was fitted with a two-cylinder engine of 90 indicated horsepower—a highly optimistic rating. Her first propeller was a single-threaded screw of one complete turn, 5 ft 9 in. in diameter and 8 ft pitch. One would not expect this to have been very satisfactory; not surprisingly, it was removed quite soon and substituted by a double-threaded or two-bladed propeller, each blade or thread being but half a turn, with the same diameter and pitch as before. After preliminary trials in 1839, *Archimedes* was tested in the Channel against Dover Mail Steam packets. Captain Chappell, R.N., was appointed by the Government to conduct these trials in early 1840, and four packets were used. *Archimedes* was in fact slightly larger than any of them but one, *Widgeon*, was the fastest packet on the Dover Station. To quote Captain Chappell:

These (cross-Channel) trials clearly prove the speed of *Archimedes* is slightly inferior to that of the *Widgeon* in light airs and calms and in smooth water; but as the steam power of the former is 10 horses less and her burthen 75 tons more than *Widgeon* it is evident that in this vessel the propelling power of the screw is equal if not superior to that of the ordinary paddle wheel. Mr Smith's invention may be considered completely successful.[1]

Archimedes was then placed at the disposal of Captain Chappell in order to test the screw propeller in various service conditions, including a

45 *Archimedes* off the Nore—14 May

voyage round the coast of England and Scotland and one from Plymouth to Oporto, which she made in 69 hrs, the fastest steam passage to that date.

Basically a propeller is a number of wings working in water—obtaining lift and hence thrust exactly as does an aircraft wing. A long narrow wing is more efficient than a short broad one and so a very short segment of a screw produces thrust better than an axially long one of little span. James Lowe patented just this in 1839 and wrote in 1842:

> . . . any success which the *Archimedes* gained was when my patent segments were applied instead of Mr Smith's whole screw. The voyage from Plymouth to Oporto was performed by a propeller of my segments. *Archimedes* left port with Mr Smith's patent which was afterwards unshipped and my patent segments fitted. On her return . . . she was obliged to come back to the Thames with my propeller still fixed to the stern.[2]

Certainly Lowe's type of propeller become common because it was more efficient, but to be fair to Smith he never claimed a patent screw, only a method of applying screws.

Archimedes's trips constituted a sales tour, familiarising shipbuilders, engineers and naval men around the coast with the screw propeller and illustrating how it showed to advantage by comparison with paddles.

As was normal at that time, *Archimedes* had a slow-running main engine, and this was speeded up to the screw by a system of double step-up gears of crude construction and of overall ratio $5\frac{1}{3}$: 1. In May, 1840, during this tour, the ship made a highly significant visit to Bristol. There were the usual demonstration runs, in this case in the Floating Harbour, and the Building Committee was most interested. An excursion was made to the Holmes and as a result Guppy went round with the ship to Liverpool. During this voyage quite heavy weather was encountered and it became apparent that, contrary to what the Jonahs had said before to the Building Committee, the screw propeller was not impracticable. The Building Committee then recommended to the directors that construction of *Great Britain*'s engines be halted, together with that of those parts of the hull which would be affected by any possible change in engines. Brunel, who supported this recommendation, was asked by the directors to go into the whole question of the adoption of the screw and to report on it.

The first step was to carry out experiments, and the Great Western Company borrowed or hired the *Archimedes* from the Screw Propeller Company for some months. Altogether eight screws were tested; an engine indicator recorded the horsepower developed by the steam in the cylinders and as far as possible all trials were comparative and scientific. Appendix 2 shows the details of the screws and the speeds achieved. The last columns of the table have been added to show the relative merit of these screws together with their speeds of revolution. By this time there were other competitors in the field. Woodcroft had designed a screw propeller featuring an increasing pitch from the leading edge to the after edge of the blade, while other designs by Steinman and Sutherland were also coming to the fore. The main propellers tested by Brunel were Smith's and Woodcroft's but the eighth propeller was a design probably not dissimilar to that finally adopted for the *Great Britain*. Fig. 46 shows Smith's and Steinman's two-bladed screws.

Brunel's report to the directors dated 10 October 1840 is a long and complex document.[3] It is quite fascinating and certainly marks the birth of the scientific approach to propeller design. Too long to quote from extensively, some parts must be repeated. The opening is written in dignified Victorian English:

Gentlemen, I have now the pleasure to lay before you the result of the different experiments which I have made and of the best consideration I have been able to give to the subject of the screw propeller.

The observations which I have to make are naturally devised under two principal heads—namely—First the simple question of the applicability and efficiency of the screw considered merely as a means of propelling a vessel compared with the ordinary paddle wheel and secondly the general advantages or disadvantages attending its use.

It must be understood that at the time Brunel wrote naval architects considered that the resistance of a vessel through the water was directly proportional to the area of its midship cross-section. This is a convenient assumption but quite incorrect generally and especially so when the speed

SMITH

46 Smith & Steinman two-bladed screw

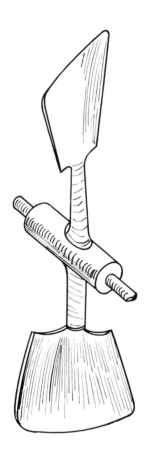

STEINMAN

of ships becomes great enough for them to make appreciable surface waves. Scott Russell, the shipbuilder responsible for the actual construction of *Great Eastern*, once remarked that that ship had to dig a channel across the Atlantic equal in cross-section to her midship section and that the power of the engines was expended directly on this work.

Much of Brunel's comparative analysis in this great report is based upon the midship section areas of the ships considered, his main comparison being between the *Archimedes* and the ship he knew best—the *Great Western*. For example, he stated that the area of the propelling surface in each case, the midship section being 100, was 20·3 in the case of the *Archimedes* screw propeller and 39·1 in the case of the *Great Western* paddle propeller. However, he said the difference of speed between the vessel and its propelling surface (or the amount of slip), the ratio of the vessel being 100, was 29·1 in the case of the *Archimedes* and 27·08 in the case of the *Great Western*. Let us use Brunel's own words:

The resistance whether to the surface of a screw or of a paddle board or of an oar or any other propelling body offered by the fluid against which it acts is of course not perfect and there is a certain amount of yielding commonly called the slip.

Thus, although the propeller had a much smaller surface with which to act upon the water than the paddle, it had no less effect. Brunel examined a number of other ships to convince the directors that this was so. He remarked that 'the mass of water pushed back by the action of the screw appears to be very large spreading from the screw . . . but there is little or no appearance of any rotatory motion in the sense that the water is not put into rapid motion as in the case of the paddle. . . .', and that '. . . comparing this with the violent displacement of the water by the action of paddle boards even under the most favourable circumstances I no longer feel surprised. . . .'

Brunel also had to contend with a misconception that existed among many people at that time, namely, that the propeller was really only a skewed paddle. In other words, that part of a propeller at, say, 45° to its axis must strike the water at 45° as it went round. Of course, if the water was motionless relative to the screw this would be so but with inflow and the vessel in forward motion the angle is much reduced and is in fact generally only about 5° or 6°, thus operating at an 'angle of incidence' rather like an aeroplane wing. Brunel commented:

As regards the oblique action also a great mistake appears to have been made generally and very naturally by most persons when first considering the working of the screw. It is generally assumed that the inclined plane formed by the thread of the screw strikes the particles of water at that angle . . . but it is forgotten that the screw is moving forward with the ship and therefore that the angle at which the water is struck by the plane is diminished by all that much as the ship with the screw advances . . . The angle at which any given part of the screw does in fact strike the water is only equal to the difference between the angle to which that part of the screw is formed and the angle or direction in which it moves by the compound motion of the revolutions of the screw and the forward motion of the ship and the screw.

In fact Brunel showed that in the case of the *Archimedes* the angle at

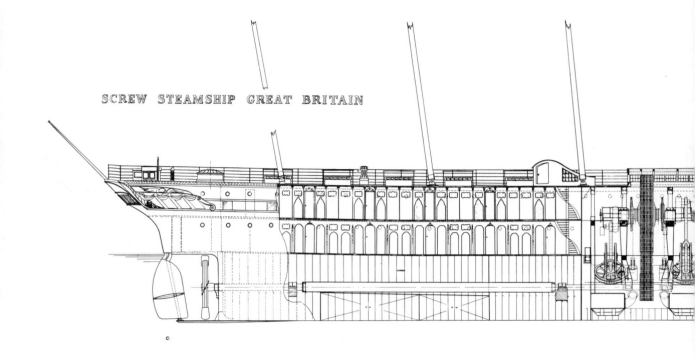

SCREW STEAMSHIP GREAT BRITAIN

47 The inboard profile of *Great Britain*, 1845

which the leading edge of the propeller struck the water was only 1 in $11\frac{1}{2}$, which is $6\frac{1}{2}°$.

However, Brunel himself did not appreciate the importance of 'camber.' or the difference in curvature between one side of a blade and the other, In February 1844 a Mr Cowper, discussing a paper on screw propulsion described a fan he had made with three or more cambered blades, like a screw propeller:

When the axis was placed vertically and a rapid rotary action imparted to it the fan rose in the air 150 ft. On reversing the fan—it would not rise at all. This fact evidently showed that the action of the curved fan on the air was like that of a screw in a solid.[4]

Cowper pointed out that a flat helicoidal fan did not show this asymmetry. Propellers soon began to have a flat face and a curved back.

Brunel went on to analyse the losses that would arise in the propeller: the friction of the propeller as it went through the water and the resistance of the water to penetration of the 'cutting edge'. We must remember that in Brunel's day nothing of the modern sciences of hydro- and aerodynamics existed. Brunel was not aware of the lifting capabilities of a wing and had to reason from more mechanistic bases. But if his analysis can be faulted his conclusion is nevertheless sound:

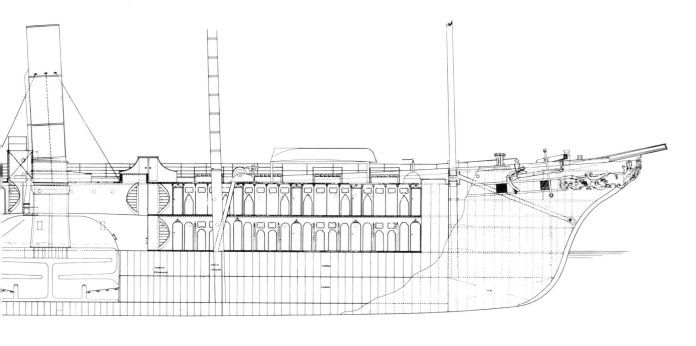

I think that one conclusion can be drawn from the results of the experiments quoted and that is that as compared with the ordinary paddle wheel of Sea-going Steamers the Screw is both, as regards the effect produced and the proportion of power required to obtain that effect, an efficient propeller.

The report then dealt with the supposed disadvantages of the screw propeller. These were: first, 'the necessity of a peculiar form of vessel'; secondly, the fact that the screw, being underwater, was to some extent unseen, inaccessible and possibly liable to injury; thirdly, that it might be lifted out of the water as the ship pitched; and fourthly, the difficulty of achieving the required number of revolutions which was much greater than that required by a paddle wheel.

A clean run is the most essential condition and I should suppose no ship was ever built in which this principle of form was carried to a greater extent than in our new Iron Ship—Her present form I believe to be excellent for the screw and with the very slight dropping of the keel towards the stern which can easily be done now without any expense, assisted by the different trim which I shall presently show will be effected by the use of the screw the required draught of water will be attained.

This is a very interesting statement because the way Brunel accommodated the screw in *Great Britain* was in fact to drop the horizontal member at the bottom of the propeller aperture—the solepiece—below the line of keel. This arrangement can still be seen today. As regards the second objection, he felt, after considering the matter, that the screw was far less exposed to injury than the paddle wheel. It was by no means inaccessible and could be stopped during heavy weather, which was not the case with paddles; the whole of the screw bearings could be examined, and, if necessary, 'men sent down with common diving jackets and hoods—to replace bearings or attach tackle to remove the screw or clear away any obstacle entangled in it'.

The third point was examined in detail. Captain Claxton's son, Berkeley, who was an engineer and draughtsman and worked for the Steamship Company, was sent by Brunel on a number of voyages aboard *Great Western* and made many measurements of pitching and rolling angles, as well as observing visually through a port cut in the stern of the ship the rise and fall of the sea at the stern. Brunel wrote:

From this it was evident that the vessel never pitches to so great an angle as that to which she rises. Such a result might indeed have been anticipated by considering the form of the vessel forward and aft, and the circumstance that a **Steamer** is always invariably meeting or passing the Seas or if overtaken by them **is still** going at a good rate which reduces the relative Speed of the Sea—Con**sequent**ly although the vessel may be frequently thrown up very violent forward —**yet** the Stern which has no displacement under water settles down heavily **upon** the surface. Or considering it another way Variation of displacement at the stern is very rapid falling off to almost nothing in a few feet below the waterline and spreading out to a greater extent at a few feet above, whilst forward the difference of displacement is comparatively small. The centre of motion is therefore thrown very far aft and while the bows are thrown high out of the water and plunge deeply into it—the Stern floats nearly steady resting on its broad counter.

In the *Great Western* the whole cut water and it is said a considerable length of keel is frequently seen out of water from the bowsprit, while astern it is doubtful whether more than half the stern post was ever seen. Marks have been made by my direction on the rudder to observe this. As yet the 9 ft mark is the lowest seen and this occurring rarely and only for very short intervals.[5]

Brunel also sent Berkeley Claxton with *Archimedes* on her voyage from Plymouth to Oporto, and the facts he collected agreed so closely with those obtained from the *Great Western* that Brunel was able to dispose of this potential difficulty with ease.

On the fourth point it must be remembered that up to this period marine engines had been developed to supply power for the paddle wheel and as this required a speed of rotation of the order of 15 to 20 revolutions per minute such machinery was quite unsuitable for the 50 or 60 revolutions that the propeller demanded. Brunel was very critical of the speed-increasing arrangement on board the *Archimedes*: 'The Archimedes offers but a miserable example and the result is almost enough to prejudice the mind of any person against the whole scheme.'[6] Apart from the fact that the required speed of the screw was not achieved 'the noise and tremour caused by the machinery is such as to render the Vessel uninhabitable and perfectly unfit for passengers, I should almost say for a crew.' However, this was a mere mechanical difficulty which could be overcome by the use of straps instead of gearing. He described how this should be done and in fact was to adopt variations of the method both for the experimental naval vessel *Rattler* and for the *Great Britain*.

Brunel then turned to the advantages of the screw propeller which he concluded were: (1) a considerable saving of weight, principally top weight; (2) the introduction of a better and simpler form of vessel, having greater structural stiffness with the same quantity of material and offering less resistance to headwinds and seas; (3) the fact that the operation of the screw was unaffected by the trim or rolling of the vessel and allowed the free use of sails; (4) perfect regularity of motion and freedom from shocks to the engine; (5) the singularly increased power of steering given to the vessel; (6) a great reduction in the overall breadth.

In the case of *Great Britain* he estimated that the weight saved by adopting screw propulsion would be over 96 tons and that a greater weight than that was moved from the top of the ship to the bottom: '. . . no less than 160 tons is removed from the level of the paddle shaft or about 10 ft above the waterline and replaced with 55 tons at about 7 ft below the waterline'. This of course is quite correct, and the screw vessel required less breadth for stability than did the paddle ship. The other advantages were explored in detail. Perhaps comment is justified on Nos. (5) and (6). The propeller being in front of the rudder, if a screw vessel is at rest it is possible to direct a considerable stream of water over the rudder and thus obtain steerage even though the vessel itself hardly moves. This is quite a distinct advantage and one of which Brunel was well aware. The sixth point was very close to home as far as the Great Western Steamship Company directors were concerned. 'Important as this alteration would be to any Vessel,' said Brunel, 'it is peculiarly so as connected with Bristol. Her total breadth including paddle boxes would be at least 78 ft—with the screw it would be under 50. Very nearly 30 ft of difference—One of the principal objections to her coming up the River would be removed—and the Dock Gates might easily be made to receive her.' A technically impeccable argument, though politically it was not quite as easy as this.

At the end of this long and brilliant report Brunel concluded:

From all that I have said it must be evident to you Gentlemen that my opinion is strong and decidedly in favour of the advantage of employing the screw in the new ship—it certainly is so. I am fully aware of the responsibilities I take upon myself by giving this advice.

Brunel was indeed worried by his responsibility. In August 1843, he wrote to Guppy:

If all goes well we shall all gain credit but 'quad scriptum est manet' if the result disappoint anybody, my written report will be remembered by everybody and I shall have to bear the storm—and all that spite and revenge can do at the Admiralty will be done! The words 'better sailing qualities than could be given to the *Polyphemus*, which I used in my report to the Admiralty I believe have never been forgotten.

Well, the result of all my anxious thoughts—for I assure you I feel more anxious about this than about most things I have had to deal with—is first that we must adopt a *principle not to be departed from*, that all mechanical difficulties of construction must give away, must in fact be lost sight of in determining the most perfect form. If we find that the screw determined upon *cannot* be made (and what cannot be done?) then it is quite time to try another form and even then *my* rule would be to try again at making it.[7]

In a few words of his own, the whole creed of the man.

Brunel attended a special meeting of the Board and read and explained the report. A resolution was passed in December 1840 adopting screw propulsion for the *Great Britain*. It was found impracticable to retain the Humphreys engines; as the company had by now erected a complete engine-building shop, it was necessary to build the new engines themselves. On Humphreys's resignation Guppy was appointed Engineer-in-Charge of the whole establishment with a Mr Harman as assistant under him. Later Harman was the ship's first Chief Engineer.

Soon after this and possibly because his report was so striking that it was much discussed, Isambard Brunel was asked to send a copy to the Admiralty. Shortly afterwards he was invited to attend the Board which he did on 27 April 1841. We have his own account.[8] Lord Minto stated that he wished an experiment to be made on the screw and proposed to place the conduct of the experiment 'in my hands as a professional man'. Brunel was pleased and interested to do so 'provided they intended to make a good experiment and would place it entirely in my hands without the intervention of any Government Officers but that I should communicate direct with the Lords and of course with Sir Edward Parry'. Parry, the Controller of Steam Machinery, was an advocate of the screw but the Surveyor of the Navy had very strong objections to it. The interesting but lengthy history of the delays and confusion caused by the Admiralty and their discourteous treatment of Brunel is best referred to in the biography of Isambard by his son. As a result, the *Rattler*, the vessel specially built for the experiment, did not run her trials against paddle vessels until the end of 1843. While these succeeded in demonstrating to the Admiralty the superiority of screw propulsion, they were far too late to provide Brunel with data for the design of the *Great Britain*'s first screw. He was thus forced to proceed almost from scratch, with only the *Archimedes* experiments to help him.[9]

Two screws were in fact designed for the ship. The first, which was used on trials and on her first two trans-Atlantic voyages was six-bladed, of 15 ft 6 in. diameter and 25 ft pitch. The propeller was of peculiar construction. The boss was made in several parts, the main one being a simple cylinder 17 in. long and 2 ft in diameter, to which were fire-welded six wrought iron arms each 6 in. thick and twisted into a helix of the correct pitch. This basic boss and the arms were then milled off flat at right angles to the propeller axis. A picture of a modern model of this screw made for tank-testing purposes perhaps explains better than words do. To the arms were riveted palms 4 ft 3 in. wide at the tip, 2 ft 7 in. at their inner circumference and 2 ft 10 in. long radially. These were $\frac{7}{8}$ in. thick and constituted the main driving portion of the screw. The boss was then completed with fore and aft closing portions which were held together by long iron screws and rivets. The whole was buffed up,

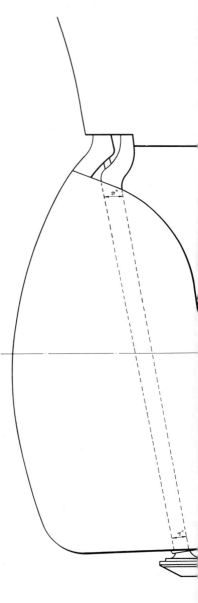

49 Photograph of tank-test model propeller

polished, painted and varnished to give a good surface which would reduce friction. The finished weight was 3·85 tons.[10] The second screw was intended as a longstop in case the first one was wide of the mark but it was decided to defer final design decisions until trials data were obtained from the first one.[11] Its final appearance may be judged from Fig. 50. Technical details of both screws are given in Appendix 3.

Modern tank tests show that to obtain sufficient thrust to propel the ship at 12 knots each blade would have to bear a steady load of about $2\frac{1}{2}$ tons. The calculated stress in the root of the arm would therefore be about $4\frac{1}{2}$ tons per sq. in. While this figure was inside the limit recommended for wrought iron by the British Government at the time, it is high when one considers that it represented a live load on a propeller blade. It was certainly too great a strain to impose upon blades fixed to

48 The original propeller and sternframe arrangement of *Great Britain*

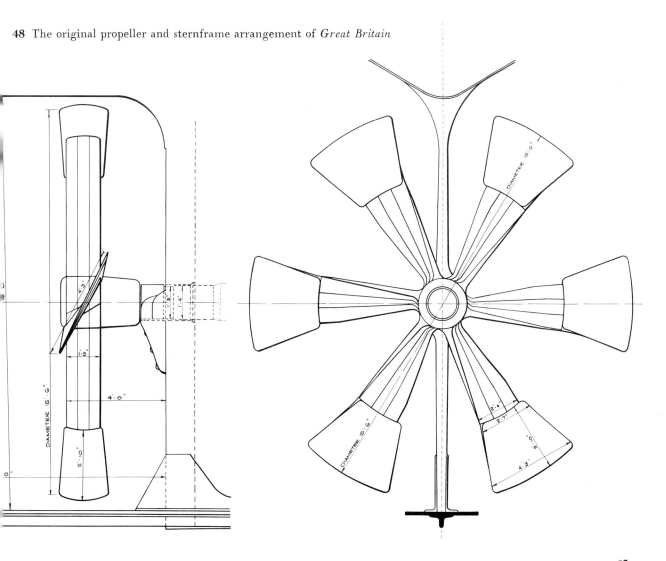

their boss by crude fire-welding, though with modern steel and welding methods it would be quite acceptable. The screw or tailshaft was 18 in. in diameter, decreasing to 16 in. in the sternpost and 15 in. in the bearing and propeller boss. Between the sternpost and the boss, a distance of 1 ft, a rope guard was fitted, supported from the post below the shaft. The main function of this feature was to form the after bearing for the tailshaft. The triangular bearing support was attached to the sternpost and formed a shelf on which the bearing and the shaft could rest. The arrangement was not uncommon at that time but of questionable efficiency. Water was kept out by a leather and copper stuffing gland just inside the sternpost which could be reached from inboard. The aftermost inboard shaft bearing was on the 18-in. portion just forward of the sternpost so that the screw was well supported, but the aftermost bearing could not have been large enough to give adequate bearing area for continuous service.

The way a screw is applied is as important as the propeller itself. Brunel fitted his in an aperture 13 ft long with its top 16 ft above the line of keel, which was dropped some 8 in. in this part of the ship. The bottom bearing of the rudder was 10 ft 6 in. aft of the sternpost, as it was a balanced one with part of its area forward of the bearing; the leading edge of the rudder was only 4 ft aft of the screw blades.

The rudder was a unique feature—brilliantly designed to suit screw propulsion and much ahead of its time. It had a removable post with a palm at the top which could be bolted on to the ship's structure. The post tapered from 9 in. diameter at the top to 7 in. at the bottom, structurally correctly reflecting the loads on it. It formed a support and a bearing for the rudder which was balanced and streamlined, about 14 ft in mean height and 7 ft 6 in. in mean width or chord. The whole structure was raked, including the rudder stock. This was of modern type, cranked around the top of the rudder post and with a steady bearing on to it. As can be seen, it was, like most modern rudders, overbalanced and would require careful handling for sailing (as distinct from steaming) as, lacking a central position, it would tend to fly over if the wheel were released. Fig. 51 shows how the steering gear was arranged. The raked stock carried an aft-facing tiller just over 6 ft long at promenade-saloon level. This was pulled to port and starboard by ropes leading from it over pulleys up to the weather deck where they wrapped over a geared drum attached to the steering wheel. The maximum force needed to turn the wheel was about 75 lb. at the spokes, and it needed about six turns from Hard Over to Hard Over.

From contemporary documents it seems clear that the whole of this arrangement was devised by Brunel, who was also responsible for the second propeller. He predicted a speed of 12 knots for the vessel and of one knot for every 1½ revolutions per minute of the engine, i.e. for every 4·5 revolutions per minute of the propeller. These predictions were probably based simply on an assumed slip of just over 9 per cent. Without slip the 25-ft-pitch propeller revolving at 53 revolutions per minute would travel some 13·1 nautical miles per hr, and Brunel expected the

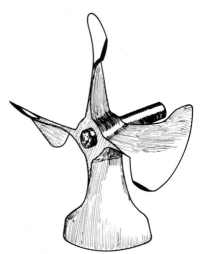

50 The four-bladed spare propeller designed after the original trials

ship to travel 12. Indeed it is probable that he arrived at the pitch by assuming the slip and working from the desired speed. This reckoning, gives no indication at all of the power required and there is no direct record of how Brunel in fact calculated this. It is practically certain, however, that he would work from *Great Western*, the ship he knew so well; that he would employ his famous principle governing the increase of resistance with size; and that he would draw comparative conclusions regarding the screw propulsion of the new ship by relating the paddle propulsion of the *Great Western* to the experiments in *Archimedes*. He had concluded that *Archimedes* and *Great Western* were almost identical

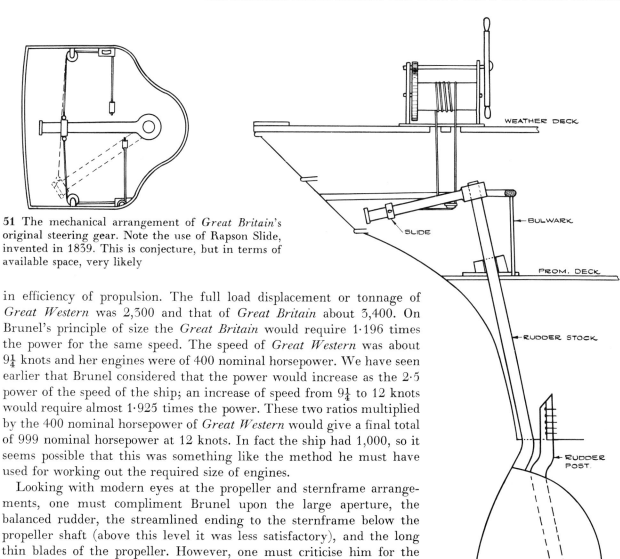

51 The mechanical arrangement of *Great Britain*'s original steering gear. Note the use of Rapson Slide, invented in 1839. This is conjecture, but in terms of available space, very likely

in efficiency of propulsion. The full load displacement or tonnage of *Great Western* was 2,300 and that of *Great Britain* about 3,400. On Brunel's principle of size the *Great Britain* would require 1·196 times the power for the same speed. The speed of *Great Western* was about $9\frac{1}{4}$ knots and her engines were of 400 nominal horsepower. We have seen earlier that Brunel considered that the power would increase as the 2·5 power of the speed of the ship; an increase of speed from $9\frac{1}{4}$ to 12 knots would require almost 1·925 times the power. These two ratios multiplied by the 400 nominal horsepower of *Great Western* would give a final total of 999 nominal horsepower at 12 knots. In fact the ship had 1,000, so it seems possible that this was something like the method he must have used for working out the required size of engines.

Looking with modern eyes at the propeller and sternframe arrangements, one must compliment Brunel upon the large aperture, the balanced rudder, the streamlined ending to the sternframe below the propeller shaft (above this level it was less satisfactory), and the long thin blades of the propeller. However, one must criticise him for the lozenge-shaped cross-section of the propeller arms, which one would not expect to be efficient, for the propeller's size, too great for the draught of the ship, and for its position too near the sternpost.[12]

CHAPTER SEVEN

The screw-propeller machinery

We have seen how the decision to adopt screw-propulsion led to the cancellation of the Humphreys trunk engines, albeit well advanced in construction, and to the subsequent resignation and death of Humphreys. Guppy took charge of the construction of the new engines with Harman as his assistant. Neither of them, however, was an engine designer and Isambard Brunel must have had a great deal to do with the actual design of the machinery.

The history of the steam engine went back to the first atmospheric engine of Newcomen, built in 1712, which worked entirely below atmospheric pressure by condensing the steam underneath a cylinder. Although originally extremely inefficient, this type of engine which worked a beam above it was widely applied for pumping of mines; its popularity and efficiency were greatly increased by James Watt's invention of the external condenser. By the end of the eighteenth century the design of both steam engines and boilers had reached a fair degree of sophistication. The compound engine, where high pressure steam expanded in one cylinder was exhausted to another cylinder and further expanded had been invented by Jonathan Hornblower, the uncle of the legendary naval officer, in 1781. In 1783 rotary motion was first produced from a steam engine by cranks, and slightly earlier James Watt had conceived the idea of expansive working where pressure steam was admitted to a cylinder but shut off after the piston had only moved a small distance, the expansion of the steam carrying out the rest of the work. This further improved the efficiency of engines. In 1790 Watt invented the indicator, a mechanism for indicating the pressure in the cylinder during the whole of the working stroke; Southern improved it a few years later by attaching paper to a rotating drum so that the actual pressure cycle in the cylinder could be drawn.

Around the turn of the century progress began to be rapid. Trevithick invented and developed high-pressure engines working up to 50 lb. per sq. in. and other engineers followed suit. Indeed, Jacob Perkins, an American inventor who emigrated to England, was experimenting by 1827 with pressures as high as 1,500 lb. per sq. in., and Dr Alban of the Grand Duchy of Mecklenburg-Strelitz actually built engines resembling Trevithick's which worked at 650 lb. per sq. in. Steam-engine development branched at this point into the high-pressure relatively small engine and the low-pressure slow engine mainly of beam type. In 1811 Woolf, the Cornish engineer, developed practical compound engines with only two-thirds the fuel consumption of Watt's engines. He received no encouragement in England where fuel was cheap, and emigrated to France where for many years compound engines were called Woolf engines.[1]

Marine engineering was at this period tied inevitably to the paddle propeller. Paddles are high-torque, slow-speed devices and require slow-turning engines which drive upwards to the crankshaft. Furthermore, it was necessary to feed the boilers of seagoing ships with sea-water, and high pressures could not be used in such boilers without the risk of priming, where water and salt came up with the steam into the engine. The beam engines of Newcomen and Watt lingered on in marine form to the end of the nineteenth century in the walking-beam engines of American paddle boats, and until the advent of the early screw steamers such as *Great Britain* there was little impetus to change from this heavy low-speed machinery. We have seen that Joseph Maudslay offered oscillating engines in the early stages of the building of the *Mammoth*; he revived this engine in 1827 and it later became a great favourite for smaller ships and especially for river vessels. But as far as the *Great Britain* was concerned, perhaps the most significant inventor was Isambard's father, Sir Marc Brunel.

In 1822 Sir Marc filed patent No. 4683 wherein he describes what he and his son called between themselves the 'Triangle' engine. This was the first engine of 'Vee' type, and drove upwards to a crankshaft above the cylinders. The cylinders were arranged in his parent drawings at 90° to each other but 'though the right angle is the most favourable position for the respective powers, I do not confine myself to that angle only as I may contract or increase to a certain extent, as necessity may require'. At that time engineers were needlessly worried by the possibility of wear by the piston if cylinders were other than vertical, and so this engine had an arrangement for supporting the piston and crosshead on wheels running in the trunk guides. The cylinders had domed ends and pistons while the steam sealing on the piston was by metallic rings stuffed behind with cotton. The engine was governed and regulated by a Watt's-type governor, improved by Sir Marc who turned it so that the balls rotated in a vertical plane and replaced the effect of gravity with a spring. As Sir Marc pointed out, with this governor 'all effect of gravitation or any other power except centrifugal force is neutralised'. This was a most important invention.

Other noteworthy features were the boiler and condenser. The former was tubular with domed ends, and completely filled with fresh water. It had extensive fire tubes and was to be fed with pulverised coal by a mechanical rotary stoker; its steam dome was to facilitate the collection of steam without priming. The multi-tube condenser was to be of advanced type, formed from modular nests of small pipes inside large ones. All the pipes were to be in a rectangular iron box filled with water and the steam condensed in the pipes was to be returned to the boiler by feed pumps. It must be realised that at this time all existing condensers were of the jet type; this modular-surface condenser, though quite within the scope of contemporary technology, was very advanced both in concept and construction. In 1834 Samuel Hall revived the surface condenser for marine engines but the jet condenser persisted for many years after that date, indeed right up to the latter part of the nineteenth century.

When pumping engines were required for the construction of the Thames Tunnel, Sir Marc and Isambard naturally decided to use Triangle engines. Built by Maudslay's, these gave very good service. Thus at the time of the decision to re-engine the *Mammoth* Isambard was well aware of his father's work and had actually used engines of this type. In 1840 no really large marine engine running at more than about 20 rpm had ever been built, and so in deciding to use Sir Marc's Triangle engine Isambard Brunel was forced to consider a 'multiplying gear' between it and the propeller. The Triangle engine was simply turned through 90° so that the cylinders lay athwartships. The original cylinder diameter chosen was 80 in. but as Brunel was keen on expansive working it was decided to increase this diameter to 88 in., a 21 per cent. increase in cylinder volume. In criticising the gear of the *Archimedes* which Brunel had felt so intolerably noisy and crude, he had come to the conclusion that 'straps' would be the best answer. Transmitting nearly 2,000 horse-power at 18 rpm through 'straps' is not a very practical proposition as Brunel no doubt soon found, so he decided to transmit the power from the crankshaft to the propeller shaft by chains. To get the necessary power he needed four 88-in.-diameter cylinders; using the Triangle engine concept this resulted in placing a pair of engines at each end of an overhead

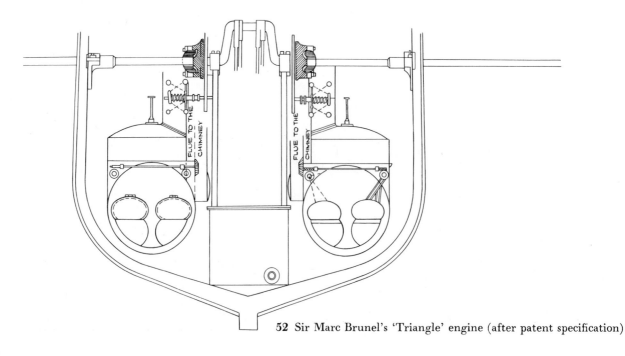

52 Sir Marc Brunel's 'Triangle' engine (after patent specification)

fore-and-aft crankshaft with the chain-wheel drive between them. Fig. 47 shows a longitudinal section through the engines as fitted to the *Great Britain*.

The angle between the cylinders, though only 60°, was inside the bounds of Sir Marc's patent. As was common in those days, the engine framework was incorporated in the ship structure—Fig. 56 shows a contemporary model of this engine which illustrates this point well. The cylinders were domed as in Sir Marc's patent and so was the piston. The crosshead ran on guides and the crankshaft was so arranged that there was a power stroke from one of the four cylinders every eighth of a revolution. The massive crankshaft, some 2 ft 4 in. in maximum diameter, was water-cooled: a 10-in. hole was drilled right through it and water feed came through the crankpin from a telescopic feed tube. As can be seen, the crankpins were turned spherical to avoid side loads due to any mis-alignment of the connecting rods. This crank was fabricated by the Mersey Iron Works and attracted much attention in its day as it was such a massive forging. The cylinders were 88 in. bore and 72 in. piston stroke. The pistons were interesting: each was fitted with a 15-in. manhole to allow inspection of the bore and the packing was metallic consisting of a complete ring of cast iron cut open at one point with a half-lap joint very like a modern motor-car piston ring. It was packed behind with cotton. This type of ring was really the invention of Jonathan Horn-blower, who called it the 'Lantern Brass'; modern pistons often use a variation of the design.

The main drive wheel was 18 ft 3 in. in overall diameter and 18 ft on

53 Sir Marc Brunel's 'Triangle' engine

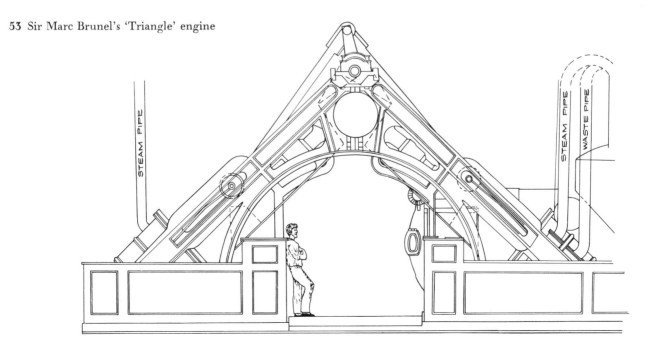

the pitch circle. The lower drum was 6 ft in diameter, lined with lignum vitae. It is evident that Brunel gave a great deal of thought to the drive, which consisted of four chains weighing 7 tons, placed side by side and of the 'inverted tooth chain' type commonly used in engineering to give quiet running and to be self-compensating for stretching. In this type of chain the links have wedge-shaped teeth at each end, and these teeth engage in grooves in the drum. In the *Great Britain* the main drum was lined with teak in which the grooves were formed. As the chain stretched and its pitch increased, the links would ride on the grooves at a slightly increased radius and thus automatically correct the small change in the pitch. There is no relative sliding between the drive-wheel grooves and the teeth of an inverted tooth chain, and the type has an excellent life, running very smoothly and quietly provided it is properly lubricated. It is commonly used today where silent running and good life are required and there can be no doubt but that Brunel's choice was reasoned and sound. The links were forged, and according to Guppy,

They were then brought to a dull red heat and placed in a proving machine, where they were stretched ⅛th of an inch, and while in that state they were rigidly examined. After boring and planing they were all finished on one gauging tool and case hardened.[2]

The four sets of chains had a working width of 38 in., a cross-sectional area of links of 24 sq. in., and to cut down noise still further each chain consisted of alternate groups of two and three links. To quote Guppy again, 'The motion [of the pitched chains] is remarkably smooth and noiseless.' The gear ratio was 2·95:1 and the design speed of the engines 18 rpm: the design of the propeller was therefore 53 rpm.

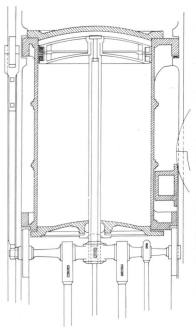

54 Piston rings and seals—'Triangle' engine

The lower drum was keyed to the propeller shaft which was of 18-in. diameter in that region. At the forward end of this shaft was the thrust bearing which at full power of 12 knots would take a load of about 10 tons and when accelerating from rest would probably double this. It consisted of a circular steel plate 2 ft in diameter supported by a block attached to the engine beds, against which a gunmetal plate, also of 2 ft in diameter and attached to the shaft itself, pressed. Water under pressure was fed to a cavity in the centre of the two plates, escaping radially; this, according to Guppy, 'very satisfactorily lubricates them'. It would be necessary to work at a pressure of the order of 200 lb. per sq. in. maximum and about 80 to 90 lb. at sea; we must assume that this was in fact supplied.

The screw shaft ran aft between the after pair of cylinders through a watertight gland in the after engine room bulkhead (which, incidentally, was also fitted with a watertight door for the engineers) and then joined the intermediate shaft which was a quite extraordinary feature of this ship. 61 ft 8 in. in length and 30 in. in internal diameter this shaft was formed from two strakes of plate, each ¾ in. thick, riveted together by countersunk rivets. Bearing in mind the small size of plates available in those days, to construct such a shaft was a difficult feat, although obviously one performed successfully. We can assume that the plates were smithed red-hot into a cast-iron former and trimmed exactly to

55 Sir Marc Brunel's boiler

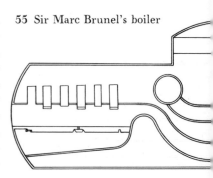

56 A contemporary model of the original machinery of *Great Britain*

57 The *Great Britain*'s original crankshaft

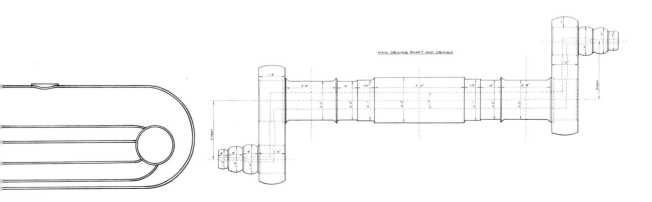

shape from marks made in the former. The plating could then be laid with butts shifted and internal butt straps, and if great care had been taken at all stages a true shaft could be produced. This shaft was in effect a torque tube and very light and stiff for its length. It could not, however, have bearings in its length. Such shafting is still not in common use in merchant ships although there are research programmes into its development.

Aft of the hollow intermediate shaft was the tailshaft, 25 ft 6 in. in length, the after end of which we have considered in a previous chapter. The two shaft bearings were supported on massive wood stools. The forward one was located by a curved plated recess in the floors, 1 ft deep and three frame spaces long, which still exists. The wide 6-ft base to the stool would have given excellent sideways support, necessary as the intermediate shaft would hardly have run true. This wood support was a good solution, giving low bearing pressures and a fairly soft support with good vibration-damping properties. It is a fascinating link with long-obsolete practice and indeed with wooden ships.

Steam was generated from sea-water in a rectangular boiler 34 ft long, 31 ft wide and 21 ft 8 in. high, divided into three bays by longitudinal bulkheads. Stoked from each end, it had a total of 24 furnaces, and the flue gases pursued a tortuous path upwards to escape finally through a central casing, which was jacketed at about the weather deck to form a feed-water heater. Water was pumped up into this space and when the boiler needed topping up a tap could be opened and the water run under gravity into the boiler against its pressure. The average working pressure was about 5 lb. per sq. in. above atmospheric, equivalent to a head of just over 10 ft of water of normal salinity. At the time of the *Great Britain*, boiler pressures at sea were generally little if anything above the 5 lb. per sq. in. of Watt's day. Fig. 60 shows the steam pressures of the P. & O. fleet during the entire era of iron shipbuilding and the slowness with which marine pressures rose in the early days of metal ships.[3]

Steam was drawn off from the after end of the boiler through shut-off valves of wedge type which could be withdrawn vertically by means of a wheel and screw. To get to these the steam had to pass over a priming plate at the aft end of the boiler, which can be seen clearly in Fig. 47 on the profile of the boiler. The steam was then collected from the three sections into a transverse steam pipe; as pressure was so low this could be of rectangular cross-section. From this pipe the steam was passed to the cylinders through circular pipes 2 ft 4 in. in diameter.

The boiler used brine, which became steadily more concentrated with the amount of feed supplied. Blowing-off generally took place when the concentration of salt reached a level three times that of seawater; each of the three sections of the boiler could be blown off individually, steam being kept on the engine by the other two sections. The salt gave a hard glazed surface to the boiler which did not lead to excessive corrosion but must have cut down the rate of heat transfer and greatly reduced efficiency. Waste gases were vented through a single casing chimney 8 ft in

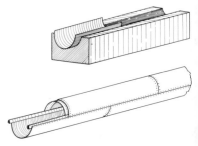

58 The cast-iron former and furnace-tube method possibly used for forming the intermediate shaft

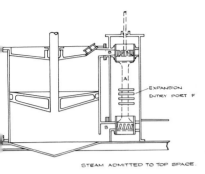

STEAM ADMITTED TO TOP SPACE.

59 Valve arrangements of
original engines

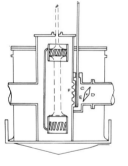

STEAM ADMITTED TO LOWER SPACE

diameter extending 38 ft above the weather deck. Up the aft side of this ran the elliptical waste steam pipe—2 ft wide, 1 ft fore and aft—which was presumably a casting. Coal was stored in wing bunkers outboard of the engines at the lower deck levels. These spaces were coaled through side shell-openings which can be seen in the drawings and the small bunkers forward of the engine room were coaled through circular deck lids and diagonal chutes to the bunkers.

Steam was admitted from the main steam pipe to the central steam space (A) through an antechamber (C), past a butterfly valve (D) which was used for regulating the flow of steam, and past a slide valve (E) which was used to vary the expansion of the steam. The engines were designed to work at approximately a 6:1 expansion, cutting off the steam at 12 in. out of the 72 in. of stroke available. However, this expansion could be varied by adjusting the stroke of the slide valve, and on trials expansion was tried between 4:1 and 6:1. The valves for admitting steam to the two sides of the piston were of piston type, working in brass liners, with twisted steam openings in order to keep wear uniform. As the piston valve worked up and down, the two rows of ports would be opened alternately, steam thereby being admitted from the central steam chamber (A) into the belt round the cylinder shells (B). The stroke of the piston valves was 4½ in. with 2½-in. lap and like the main pistons these had metallic split rings similar to those of a motor-car. This was quite a sophisticated arrangement. Particularly remarkable is the care with which the possibility of excessive wear was avoided in the piston valves: everything was balanced, the ports skewed and low-wear-type pistons used.

The drive to the valve gear was by eccentric. This device, really a crank of small radius, had been invented in about 1800 by Murdoch. It consisted of an eccentric circle of plate keyed to the shaft and encircled by a strap to which the valve rod was fixed. Means had to be provided for reversing the drive. At the time *Great Britain*'s engines were designed the valve gear known as a Stephenson link (but actually invented by

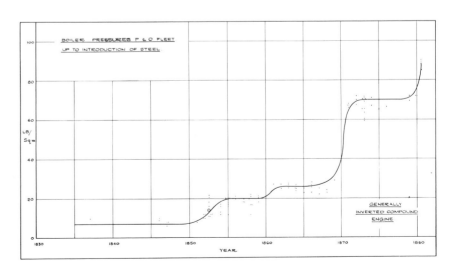

60 The steam pressures of early
P. & O. ships

William Howe in 1842) was not available and a cruder arrangement had to be adopted. In this the valve-gear eccentric which had a stroke of 9 in. was attached to a large spur wheel 8 ft in diameter which was concentric with the crankshaft. The spur wheel and the eccentric were locked by a sliding collar with a projecting tooth which could be engaged in a slot in the eccentric wheel. There were two slots at rather more than 90° angular separation so that the eccentric could be locked in the appropriate position for ahead or astern running. Leading aft and forward from these two great spur wheels were shafts terminating in small spur wheels at the eccentric end and large hand-wheels on the control platform. These two shafts could be slid forward and aft so that they could be disengaged from the spur wheels when the engine was running but pulled back to engage when it was stopped. The procedure for reversing was to stop the engine, slide out the dog clutch by means of a lever, engage the spur-wheel pinion, turn the eccentric through 90° plus the advance, and re-engage the dog clutch. The sliding or Stephenson-link motion could, of course, be reversed with the engine running. Expansion was varied by disconnecting gears running in slotted quadrants. With the engines stopped, the stroke of the slide valves could be varied by moving the attachment points in the quadrants.[4]

It remains to describe the air pumps, condensers and auxiliary pumps. The two end sections of the crank pins on each end of the crankshaft were used for the air-pump connecting rods. These were 11 ft 6 in. long and had the same stroke as the pistons. The air pumps themselves were $45\frac{1}{2}$ in. in diameter and were set into the condensers which, as can be seen in Fig. 61, lie beneath the cylinders themselves. They were formed from $\frac{3}{4}$-in.-thick wrought-iron plate and were 12 ft long, 8 ft 6 in. wide and about 4 ft deep. The air pumps were set into them at a slight angle to the vertical. The connecting-rod pin was kept in line by a parallel link motion as shown. This is a variation of the so-called 'grasshopper' parallel mechanism and consisted of a swinging link (A) 5·6 ft long, attached to the ship's structure and supporting a transverse rocking link (B) 6·75 ft long, the cross-head of the piston rod being 2·75 ft from the swinging link attachment. The other end of the rocking link, 4 ft from the swinging link attachment, was hinged to a second rocking link suspended from the engine frame. It can be seen that this arrangement gives a virtually linear motion to the cross-head of the connecting rod. The boiler feed and bilge pumps were worked from one of these rocking arms, as shown. The total pump capacity can be calculated at approximately 180 tons per hour.

This machinery* has many interesting features and was certainly in advance of most of its contemporaries. The valve gear was undoubtedly more practical than that of Sir Marc's Triangle engine, and the chain drive was, in this author's opinion, a triumph of logical and practical engineering. However, it must be confessed that in most other respects the original Triangle engine was considerably more sophisticated and ingenious, and that the *Great Britain*'s boiler was a travesty of Sir Marc's fine effort.[5]

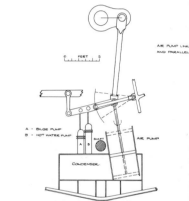

61 Pump-drive arrangements of original engines

* A summary of its dimensions is given in Appendix 4.

CHAPTER EIGHT

General arrangement of the 'Great Britain'

By the time the *Mammoth* was well advanced in construction it was decided to call the ship the *Great Britain*, and this name will be used from here on. Lengthwise, the *Great Britain* was divided into four main spaces: the after accommodation with the shaft space below it, extending to the after engine-room bulkhead; the machinery space; the forward accommodation; and the forecastle, used for crew accommodation. This simple arrangement makes a description of the ship very easy.

The machinery space was very nearly centred about amidships. The funnel was placed about 15 ft forward of admidships, but with the bowsprit the profile was nicely balanced. The engine and boiler room, as can be seen from Fig. 67, was bounded aft by a flat bulkhead running right up to weather-deck level and forward by a stepped bulkhead running from the keel to the lower 'tween deck, then picking up again aft of this and running to the weather deck. This resulted in the engine room being longer at lower-platform level (93 ft) than higher up (79 ft).

The after accommodation was allocated to the first class and ran from the extreme stern at lower 'tween-deck level to the engine room bulkhead, and from the stern windows and the tiller bulwark at upper 'tween-deck level to the bulkhead. The lower of these two spaces was the dining saloon with cabins outboard of it to port and starboard. The upper was a promenade saloon, again with cabins in the wings. The forward accommodation, which was second-class, had the same arrangement of dining saloon and outboard cabins in the lower 'tween deck and promenade saloon and wing cabins in the upper. It was, of course, stepped over the forward stoke hole and coal bunker which extended underneath it almost to No. 2 mast. At the forward end of this space there was a cargo trunk on the centreline with a hatch at the weather-deck level leading to the lower cargo holds. The passenger accommodation ended short of the forecastle bulkhead, and doors were arranged from the trunk so that at these two deck levels there were cargo lockers to port and starboard. Below the forward accommodation were the two iron cargo decks which were served by the above mentioned trunk and hatch. Thus forward *Great Britain* could stow cargo at four levels: in two cargo decks over 70 ft long and the full breadth of the ship, and in two cargo lockers about 10 ft long and the full breadth of the ship at the lower and upper 'tween deck levels.

Right forward, as has been said, was the officers' and crew's accommo-

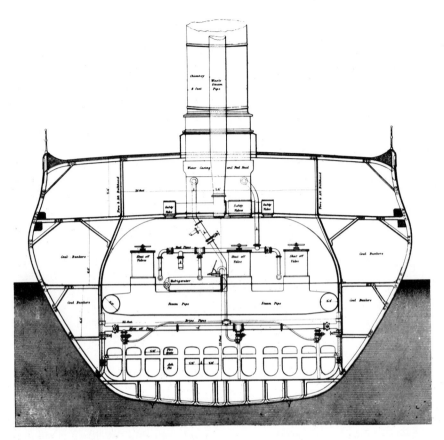

62 Transverse section through the boiler room

63 Main promenade saloon

dation, again at four levels. The lowest, which was on top of the forepeak fresh-water tank, was a store; then there were two levels of crew accommodation, and the upper forecastle was for officers. Aft, the space under the two passenger decks contained the great tubular intermediate shaft and below that, running up to the 6-ft level, were the ship's fresh-water tanks, divided athwartships into two sections. The forward and aft compartments held 30 tons and 34 tons of water respectively.

Before describing the rest of the accommodation it is as well to cover what is known of the accommodation amidships abreast of the machinery and boiler rooms. The two middle levels of the ship (the lower deck and the lower 'tween deck above it) were occupied in this area by coal-bunkers which ran the whole length of the machinery space. These were bounded by fore and aft bulkheads, each 13 ft from the centreline, which ran right through the engine space and then bulged out round the boiler, fitting it very closely. In the upper 'tween decks, however, the two fore and aft bulkheads, 26 ft apart, ran the whole length of the machinery, and the spaces outboard of them were available for accommodation. Unfortunately, lay-out details of these two spaces, 74 ft in length and about 8 ft in width, have not survived. They certainly incorporated a fore and aft passage which we may surmise ran on the inside, alongside the engine-room casings. Outboard we know from Captain

Claxton's account of the ship that there were 'the servants' accommodation on one side, engineers' cabins and stokers' accommodations on the other, besides 26 water closets'.[1] It is possible to reconstruct approximately the situation of these w.c.s. We know that from the after accommodation there were w.c. passages leading from the port and starboard ladies' boudoirs and also from the starboard general accommodation. From the forward accommodation there was a w.c. passage leading from the starboard second-class accommodation. It is probable, therefore, that there was a block of w.c.s port and starboard aft for first-class passengers and the captain, and that forward crew's w.c.s were to port and those for second-class passengers to starboard. (There were also two officers' w.c.s in the forecastle, by the towing bits.) These wing spaces amidships also contained the galleys. Food would be taken along the alleyways and down the stairs to the dining saloons. It is likely that it was not too warm when it arrived, although the stewards' pantries may have had charcoal ovens or similar warming arrangements.

The first-class after accommodation ran right out to the transom windows. As has been seen, the tiller was housed at this level in a fan-shaped recess formed by a bulwark in the after accommodation; the entire steering mechanism was thus visible to the first-class passengers. In Fig. 63, a contemporary illustration of the promenade saloon, the bulwark can just be seen; the windows on the centreline were, of course, visible over it. Across the after end on a stringer shelf that still exists were settees which ran forward to the aft side of the sleeping-cabin bulkheads.

The width of the promenade space, which was about 22 ft at the forward end, tapered to about 19 ft at the after end. The cabins were divided

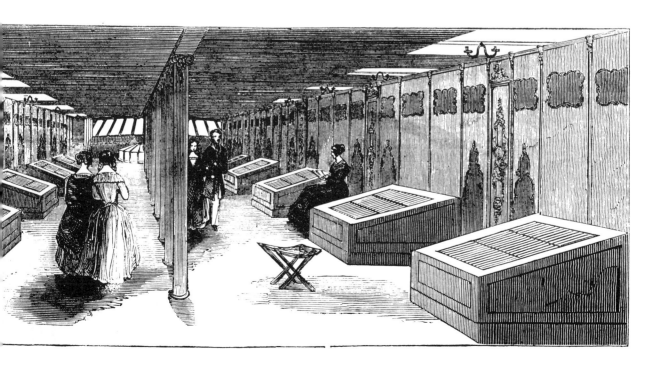

into blocks of four, by four transverse passages to port and five to starboard, which were closed off by doors, giving an unbroken appearance to the longitudinal bulkhead. Towards the forward end of each block was a ladies' boudoir; the captain's sleeping berth and some of the stewardesses' accommodation were situated on the port side, and more stewardesses on the starboard side. Each ladies' boudoir was fitted with a settee along the ship's side, a table, and another settee on the inboard side. The captain's day-room, on the centreline forward, was fairly spacious—nearly 13 ft long and 8 ft broad—and may well have also been used as a chart-room. There was a lobby on either side of this, closed off by doors, and then stairs leading upwards to the weather deck and downwards to the dining-saloon. The framework of these staircases was of iron and they were of semi-spiral type. Access to the promenade deck was also provided at the after end from both the weather deck and the dining saloon, but the weather deck ladders were probably not intended for normal passenger use, consisting as they did of single string ladders terminating in deck companionways. They provided emergency escape routes but were probably mainly used by crew ascending and descending from the navigating position. The two transverse staircases down to the dining-saloon deck were again of single flight type, and led nearly on to the centreline port and starboard. There were thus four ways up from the dining saloon to the promenade deck and four up from that to the weather deck, while from the forward end of the promenade saloon one could reach other parts of the ship by longitudinal passages fore and aft. (Fig. 47). This arrangement is quite in conformity with modern Safety of Life at Sea Regulations and a good deal better than that of many passenger ships of even quite recent vintage. It must be said, however, that the types of stairs and their fire protection would be quite inadequate by modern standards.

64 First-class dining saloon in lower 'tween decks

The cabins were very small—exactly 6 ft between the insides of the bulkheads, and generally about 6 ft wide. On the upper 'tween deck there were 32 two-berth cabins and a block of four single-berth cabins port and starboard. Thus the total number of first-class berths on this deck was 72. The lighting of this space was by five skylights on each side of the weather deck and sidelights or ports in the ship's side-plating. The skylights, about 6 ft × 4 ft 6 in. internally, were matched below on the upper 'tween deck level by similar ones like cucumber frames which allowed light down into the dining saloon, where they were positioned right over the outer lines of tables. This can be seen in Fig. 64. A large round skylight was fitted just aft of the mizzen mast and this was matched by a further one below, again giving light to the after part of the dining saloon. Light was also obtained from the 10 transom windows, while at night there were oil lights suspended from the centre of each skylight position. Captain Claxton describes this area as follows:

The walls of the after or principal promenade saloon are painted in delicate tints and along the sides are several fixed chairs of oak. A row of well proportioned pillars which range down the centre of the promenade serve the double purpose of ornament to the room and support to the deck. In this saloon on either side is a range of exceedingly comfortable staterooms and sleeping berths. About 12 of these on each side of the deck will be reserved for the ladies as they are made to communicate with two commodious ladies' boudoirs. The advantages of this arrangement must be obvious as ladies who may be indisposed or in negligée will be enabled to reach their sleeping berths without there being the slightest necessity for their appearing in public.[2]

(Actually he was very optimistic as, including the stewardesses' cabins, only six berths on each side communicated with the boudoirs.)

The forward promenade deck accommodation was generally similar: the cabins were the same size and the lighting system identical but there was only one staircase each side going up to the weather deck and down to the dining saloon. On the centreline at the aft end of this space was a stewards' pantry. There were pillars running along the centreline as on the after promenade deck; No. 2 mast and the navel pipes carrying the anchor cables also ran through this space.

Descending by the stairs from the two promenade saloons, one reached the dining saloons. Aft there were three long tables; allowing each diner only 17 in. these could sit 228, and the two rows of forward-saloon table 132. This gives a total of 360 which agrees with Claxton's account, though diners would certainly have to eat very politely with elbows well tucked in. In the after dining saloon the cabin bulkheads were generally parallel to the centreline but were angled towards the after end. The dining saloon space was 30 ft in width, with cabins in the wings and, at the forward end, a storeroom to port and a large stewards' pantry to starboard. There were three rows of pillars, one on the centreline and one each side outboard of the seats and tables. Fig. 64 shows the general appearance of this space.

At the forward end of the first class on this deck the cabins—eight to starboard and 10 to port—were single-berth, although outboard of the storeroom there was one two-berth cabin. Aft of these single-berth cabins were two-berth cabins, some with the berths disposed longitudinally and others transversely. Transverse bunks are an abomination, especially in a ship that rolls heavily as did the *Great Britain*. Although the after cabins in this block were large, their deck must have consisted almost entirely of the sloping side shell of the ship, with virtually no flat surface, as can be seen from the drawing. There was a total of 44 berths on this deck, making a gross total of 116 first-class berths plus the four steward-esses' berths which were numbered for sale if bookings were heavy. The aft end of the dining saloon was an open space lit by the large skylight above and by the aftermost 'cucumber-frame' skylights. Right aft on the centreline were the two port and starboard transverse stairs mentioned earlier, partitioned off by a partial bulkhead. In the wings of the aft end of the saloon were settees laid along the shell. Again there must have been a sloping floor up to them laid on the ship's side shell. The whole arrangement was a peculiar one. On the appearance of the main dining saloon Claxton is again worth quoting:

This is really a beautiful room. . . . Its fittings are alike chaste and elegant. Down the centre are 12 principal columns of white and gold with ornamental capitals of great beauty. Twelve similar columns also ranged down the walls on either side. [There cannot have been 12 on the centreline—the aftermost one would come under the circular skylight.] Between these latter and the entrances to the sleeping berth are [on each side of the deck] eight pilasters in the arabesque style [of which character the saloon generally partakes], beautifully painted with oriental birds and flowers. On either side are seven doors which open into as many passages each of which communicates with four bedrooms. [Again, his description is not very accurate as the cabin arrangement shown is developed from his own drawings.] The archways of the several doors are tastefully carved and gilded and are surmounted with neat medallion heads. Some looking glasses are so arranged as to reflect the saloon lengthwise, at two opposite sides, from which a very pleasing illusion is produced. The walls of this apartment are of a delicate lemon tinted drab hue relieved with blue white and gold. At the stern end are a number of sofas which range one above the other nearly up to the stern lights. . . .

Artificial lighting was again by means of candles or oil lamps suspended from the centre of the skylight shafts. The pictures of the promenade deck and the saloons which appeared in the *Illustrated London News* are most amusing because we know that the actual headroom available was just over 6 ft 6 in. clear in the promenade deck and 7 ft 6 in. in the dining saloon. If we are to believe the artist, the ladies and gentlemen shown must have been little over 4 ft tall.

The forward dining-saloon was generally similar. The cabins outboard of it were generally two-berth but right at the forward end port and starboard two cabins were arranged to be sold as one space with communicating doors. This was presumably ideal for parents travelling with children. The cabins had sofas along the ship's side and were quite commodious. Altogether there were 72 berths in the second-class promenade deck cabins and 60 on the saloon deck. The decks of all the saloons were covered with fitted carpet described by the *Illustrated London News* reporter as

superb Brussels carpet expressly manufactured for the purpose by Messrs Mogg of Bristol. The fabric takes its name from the vessel it is calculated to ornament and is of scarlet and royal purple, of dice pattern, the ground profusely covered with small figures.

This, then, completed the passenger accommodation. The cabins were small, ventilation was undoubtedly deficient—the lack of ventilators on the weather deck is painfully obvious—and bathrooms seem noticeable by their omission, although they may well have been provided in the same area as the w.c.s Nevertheless, especially with servants available, a reasonably comfortable passage could be made, and certainly the ship was more luxurious than other ships in service at the time. The fares were charged on the basis of the accommodation bought. This was a great change as the common practice on the Atlantic routes was to charge at one rate as, for example, in the *Great Western* and Cunard ships where 30 guineas was the standard fare. *Great Britain's* rates descended from 35 guineas to 28, 25, 22 and a minimum of 20 guineas—which was presumably for one berth in a second-class double state-room.

Forward of the passenger accommodation there was a space between the end bulkhead and the forecastle bulkhead, 10 ft 6 in. wide in the upper 'tween deck and 9 ft in the lower. Through the centreline of this space the trunk ran down from the small hatch which still exists at the break of the forecastle. This was the only means of putting cargo into the two lower holds, but doors port and starboard in the sides of the trunk gave access to the space between the accommodation and the forecastle bulkhead. This was probably used for small parcels of cargo, mail, etc., while the lower holds were used for the more bulky and weighty items of cargo. The approximate net volumes of these spaces were as follows:

Upper cargo locker	1,900 cu. ft
Lower cargo locker	2,100 cu. ft
Upper cargo deck	10,500 cu. ft
Lower cargo deck	7,500 cu. ft
Totalling	22,000 cu. ft

The ship carried 360 tons of light cargo on her maiden voyage. A measurement ton is 40 cu. ft, so the spaces would be two-thirds full with perhaps a weight of only 200 tons of cargo. To the modern eye, these cargo spaces appear incredibly ill-designed. Access to them is from one end only, necessitating a long drag to the after ends, and they are so low that a man of even medium height must bend to go from one end to the other. The only way to work would be to drag cargo over the decks; that this was done is shown by the dreadful state of the only remaining cargo deck forward which has been worn right away. A combination of corrosion and erosion is obviously responsible: the continual dragging of weights removed the paint and the rust, and the ship's long submersion completed the damage. The beams themselves are in relatively good shape.

The forecastle housed the officers in its upper level. There is a broad shelf or stringer right along each side of it which is a continuation of the weather-deck stringer. This shelf would have been ideal for berths and four officers could be accommodated each side. It is probable that this was the arrangement and that the centre of the space, being fairly commodious—24 ft long and the breadth of the ship—was used as general living accommodation and contained a mess table and lockers. There was a bogey stove here as can be seen today from charring of the king beam round the pipe. Forward of this again, on the other side of an iron bulkhead, were the officers' heads. Access was from the forecastle itself down through hatches aft of the towing bits, and there was a water closet on each side of the ship, the soil pipes of which still exist. Complete with traps, these vented well down below the waterline.

Seamen were accommodated on the next two levels below. These spaces, which ran right out to the ship's stem, were about 5 ft 9 in. high from beam to plank and could have had little or no ventilation. Access to them was by a companion on the port side of the forecastle deck and a trunk down through the officers' space. The seamen accommodated here, some 36 in number, slept in hammocks—some of the hooks for these are still in existence. The lowest level above the forepeak tank was used as a boatswain's store. The hawse-pipes ran diagonally up through the top tier of the sailors' accommodation, through the deck and up through the officers' forecastle. The complete arrangement for crew accommodation seems to have been as follows: the captain was accommodated in the first-class aft, and the chief engineer and other engineering officers were probably in the space abreast of the engine room; all the other officers slept in the upper forecastle, and the bulk of the seamen in the two lower forecastles; firemen and saloon crew were also probably accommodated in the upper 'tween deck space abreast of the engines.

The arrangements on deck were very simple by modern standards. Right aft there was the wheel with its rope drum and box, and forward of it the compass. On either side of the companion, hatches led down into the aft end of the first-class promenade saloon. Forward of the compass was the round skylight mentioned earlier and on either side, leading forward, the five skylights also mentioned. Abreast of the aftermost skylight was the mizzen mast and rather forward of this the after capstan, a hand type with radial battens on the deck to give the seamen a grip as they trudged around it. Forward again was No. 5 mast and, right on the after engine room, bulkhead No. 4. The stairs port and starboard from the promenade saloon came out on to the weather deck abreast of this mast through a companion with a curved top and windows. This had doors to port and starboard so that the lee door could always be used.

Port and starboard of the weather deck the *Great Britain* carried what may have been the first iron lifeboats ever built. These were patterned on an invention by Guppy—an engineer of considerable ingenuity and initiative—whose patent describes the construction both of iron boats and of iron buoyancy tanks within them. In davits aft there were four of these, 30 ft long, 8 ft broad and 5 ft deep, while inverted on skids forward of the main mast there was a boat of similar size but of wood construction. This was how the ship was equipped when she set sail from Bristol; in London, a further two boats were fitted in davits just forward of the four iron ones. These were of the same size and type but probably built of wood. The four original iron boats and the wood one were stated to be capable of carrying 400 people—80 per boat—but, of course, the total of berthed passengers plus crew came to very nearly this and to launch the upside-down boat quickly in an emergency would be quite impracticable. The six boats fitted in davits when she left London would accommodate 480 people and would give a margin of perhaps one boat, apart from the one carried on deck, in a total emergency.

Further forward was a large skylight over the engines. As the top of the main drive wheel reached some 2 ft 6 in. above the upper deck it was necessary to enclose it with a skylight, and this was extended right over the forward pair of cylinders. In the famous Lundy Island lithograph a number of people ignoring the raging of the sea and the spray about to engulf them are gazing through this skylight, fascinated, as well they might be, by the massive wheel and chain revolving immediately below them. Forward again was a grating over the after stoke hole, matched forward of the funnel by a similar but smaller one over the forward stoke hole—or hell hole, as one might describe it, considering that these two gratings were the unfortunate engineers' and stokers' only ventilation.

65 Windlass and cable clamping arrangements photographed during the salvage survey, 1968

On the centreline, just forward of the after grating, was a small deck-house which may have been used as a chart-room, from which stairs led down on to the gratings immediately aft of the boiler. There was a door in the after centre of this house, and above the house a light flying bridge, which was supported on stanchions and attached also to the funnel, extended port and starboard to the ship's sides. This feature was in existence from the beginning right through to the 1856–7 refit, and can be seen on the early lithographs and paintings, and also, in a dismounted position, in the Fox Talbot photograph. It was probably used mainly for docking: at sea the ship was conned and navigated from the wheel right aft, but when working in port the captain of such a large vessel needed a better vantage-point.

The funnel or 'chimney' was common with the forward end of the deckhouse. Towering 38 ft above the deck, it was of single construction with no casing, had a large elliptical steam pipe on the after end and was supported on a shallow oval casing bolted directly to the deck. Forward of the funnel on each side of the forward stoke hole grating, there were double companions giving access down and forward to the second-class and down and aft to the engineers' and saloon crews' accommodation. Two sets of doors were fitted to each companion allowing the use of the lee door. Outboard of these companions there were coal-bunkering lids set in the deck which delivered to the forward bunkers by means of diagonal chutes across the forward side of the engine-room bulkhead. The remains of these still exist.

Forward again, No. 2 mast was stepped right through the deck and on to the keel, while just forward of this was the windlass—a massive and beautiful pump-handle machine. The handles were outboard of the line of skylights and had a span of 24 ft. Eight to 12 men a side were probably detailed to pump these and so raise the $2\frac{1}{2}$-in. cable. The principle was that the handles worked two ratchet boxes by swinging links, and these 'crabbed' their way down the toothed drums and on the return stroke pulled the drums and the cable gypsies round a little. A description of a contemporary (1845) agricultural machine, the 'Etzler iron slave', outlines the mode of operation:

A long lever of 20 ft swinging backwards and forwards on a spindle and pulling alternately two levers of 3 ft in a box on two wheels fixed to the shaft similar to the capstan on the *Great Britain* steamship.[3]

This description fits the mechanism of the present windlass and would seem to confirm that it is the original one.

On each side of the fore deck were four skylights and on the centreline between these and forward of the windlass was the above-mentioned 30-ft wood boat on skids, supported upside-down. This boat would be handled into the water in the normal sailing-ship way, using the only main yard in the ship, namely that on No. 2 mast, as a boat derrick. The centreline hatch at the break of the forecastle has been mentioned earlier; set just forward of the forecastle bulkhead was No. 1 mast, with the hawse-pipes to port and starboard of it. The forecastle was parallel to the weather deck, without sheer; the iron rails and wood bulwarks at the forward end of it increased in height owing to their own sheer. Access to the forecastle accommodation and to the officers' heads in the eyes of the ship was through companions port and starboard. On the centre of the forecastle deck was another capstan similar to the one aft but of heavier construction, again with radial slats to give the seamen a good grip. The forecastle was complete with three bulwark-mounted bollards very similar to those on the *Great Western* and heavy wooden catheads port and starboard for the anchors. The single spike-type bowsprit was butted at the bits, and the wood and iron bulwarks were stopped on the centreline to provide a notch for it.

The *Great Britain* carried a considerable amount of sail—though much less than a sailing ship of the same size. Apart from No. 2 mast which was square-rigged, she was rigged as a six-masted schooner. She had two jibs, a loose-footed brailing mainsail and a spencer above masts Nos. 1, 3, 4, 5 and 6, and square sails on the main and topmast yards of No. 2 mast—a total area of approximately 16,000 sq. ft of sail.[4] Additionally, she could carry studding sails on the main yard, but it seems unlikely that these were ever used. The four after masts were stepped on deck in hinges, the appearance of which can be seen on the inboard profile. This was virtually a necessity, as Nos. 4, 5 and 6 had the propeller shaft below them, while No. 3 was over the aft end of the boiler and similarly limited. No. 1 mast, however, was stepped on a stub mast which ran right through from the weather deck to the tank top and provided a support for the hinge. No. 2 mast was quite different from all the others. It was bigger—34 in. in diameter—and continued right down to the platform level just above the keel. This mast was fixed and square-rigged, and carried a main yard and a single topsail yard. Appendix 5 gives mast dimensions and detailed particulars, partly taken from Captain Claxton's account and partly calculated and measured.

With the exception of No. 2, all the masts carried fore and aft sails of loose-footed brailing type so that they could be handled from the deck. As Captain Claxton said,

Economy of labour is a principle which has in a great degree affected the mode of rigging both the *Great Western* and the *Great Britain*. Nothing is so different to handle under a variety of circumstances as the sails of a steamer unless the engines be stopped, which should never be allowed in Atlantic steaming, where onwards. and for ever onwards is the rule.[5]

As he pointed out, although the sail area was much the same as that of a frigate, the *Great Britain* only required 20 seamen in a watch and in fact there was but one sail—the square main sail—which under any circumstances could require all hands to furl it. He went on,

No *steamer* has any business with lofty spars or flying kites . . . five masts of the six are hinged for lowering, when, in the captain's judgement, contrary gales shall appear to have set in as the westerlies do at certain seasons of the year.

In fact a little reflection shows that these masts could never have been lowered. The type of hinge used, which is similar to that of the mizzen mast on the *Great Eastern*, only allows a deviation from the vertical of approximately 40°. In any case, No. 1 mast could not have been lowered because of the presence of the fixed No. 2 mast, and to lower Nos. 3, 4 and 5 masts would have rendered the deck and in particular the steering position aft completely uninhabitable. It is probable that Claxton was labouring under a misapprehension.

Great Britain was the first large ship to be fitted with wire rigging which had a number of theoretical advantages. It presented less surface when the ship was under 'bare poles'; it was lighter than rope, strength for strength; and, as Mr John Hill said,

It maintains nearly a permanent length, and not requiring frequent 'setting up', as is the case with rope and probably it is more particularly applicable to iron vessels than wooden ones from the rigidity of the former not requiring the elasticity that may be serviceable in the latter.[6]

Perhaps Hill has the essence of it here. The inelasticity of the iron wire and the rigidity of the hull allowed Brunel to set up his masts on hinges on deck; once set up, they would remain at the correct rake and rig indefinitely. As one could not in any case step the after masts down to the keel because of the screw shaft, it would be logical to use hinges with a limited degree of movement on the deck. All that was necessary was to set the hinge in position and haul the mast upright, finally tensioning off the rigging at the correct rake. This was an engineer's solution, likely to receive bitter opposition from the old school of seamen: indeed, in her first refit the ship was re-rigged with hemp and the after masts stepped down through the decks—a triumph for conservatism. Grantham, writing in 1842, compared the outcry at that time against wire rigging with the earlier reaction to chain cables:

When chain cables were first introduced the greatest outcry was raised against them by those of the old school, a ship provided with them could not then be insured, but where now is the well found ship that has a hempen cable? At present indeed it is a question whether the underwriters would not be inclined to dispute the payment of a loss by a vessel in which iron cables were not used. Iron rigging has for some time been struggling against the opposition of seamen who view innovations with an extraordinary degree of abhorrence, but since the introduction of wire rope I have no doubt that all standing rigging will shortly be made of that material for its superior strength and the power of retaining its tension etc. Iron running rigging in chains, by halyards, topsail sheets etc. is also extensively used and is found to be superior to hemp and cordage. . . .[7]

In an interesting footnote Grantham referred to a contemporary document which stated that 3-in. wire rope weighed 6¾ lb. per fathom, hemp rope 14½ lb. and 1¾-in. chains 36 lb.: all would be capable of taking a strain of 16 tons. The comparative costs were: wire rope, 3s. 8d. a fathom; hemp rope, 6s. 3d., and chain 7s. 6d. Of course, iron wire rigging would rust, but kept well greased or tarred it would certainly last better than hemp. Only prejudice and extreme conservatism held it back so long.

The masts had twin forestays which in the case of the hingeing masts were used for adjusting the rake. Brunel in his efforts to save labour arranged that the topmasts could be lowered from the deck, and heavy tackles port and starboard were provided in order to do this. Normally a topmast is supported at its foot by what is known as a fid—a wedge driven in across the bottom of the mast so that it rests on the cap structure of the lower mast and prevents the topmast sliding down. As Brunel's objective was to enable most of the rigging to be worked from the deck it is probable that the masts must have been unfidded. This innovation alone would have given rise to some apprehension on the part of seamen such as Captain Claxton. The shrouds, however, were set up in the customary way, with dead eyes—rigging screws not yet having been invented. The combination of old-fashioned and advanced is part of the fascination of *Great Britain*: wire rigging and dead eyes; an iron hull with quite modern screw propulsion; and a stern crowned by false quarter galleries and a row of windows which would have done justice to an East Indiaman the best part of a century earlier.

To complete the description of the ship's fixtures, mention must be made of the adornment of the hull. Around this, 4 ft below the gunwale and 3 ft wide, ran a white band painted with imitation black gunports. At the forward end of this band, to port and starboard, were trailboards, about 16 ft in length, consisting of gilt scrollwork surrounds with white centres on which were displayed various symbols of Victorian trade, industry, learning, art and agriculture. To port were portrayed a caduceus, a carpenter's square, a dove of peace, gear wheels and a rope coil—a somewhat incongruous mixture—while to starboard were a sheaf of corn, a globe, a lyre and trumpets, an artist's pallet, a book and a bunch of flowers. The colourful figurehead was the Royal Arms, 6 ft high and flanked by a gilt lion to starboard and a unicorn to port. Each side of the stern there were false quarter galleries whose windows were decorated with scrollwork and gilt curtains; a gilt cornucopia ornamented each corner and a gilt swan stretched its wings and curved its neck over each set of four windows. Across the stern were ten glazed windows bounded by gilt wood ropework and above two Unicorns supporting the Arms of the City of Bristol with the name *Great Britain* underneath the windows. Palm fronds outboard of the Unicorns and sprays of oakleaves between the windows together with cornucopia on the transom corners completed the decoration. The whole of this decoration was very flamboyant, quite anachronistic on an otherwise extremely modern ship, but really rather splendid (*see* p. 90 for transom decoration).*

All round the hull was an iron railing, five bars high, of modern type.

* The sources for these (and for Fig. 47) are various prints and paintings, the *Illustrated London News*, and for the stern the Science Museum model and Fig. 115—the only illustration of the stern.

The early lithographs and the Weale plates show two rails on a curved wood gunwale,[8] but the Fox Talbot photograph shows that this was not in fact how the ship was built. In this photograph the five-barred rail is clearly outlined against the gable of the houses in Queens Terrace; it can be seen that it was 3 ft 3 in. in height and also that the gunwale had the knuckle in the iron shell forward—one of the original features which still survives.[*] Below the waterline the hull was painted with red lead paint; above, the paint was black except for the white band and the gilt decoration. The funnel was all black, the deck erections and most of the masts were of varnished wood, and the bowsprit and the lower mast of No. 2 were painted white. With her rows of glinting portholes—such a large number constituted a novelty—and her undoubted grace, *Great Britain* must have been an impressive sight at sea.

Turning to navigation, the ship was built and designed, as we have seen, with a light bridge amidships on top of a small deckhouse abaft the funnel, though the handling of the ship at sea was carried out from

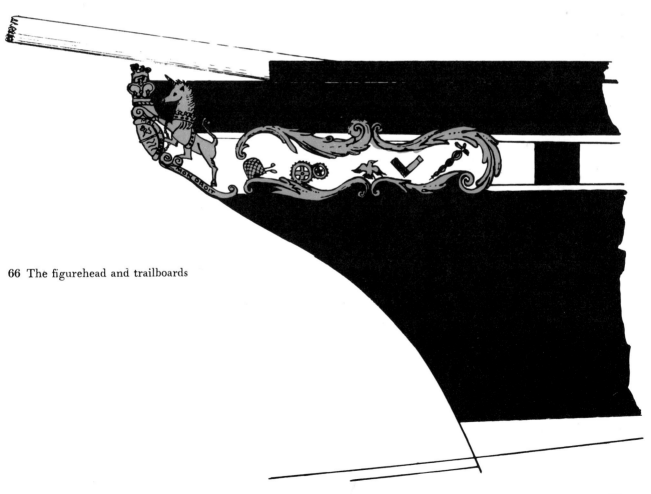

66 The figurehead and trailboards

the poop. It is by no means clear where charts were kept and worked although it is possible that the chart-room was in the small deckhouse or the captain's day-room. If so, it was a very long way from the officer of the watch and from the wheel. The oil sidelights were in light boxes on the shrouds of the main mast. The compass was immediately forward of the wheel and was corrected according to the methods described in an earlier chapter. Tiller interference—a constant bugbear of previous iron ships—would not have caused much trouble, as the tiller led aft. In her main navigation arrangements the *Great Britain* was really much the same as any sailing ship; indeed, she compared unfavourably with those whose officers' accommodation and chart-room were conveniently situated right aft.

Speed measurement was by two means: casting of the common log, and an ingenious electric fan. The common log was a little ' drogue attached to a knotted line; the number of knots which ran out in 14 seconds (timed by a sand glass) was the vessel's speed. Some disputed the device's accuracy. In the discussion of Guppy's 1845 paper on the *Great Britain* to the Institution of Civil Engineers, Captain Hosken of the *Great Britain* and a Mr Curtis crossed swords on this point.[9] Curtis, having looked into the subject, said that

persons unacquainted with the subject would not be surprised to learn that he had heard it expressed as an opinion, by most naval officers, and had found by his own practice that the rate of a ship, going more than 10 knots, could scarcely be obtained within a mile under unfavourable circumstances.

Captain Hosken could not agree:

He was convinced that with a correct glass and a log properly 'hove' by an experienced seaman the rate would be given to one-eighth of a mile. Under all circumstances he thought the common log was the best means of ascertaining speed at sea.

The electric fan was an extraordinary feature. It was described in a contemporary account of the ship as follows:

A new electro-galvanic instrument for registering the speed of vessels. It consists of a dial plate which may be placed in the cabin or any other convenient part of the ship. By the agency of an electric current the space passed over and the speed of the vessel in knots per hour is registered on this dial attached to one of Massey's ordinary fans and immersed with it in the water is an apparatus which every time the fan has made a certain number of revolutions and consequently when the vessel has passed through a given space, brings the ends of two wires in contact. These wires connect the fan with a galvanic battery and clock movement in the vessel whenever contact is procured by the fan, and a circuit is thus completed for the electric current, the indices in the dial of the clock movement are acted upon by means of electromagnets and register the speed and distance passed over by the vessel. The instrument is exceedingly simple and the fan may remain in the water during the whole voyage, the indices registering continually the speed and distance passed over.[12]

This is a modern type of device and is still used to this day, though with an electronic integrator instead of the clockwork one. Captain Hosken said it was the best of all the instruments he had seen and tried. However, it under-read when the vessel was going at less than five or over eight knots. Modern knowledge shows this to be simply an error of location, reflecting a lack of outreach from the disturbed water around the hull.

The arrangements for expelling water from the ship were interesting. *Great Britain* was fitted with a complete bilge system arranged with pipes which could draw from every compartment. The bilge pumps, as we have seen, were attached to the air-pump cross-lever and the circulating pump could also be applied to the bilge lines. This was perhaps the most powerful pumping system afloat at the time, and capable of discharging 180 tons of water per hr from the ship. In addition to these mechanical pumps the ship was fitted with the ordinary manual wheel-type plunger pumps, which still exist with the name *Great Britain* cast upon their barrels. These were mainly for emergency purpose but may have been used for discharging small quantities of water and for deck-washing. Water on the deck was collected by wooden gutter planks which took it to lead-lined scupper pipes; those ran out through the ship's side and discharged overboard. The scuppers were quite small, but deck-water could also escape between the rails. With a trim by the stern the few inches of wood gunwale protruding above the weather deck would only trap a little water, and the ship could rid herself of this quite quickly.

67 Lead scupper leading through the two-ft wooden gunwale

Mooring was by means of bollards aft and at the break of the forecastle, and bollard posts on the forecastle gunwale. Iron bull's-eye mooring pipes led out port and starboard through the heavy bulwarks at the break of the forecastle; these must have been extraordinarily difficult to work as they were some 2 ft in length through the bulwark. The anchoring arrangements were again a mixture of old and new. The anchors were suspended from catheads and were hooked and lifted on deck in the sailing-ship way by means of a fish tackle—a heavy block and tackle leading from the foremast, parallel to the forestay. The catheads were of classical wooden sailing-ship type but the cable was stud-type chain of $2\frac{1}{2}$-in. link thickness while the anchors were all-iron Trotmans with the crown and flukes hinged on the shank. This type of anchor, which is still used today in some countries, is quite efficient and has the outstanding advantage over the Admiralty anchor that when dug into the ground the fluke not in the ground comes over to lie flush with the shank of the anchor. This could be important because if a ship goes round her anchor she may wrap her cable round an outstanding fluke. This often happens with the Admiralty anchor which sticks right up from the seabed in such conditions. The *Great Britain*'s anchors weigh nearly four tons and both survive. That they were put to severe test is shown by the bent shank of one, obviously the result of a pull of many tons on the anchor cable. This kink is a silent witness of some frightening incident in the history of the old ship.

No doubt Brunel and his Committee submitted estimates of running costs to their directors, and it is interesting to speculate on what these must have been. The cost of the *Great Britain* was about £120,000. Contemporary accounts make it clear that the normal practice was to allow an annual 10 per cent. of the cost of the ship for wear and tear, and 5 per cent. each for depreciation, insurance and interest, amounting to an

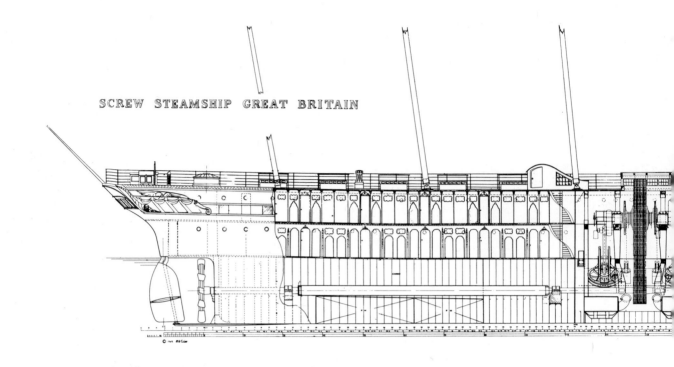

SCREW STEAMSHIP GREAT BRITAIN

68 Profile of the *Great Britain*; drawing by the author

69 The transom decoration

THE GREAT BRITAIN

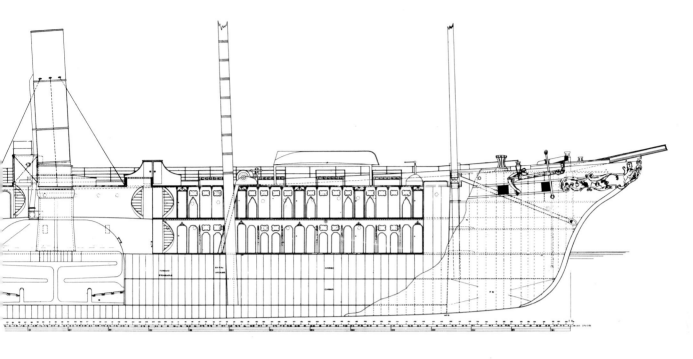

annual capital charge of 25 per cent., or £30,000. This is very heavy by modern standards.

Crew costs would have been another heavy item. At that time captains were paid £16 a month with 5s. 6d. per day for victuals, other deck officers £4 a month plus 3s. 6d. per day, the chief engineer £8 a month and 3s. 6d. a day, seamen £2 10s. a month and 1s. 6d. a day, and firemen £3 10s. a month and 1s. 6d. a day. The ship's officers probably consisted of the following: captain, mate, second, third and fourth officers, surgeon and purser. It is questionable whether the engineers, apart from the chief, were considered as officers; if so, the total of ten officers would cost between them about £1,500 per annum. We know that *Great Britain* required 20 seamen to handle her sails; assuming this to be one of two watches, the total of 40 men would cost about £2,300 a year. There must have been three watches of firemen; allowing five men for each stoke hole, this gives a total of 60. It is not unreasonable to assume 20 stewards —roughly one for every 10 passengers. The annual cost for seamen, firemen and stewards would then be about £7,300. The gross total would therefore be around £9,000 per annum for the crew, which was known to total 130 officers and men.

Coal at that time cost around £1 a ton, and *Great Britain*'s design consumption was of the order of 60 tons per day. Supposing a round trip to take 47 days (15 to the west and 12 to the east, with 10 days at each end), seven round trips a year would mean 189 days' steaming. Her annual coal consumption would therefore be around 11,500 tons—approximately £12,000-worth of coal. Making an arbitrary allowance of £10,000 for management, the cost of running this ship on the Atlantic for one year would be about £61,000.

The income is difficult to calculate because of the range of fares, but taking the median one of £28 and a capacity of 252 berthed passengers the capacity income would be almost exactly £100,000, so that without cargo the number of passengers required to break even on costs would be about 150. Cargo was carried at £5 per ton, so that revenue from this source could reach £5,000 for a round voyage, or £35,000 per annum. On the voyage on which the ship was wrecked in Dundrum Bay she sailed from Liverpool with 180 passengers—in modern terms, a load factor of 71·5 per cent. Had that voyage been completed it should have netted her some profit. If she could have carried 200 passengers—an 80 per cent. load factor—regularly, she should according to these calculations have made a profit of the order of 16 per cent. of the capital invested in her, excluding all income from mails and cargo. It would not be unreasonable to anticipate a further £20,000 of net profit from these sources at a similar load factor, in which case the directors might well have anticipated something of the order of a 30 per cent. return on capital: enough to justify the entire venture.

These figures, though speculative, do indicate that the *Great Britain* was no white elephant; given luck and continuing service she could have been a profitable venture for the Great Western Steamship Company.

70 Mute testimony to a long-past stor

Completion, launch and trials

The directors of the Great Western Steamship Company announced at their half-yearly General Meeting in March 1839 that they had decided to construct their next vessel of iron and that the preparations were far advanced. In April they made a formal and specific announcement that they were about to build a ship of iron of about 2,000 tons tonnage with engines of 1,000 horsepower. At this time the size of the ship on paper was still increasing rapidly, but by the middle of the year GB5 had been designed and on 19 July fabrication of the keel commenced officially. This date was probably chosen as being significant as the anniversary of the launch of *Great Western*, but the actual laying of the keel on the berth in the building dock was not until December of that year. Furthermore, we know that Claxton had been having difficulties during the construction of the dock and it is not unlikely that this delayed placing any iron structure on the actual keel blocks.

The dock was built on the site of a small and older one and its axis was at a small angle to the older dock. The latter may have been either a graving dock or a wet dock for timber seasoning; its remains still exist as a bulge on the south side of the Great Western Dock.

Curiously, a diligent search of Bristol records has failed to discover any reference to it. On 8 February 1840, the *Mechanics' Magazine* was able to report: 'A dock has been excavated for the express purpose of her construction and most excellent erecting shops fitted up for the engines with foundry, cranes and other conveniences.'—the total cost was just over £53,000. Economy was shown in the construction of the Great Western Dock and its dimensions approximate very closely to those of the ship itself. As can be seen, the entrance was tight in the extreme: shaped exactly to the midship section of the ship, it presupposed the draft when afloat and gave very little tolerance for a deeper one. Fig. 71 shows a full-scale template of the midship section being checked in this entrance prior to entry at the time of final salvage. To allow access to the bottom during construction, the ship was built on blocks higher than normal, the level at the entrance to the dock allowing an extra 2 ft to 2 ft 6 in., giving a clearance under the keel of perhaps 5 ft. When the vessel was to be floated it was intended that the dock should be pumped up to this level, the tops of the keel blocks removed and the ship lowered to her normal flotation level.[1]

71 Template of half the *Great Britain*'s midship section in the dock (February 1969), used to check that she would fit on her return

Construction was not very far advanced before two events delayed it. The first was the financial blow delivered to the Great Western Steamship Company by Cunard's acquisition of the mail contract across the Atlantic. As Claxton bitterly complained,

Nearly half a million is annually paid to the enterprising companies who have succeeded in obtaining contracts and who are all ably performing the service . . . Our fortunate competitors are paid as near as maybe the exact sum per voyage which is required to cover the expenses of the *Great Western* out and home, viz. £4,500, leaving if the case were hers a profit varying between £5,000 and £10,000 per voyage.

Great Western was profitable, indeed in 1843 her receipts were £33,400 and her expenditure only £25,600, but the great new ship was so expensive that she was a severe drain upon the capital resources of the company. Also, the baleful influence of Dr Dionysius Lardner was still felt by the company. He undoubtedly prevented the *Great Western* being provided with sister ships—very galling, as she was for some years unquestionably the finest ship on the Atlantic and it is likely that with three or four such ships the company would have been awarded the mail contracts. Lardner's discomfiture over the success of the *Great Western* was of little comfort to the directors: they would have been much more satisfied with some income from mails. The second event was, of course, the arrival of *Archimedes* at Bristol; the combined result was that construction of the ship was stopped from June 1840 until the end of the year.

Brunel had found that altering the *Great Britain* to screw propulsion was quite an easy task, mainly through the expedient of dropping the bottom sternframe below the line of keel. The design alterations to the hull could not have taken much time; and although the machinery had to be redesigned entirely the new design was probably completed during the early part of 1841.

As suggested earlier, the irregular frame spacings of *Great Britain* indicate that the shell plating was erected before the frames. To recapitulate, the small size of the shell plates necessitated so many butt straps that it would have been impossible to space frames regularly, say every 18 in., without them having to be joggled or bend them over the butt straps.

It would seem likely, therefore, that a wood cradle was erected from keel to deck, extending over perhaps 20 or 30 ft of the ship, and that the shell plating was laid up inside this and riveted together. The lines for the frames could then be marked avoiding the butt straps, templates taken off, and the frames bent and riveted in. The only alternative would have been to make a large-scale plating model showing all plate edges and to line up frame lines on the model to avoid straps.

Construction having started anew in the spring of 1841, it was not long before *Great Britain* began to attract a great deal of interest. To quote Captain Claxton:

The sides of the *Great Britain* were scarcely visible over the walls of the yard in which she was building when naval officers, shipbuilders, engineers and philosophers from all countries began to seek admittance and many have been the papers which in most languages have been written on the comparative merits of iron and wood as a material for shipbuilding, which would not probably have seen the light had not a scale of dimensions been decided upon, which may create astonishment at the present moment, but which will probably excite no more wonder in a few years than the size of the *Great Western* does at present.[2]

He referred to the prophecy of doom made at the *Great Western*'s launch that, being so long, she would break her back when she put to sea.

The project attracted its cranks, one of them being a Mr Dayman who wrote from Bideford in 1842 that

Having resided near Bristol during the time that the principal portion of the outer sheeting of the hull of the then *Mammoth*, now *Great Britain*, was being laid on it struck me very forcibly that the method adopted, that of riveting together oblong sheets of iron of short lengths was a most clumsy mode of proceeding and utterly unworthy of the advanced state to which the mechanical arts have arrived.[3]

Dayman proposed 'iron planks' where the iron was rolled out into long narrow strips and the edges preferably welded together.

Other would-be inventors were drawn to screw propulsion. Again to quote Christopher Claxton:

No sooner was it known that Mr Brunel had recommended the application [of the screw] than claimants sprang up in several directions. These gentlemen were handed over to Mr Smith's Company under whose licence the *Great Britain* was working.

The *Great Britain*'s propeller was in fact an application of the patents of James Lowe in the deadwood aperture of Smith, but it was clearly convenient to let Smith fight these battles. Opinions differed strongly as to the wisdom of the decision to use screw propulsion. One learned gentleman wrote in January 1841:

It does appear to me . . . a rather hazardous thing on the part of the Company to adopt an invention of the success of which they are not as yet fully satisfied. One voyage however to New York will be quite sufficient to decide this question.

The *Mechanics' Magazine* had no doubt: 'It is no experiment but a triumph of public spirit and laudable evaluation over pre-conceived notions of excellence and perfectability.'

Another battle soon began to rage. When the ship was first proposed she was to have been a smaller, cheaper and simpler vessel using conventional materials and machinery. The cost increased as the ship grew in size, changed to iron and then to screw propulsion, and a *cri de cœur* appeared in the press in November 1842 from an individual signing himself 'A Luckless Shareholder'.[4] While descriptions of the ship excited the public mind, he begged leave to place a few remarks upon the merit (if any) of the management and the indiscreet expenditure of the company's resources:

I am one of the unfortunate shareholders and have now become so sick of the continued demands and want of money that I feel almost reckless of the consequences.

In August last [1841] we were told the cost of the new ship would not exceed £76,116 but at the meeting held at Bristol on Friday last just three short months after we are told that the estimated cost is not to exceed £100,000. . . . I respectfully and most feelingly put it to my brother shareholders whether it is not better instead of reducing the weekly wages from £367 to £300 as proposed to increase them and *get the thing* done if possible before another three months pass over our heads. . . . A suggestion was made that the services of Mr Guppy should be dispensed with and thereby save £500 a year but I say NO! If we are to finish the ship let us procure the additional assistance of a *real practical industrious engineer* in whose ability we may place confidence for the short time we are to remain a company and that the £300 or £400 paid weekly be properly spent and that the system of making, altering and re-making which has been so long practised to our cost and of advantage to none but our salaried service be put an end to. I do not wish to be understood as hinting at any incapacity in Mr Guppy as *engineer* seeing that the title and diploma may be had even easier than by setting one's legs under the office table of a C.E. in chief for a couple of years. . . . One cannot but think that the people of Bristol with the exception of two, are perfectly innocent of sleeping with one eye open: to me it appears they keep both shut.

Criticisms by 'A Luckless Shareholder' were hardly fair. At a time of rapid change in shipbuilding it was not to be wondered at that changes should be made and costs increased.

To the technically-minded man, however, the *Great Britain* was fascinating. John Grantham wrote in 1842:

The scientific world is waiting with intense interest the completion of the iron ship the *Great Britain* now building at Bristol and better known as *The Mammoth* I have been favoured by Mr Guppy with her dimensions which are truly gigantic.

He then followed with a substantially accurate description of the ship and concluded:

It would be an endless task and without the aid of drawings a fruitless one to attempt a description in detail of this magnificent vessel. I can however state that her lines are very beautiful and adapted to the highest rate of speed. The general character of the workmanship is very good and does a great credit to the builder.[5]

Another technical man, J. R. Hill, C.E., reported to the *Mechanics' Magazine* at length in August 1842 on the ship.[6] A few weeks before a model of the machinery had been exhibited and created great interest at the Agricultural Meeting at Bristol; Hill's description, which was repeated a year later in the *Illustrated London News*, is competent and extensive. He refers to the same statement of cost as did 'A Luckless Shareholder'. Apparently this was made by one of the company's officials at the Agricultural Meeting and was £105,000 in toto and not £100,000 as quoted by 'A Luckless Shareholder'. The last official cost was as quoted by 'Luckless Shareholder'; and indeed, the actual total cost, apart from that of the shipyard, was £117,295 6s. 7d. Seventy-three per cent. of this was accounted for by the hull, $15\frac{1}{2}$ per cent. by fittings, rigging and stores, and the remainder by financial charges and so on. In fact *Great Britain* cost almost exactly twice as much as *Great Western*: quite a reasonable increase in view of the ship's size, material and complexity.

It is interesting that as late as the middle of 1842 the public still did not know how the ship was to be propelled. Commenting on John Grantham's statements, *Mechanics' Magazine* pointed out that it was not known as yet how this 'prodigious floating mass is to be propelled—that is how the power of the engines is to be made available. We gather only from the breadth assigned for the beam and the absence of all mention of paddle boxes, that it is *not* to be by paddle wheels.'

Despite complaints, money was scraped up and construction proceeded. By the late autumn of 1842 Hill stated that the machinery was in a 'forward state' and much of it ready for putting into the vessel; the boiler was nearly finished, and cabins, berths and other joinery work was well advanced. In March 1843 the directors were able to report:

The *Great Britain* is in a forward state. Frames and hull are complete. The whole of the upper decks of the forecastle, forecabins and aftercabins are laid and caulked. Nearly the whole of the staterooms and other joiners' work is finished. The forehold, afterhold and iron coal decks before the boilers and abaft the engines are nearly finished. The boilers and funnel are fixed in their places, as are the cylinders, condensers, air pumps and other weighty parts of the engines. To add to her strength and diminish the apprehension of fire, the decks and partition of the body of the ship occupied by the engines, etc., will be fitted up in iron.

Nearly all the masts and spars are made and should nothing unforeseen arise she may be floated out within three months . . . and might be at sea within six months.

The launch schedule was adhered to, and by the summer the great ship was ready. The masts were dumped on the deck and stayed temporarily in order to give the ship a suitably imposing appearance at launch. An auspicious date was chosen: 19 July, the anniversary of the launch of *Great Western* and of the start of fabrication in iron. One hundred and twenty-seven years later to the day, *Great Britain* was moved back into the same dock after being salvaged.

It seems that Prince Albert was invited to launch the ship, but that he in turn invited Mrs Miles, the wife of one of the directors of the Steamship Company, to perform the ceremony. Mrs Miles had launched *Great Western* six years earlier. It was a great occasion. Bristol was decorated with flowers and flags from the roofs and from lines between roofs. A considerable number of triumphal arches were erected in the streets, and Prince Albert was led in procession from Brunel's Temple Meads Station to the yard of the Steamship Company. Cannons were fired at intervals, and thousands of people lined Brandon Hill which forms a natural amphitheatre from which to view the building dock. Prince Albert inspected the ship and then was banqueted in a pavilion converted from the patternmaker's shop. In the centre of the royal table there was an interesting toy—a model of the *Great Britain* in full sail contrasted with two other ships, all moved by clockwork. The cold banquet was sumptuous and the importance attached to the occasion can be seen from the list of guests: Prince Albert, the Prussian, American and Sardinian Ministers and their wives, the Marquis of Exeter, the Earl of Liverpool, the Earl of Hardwick, Lord Granville, the Marquis of Northampton, the Earl of Lincoln, Lord Charles Wellesley and so on. Not least were Sir Marc and Lady Brunel, Isambard's ageing parents, to whom their son's achievements and also the use of the Triangle engine must have given great satisfaction.

After the banquet the launching party went to the pavilion on the corner of the dock, by its entrance. This pavilion can be seen in Fig. 72 with the large Royal Standard on its summit. The *Bristol Journal* commented:

The vessel was decorated with the colours of all nations and as far as the eye could reach in every direction nothing was to be seen but flags, banners and emblems and masses of human beings. All around rose the masts of ships dressed out in chequered and flaunting colours. Boats and barges were crowded and the various adjacent wharves and quays were lined with anxious spectators. . . . From the water's edge upwards rose tier upon tier of spectators. . . . Brandon Hill was covered with not less than 30,000 persons.

The ship had been floated during the banquet and was now ready to be named and floated out. A small screw steamer, the *Avon*, took a line from her bows and at the signal *Great Britain* was pulled slowly out into the harbour amid the cheers of the crowd. The shipyard workers guided the ship with lines from bow and stern, but unfortunately the *Avon*'s rope broke and Mrs Miles missed the ship by a full 10 ft. A second and larger line was substituted and she then veered over towards the royal pavilion. Prince Albert intervened and taking a second bottle of champagne threw it at the vessel, scoring a decisive hit—glass and wine showering the heads of people below who were pushing her side off from the dock. She was thus named *Great Britain* at quarter past three, and Prince Albert left almost immediately afterwards by Brunel's Great Western Railway,

72 The launch of the *Great Britain*

arriving at Paddington two hours and 40 minutes later. It was a great day and he expressed himself particularly impressed by the fact that he had spent six hours in Bristol and made a journey of 240 miles, all in 12 hours.

The ship was now ready for fitting out and the next year was so occupied. Work seems to have proceeded more slowly than was expected, however. Just before Christmas in 1843 there was a special General Meeting of the shareholders and it was announced that the ship would be ready for an experimental trip in February of the following year. The meeting unanimously agreed to place her on the New York line early in May, with which the directors agreed. They were then allowed to raise a further £10,000 to complete the ship for sea, an event which had to wait for a further year.

Possibly the first photograph ever taken of a ship shows *Great Britain* during these last stages of her construction. The survival of a number of the buildings in this photograph makes it possible to place the ship with accuracy. She is lying alongside what is now the Northern Gas Ferry steps, and the line of sight is directly north. The ship is nearly complete, her draught about 13 ft aft, and the machinery has been fitted. That some minor parts of it are still being fitted may, however, be surmised from the staging alongside the bunkering hatches and from the fact that the bridge wings are shown struck down and laid against the main mast shrouds, allowing access through the top of the deckhouse abaft the funnel. This interesting and invaluable photograph does not agree in some minor details with contemporary lithographs and thus shows their lack of complete accuracy. From the state of the ship and the trees it can be concluded that the photograph was taken in April or May 1844.

73 Possibly the first photograph ever taken of a ship—by Fox Talbot, 1844

Very many people visited the ship during this period. Some were ordinary Britons such as William Botham of Gloucester, who wrote in his diary: '18 May 1844—On Monday morning went on board the s.s. *Great Britain*, the Monster of the Deep'. Others were exalted foreigners such as the King of Saxony, who visited the ship on 8 July 1844. His physician, Dr Carus, commented at length on the visit and was clearly impressed by Brunel:

The engineer who has directed the building and who speaks German very tolerably conducted the King through the whole labyrinth of the interior and gave us the most interesting details concerning it. . . . The peculiarity about the vessel is the manner of progression being propelled by means of an Archimedian screw introduced in the keel and under the rudder.

The King was very impressed with the internal arrangements and accommodation, but the whole party seemed to be doubtful as to whether the vessel could ever get out of the narrow dock and along the Avon into the sea, and whether a ship with such dimensions would be fit for sea service at all. Obviously denigrators were at work. In Carus's words:

It is feared, and as it appears not entirely without reason, that if the vessel were to be raised at once under the bows and stern by two waves, the weight of the machinery in the centre might possibly break her in two.

74 Where the *Great Britain* lay in Fox Talbot's photograph—he stood on the Wapping Wharf looking towards Brandon Hill

There seems to have been an extraordinary lobby against the *Great Britain* in her early days, especially in Bristol. The directors did not help. To see the ship a written permit signed by two directors and a 5s. contribution to the Workmen's Sick Fund were required. 'Who ever heard of such a demand?' it was asked indignantly.[7]

In contrast to the attitude in Bristol, the City of New York was preparing to welcome the ship, and the Board of Aldermen of the City unanimously adopted a resolution allowing the extension of the pier at the foot of Clifton Street a further 70 ft into the river so that it would be suitable for the *Great Britain*. But there were further delays before the ship was to set forth for America. One problem was the design of the

propeller. This had been intentionally delayed while there was still hope that the *Rattler* experiments would be completed in time to give some useful data, but in March a directors' meeting decided that it was possible to wait no longer and that the design must be put in hand.[8] Brunel conceived and executed this great design in the spring and summer of 1844.

Another delay was caused by the controversy over the *Great Britain*'s passage from the Floating Harbour into the Cumberland Basin, and then from the Cumberland Basin into the River Avon. It had been realised at an early stage that the ship's unprecedented width would necessitate alterations to the locks into the river, but it was not originally planned to widen the gates between the Floating Harbour and the Cumberland Basin. However, the weight of the machinery, which was fitted before the ship had passed out of the Floating Harbour (instead of in the Cumberland Basin, as had been the intention), made the ship's draught too great to allow her sloping sides to overhang the entrance walls: it became apparent that these locks would also require altering if the *Great Britain* was to make her exit.

The year 1844 started badly. The *Bristol Mirror* reported:

All sorts of reports of a mischievous tendency are being most industriously propagated respecting the removal of the ship. At one moment we hear that the water is to be raised high enough to drown the city, at another that gentlemen are about to hire kitchens and cellars for the purpose of depositing goods with the intention that they shall be swamped and the value recovered from the Dock Company. At another that the walls of the outer lock into the Basin are to be pulled down altogether and the upper lock treated the same way, at another that the gates are to be removed and are too weak to be put back again, at another that the trade of the port is to be shut up for a month, at another that the expense of the removal will be £30,000 and last but not least that the *Great Britain* is a great mistake and is until the iron with which she is composed is altogether decomposed to remain in the Port of Bristol.[9]

The *Bristol Mirror* rose nobly to the occasion and refuted these various rumours at length and with strength. The ship was still advertised as due to commence operation on the New York route in May, but by this time there can have been little hope that she would be able to do so.

In March the press were still reporting that 'the Dock Company have not yet given their sanction to the passage of the *Great Britain* through the locks',[10] while in April the *Mechanics' Magazine* made a determined plea for 'the solicited mediation of the Board of Trade'.[11] The article continued:

On further consideration of the plan of floating the huge vessel out of the two narrow docks with iron tanks it appears to be so fraught with danger that we understand it must be abandoned so that the *Great Britain* is in the predicament of a fattened weasel that while feeding and fattening in the farmer's granary grew too big for the hole by which it gained admission. The mutual difficulties of the Steamship Company and the Bristol Dock directors have, however, been fairly brought under the consideration of the Board of Trade. The case is one in which the nation at large is concerned and the interests of commerce and navigation not a little involved and although it is anomalous and without precedent it surely cannot be without remedy.

The Dock Company originally refused to accept the liability for making alterations to the structure of the docks without the sanction of an Act of Parliament. Eventually, however, agreement was reached and the *Bristol Mirror* was able to report in October:

The alteration in the entrance to the Cumberland Basin for the admission of the *Great Britain* is proceeding in a most satisfactory manner and we are happy to announce that the whole vessel will enter the Cumberland Basin on or about 26 October and will proceed from thence to Kings Road on the highest tide in the early part of November.[12]

A day or two later it was reported that she had at last floated from the Dock. The Dock Company's dilatoriness had condemned her to at least six months of imprisonment.

On 10 December the ship was ready to enter the Avon. At high water a steam tug towed her into the lock but when about three-quarters of the way through she stuck. Claxton was on board the tug and immediately concluded that she must be pulled back as she was touching the lock walls on either side. He gave orders, and in the nick of time, as the tide began to fall, the ship was back in the Basin. Further widening of the lock was necessary, and Brunel wrote on the 11th:

She stuck in the lock. We *did* get her back. I have been hard at work all day altering the masonry of the lock. Tonight, our last tide, we have succeeded in getting her through but being dark we have been obliged to ground her outside. I confess I cannot leave her until I see her afloat again and all clear of her difficulties.[13]

In fact they were over. At 8 a.m. the following morning, 12 December, she floated and was towed down the Avon. The *Liverpool Mail* correspondent who saw this was greatly impressed: 'The contours presented to the eye are of the most exquisite grace—fine and beautifully rounded in her lines with a gentle sheer she sits upon the water like a racing gig.'

During her progress down the river the boilers were filled and steam raised, and a preliminary opinion of the performance of the largest screw ship ever built was formed. *The Times* correspondent reported:

Great Britain steered like a boat with one or two strokes of her wheel and came round with helm 30° in a circle of less than half a mile in diameter. The superintendent engineers Brunel and Guppy told Mr H. S. Harman the engineer-in-chief—six revolutions only for running in, at which she made four knots.

The ship's speed was gradually increased after reaching Portishead, and near the Holmes further steering trials were carried out, during which it was found that she handled best with 30° of helm. Eventually, on the way home, they reached $16\frac{1}{4}$ engine revolutions which gave 11 knots, and it was found that the slip of the propeller was only seven per cent. On this preliminary trial six of the 24 fires were not lit, but the most important thing was that the engines

worked perfectly smooth and without the slightest vibration or tremor being felt in any part of the vessel. The screw propeller was not fully immersed and the ship's draft aft was 14 ft 6 in. and 12 ft forward. . . . When going at her best speed there is no swell whatsover under the bows, her stem cutting through the water. The chains and wheels upon which they worked revolve without noise and what is still more desirable there is a complete absence of vibration in the ship.[14]

Following this preliminary trial, the superintending engineer, Guppy, felt he ought to submit a formal report to the directors:

Great Western Steamship Works
Bristol
17 December 1844

Gentlemen,

Relying upon the opinion of Mr. Brunel you boldly decided in December 1840 to alter the method of propulsion of the large steamer which you had then commenced to construct from paddle wheels to the then scarcely tried Archimedian propeller.

The triumphant result of this your decision was ascertained on Thursday last when the *Great Britain* having been towed down to King Road had her steaming powers tested for the first time. As it was not desirable to suffer such weighty machinery to run at its calculated speed for some length of time the engines commenced working at six to eight revolutions a minute and this was gradually increased to 12 or 13 revolutions. The velocity required by the vessel during this time was exactly that which had been intended being at the rate of one knot per hour for every $1\frac{1}{2}$ revolutions per minute, thus 12 revolutions gave exactly eight knots. In this manner the ship proceeded to the Holmes when some evolutions were performed with the view of trying how she steered, and it was ascertained that she was very completely under the command of the helm. On the return to King Road the speed was increased to rather more than 16 revolutions per minute when her rate of going was ascertained to be 11 knots.

During this short trial voyage much more steam could have been generated had it been required. . . . My duty in the construction of the ship and engines being performed I am now to thank you for the extreme confidence you have placed in me; and as such a valuable machine ought only to be entrusted to the management of a person fully alive to the importance of the trust reposed in him I have now to request that you will confer on Mr Harman who has so ably and zealously assisted me in the great novel work the post of Engineer in Chief. The avoidance of accidents and repairs and the great saving in the consumption of coal, oil, etc., by the management of the personal judgement constitute this situation one of importance.

The present screw has rather surpassed my expectations but as you have voted that another shall be made and its progress has only been delayed until we can make some observations with regard to this one, I have already consulted Mr Brunel on the subject; it will not be desirable to proceed far with it until we shall have had the benefit of a few more trial trips. . . .

T. R. GUPPY[15]

> *Six Masts—like princely sons to bear!*
> *"Great Britain" for my name*
> *My smoke trail black on the sun bright air,*
> *My screw as swift, and my sails as fair*
> *As the trumpet voice of Fame!"*
> *(From—'The Trial of the "Great Britain" '—Anon. 1845)*

Official trials began on 8 January 1845. Among others, engineers, scientific men and directors of the company were on board, but unfortunately there was thick fog and the pilot, after waiting at anchor for several hours, was only very reluctantly persuaded to make a run to gratify the visitors. *The Times* commented:

She came round from her moorings in the King Road in beautiful style. The

75 Finally free—*Great Britain* leaving the docks into the River Avon

engines were put in motion at 10 revolutions a minute when she made 6½ knots. At 19 minutes past one the log was again thrown 13 and nearly 14 revolutions nine knots. . . . When the ship was below the Holmes she was brought round twice and came round 32 points in a little less than seven minutes. On her return up channel the speed of the engines was increased to 18 revolutions which gave 11¾ knots. The engines worked beautifully, none of the bearings heating.[16]

This preliminary trial was followed by a dinner on board under the chairmanship of Captain Claxton who toasted the health of Mr Smith, with whom he was obviously very impressed. *The Times* somewhat sourly remarked:

Captain Claxton forgot to add one remarkable fact, that the screw applied to the *Rattler*, *Great Britain*, etc. is no more like the Archimedian screw of which Mr Smith is the patentee than a grindstone is like a wheel.[17]

The ship was then formally registered, being issued with certificate No. 10 of 1845, on 14 January. She was given the official number 25967 which she kept throughout her life: indeed, it still is carved on one of the hatch coamings. The registered owners were 'John William Miles and Thomas Bonville Were of the City of Bristol Trustees of the joint stock company called the Great Western Steamship Company'. John Miles was the husband of the Mrs Miles who had missed with the first bottle of wine at the floating ceremony.

The *Great Britain* was described as 'schooner rigged with standing bowsprit, square stern and carvel built with false galleries and a Royal

Arms figurehead'. This must surely be one of the most historic registry certificates in existence.

A more formal trial was carried out on 20 January when a run was made down the Bristol Channel to Ilfracombe and back, a distance of about 95 nautical miles, without much wind but in a head swell and with a balance of two hours of tide against the ship. The round trip was performed in eight hours 34 minutes at an average speed of over 11 knots. During this endurance run the engines reached a maximum of $18\frac{2}{3}$ strokes per minute; the condenser vacuum was 26 in.; the expansion was cut off at a quarter of a stroke and the ship's best speed was $12\frac{1}{3}$ knots.

The ship was accepted as being clearly most successful. Indeed, *Great Britain*'s performance on trials was remarkable. There was little or no difficulty with her machinery and no need for alterations, the ship met her intended speed, she steered well, and everything was in order in spite of the novelty of her construction and of her means of propulsion. Only naval architects and shipbuilders can appreciate the enormous achievement this represented in the technological context of the day.

The ship was due to sail from Bristol to London on 23 January. Upon raising the anchor at 7 p.m. it was found that it had fouled the wreck of a schooner which had sunk a few weeks before, and some time was spent in getting clear of the sunken spars and rigging. By 9.30 p.m., however, the ship was abreast of Flat Holme, where she increased speed to 14 revolutions a minute, the steam pressure being $4\frac{1}{2}$ lb. per sq. in. Shortly afterwards she had to slacken speed to adjust bearings, and she held this reduced speed until midnight when she worked up again. In the small hours of the 24th a strong north-westerly gale arose with a heavy cross sea and squalls of rain. By 10 a.m. the ship was off Lundy Island with the gale continuing from the north-north-west but still making $5\frac{1}{2}$–6 knots against a heavy sea with 13 revolutions of the engine. She was rolling tremendously but still very easily. This caused some trouble. Guppy commented:

The crew of sailors consisted chiefly of that indifferent class usually shipped for short runs to whom of course the rig of the ship was perfectly new. Some of the engineers stood well to their duty but others and nearly all the stokers were completely knocked up with sea-sickness. With the wind ahead or on either bow and with a heavy head sea she steered with the greatest ease and precision.[18]

At 3.20 on the afternoon of the 24th, with the tide ebbing strongly, the *Great Britain* was struck by a tremendous sea on the starboard bow and a smaller one at the same time on the port.

The shock was dreadful and for a moment brought her to a standstill. She recovered instanter and on examination it was found that three of her starboard bow bulls-eyes had been stove in with their frames. The diagonal bands of the foc'sle deck buckled, the woodwork started 2 in. upwards, a portion of her carved figurehead and the carpenter's work of the bulkhead carried away and the iron sheathing on both starboard and larboard bows above decks ripped in two places. Notwithstanding this shock she still held on her way.[19]

This incident has been preserved for all time by the artist Walter who

76 3 p.m. on 24 January 1845— struck by a heavy sea in a gale (after a painting by J. Walter)

was on board. The ship is flying a three-flag hoist in the Marryat code of 1845: 9, 4, 3—'The Best of All'.

At 5.30 p.m. the weather began to moderate and they were able to set sail, using four spencers, a jib and the square mainsail. The engine room raised 15 revolutions and the log showed $9\frac{3}{4}$ knots. By eight o'clock the sea was going down fast and the weather was fine and clear. An hour later there was no wind at all as the ship passed the Longships at 10 knots.

As *Great Britain* rounded the Lizard another two hours later, her speed had risen to $10\frac{1}{2}$ knots and the sails were useless. The next day she was off Portland at 9.45 a.m., making just under 11 knots with the mainsail and all fore and aft sails. The Needles were passed three hours later, by which time her speed had risen to $11\frac{1}{4}$ knots. The ship stopped for a few minutes off Cowes just after 2 p.m. to land letters.

At 1.45 a.m. on Sunday, 26 January, they came to anchor in the Downs and at 8.11 weighed anchor and set off for London. Off the Nore there was an augury of things to come. The *Prince Albert*, an American packet, was passed and responded nobly with her colours and three cheers. They were returned by the *Great Britain* who hoisted the American Ensign at the mainmast. By this time there was a stiff gale blowing from the west-north-west which persisted right up to mooring at Blackwell at 3.30 p.m. The *Great Britain* caused a sensation. To quote the *Illustrated London News*: 'As she passed up the river the crews of every vessel ran on deck to obtain a view of her. Her extraordinary length and her singular appearance rendered her an object of considerable attraction.'

Overall the average speed was between $9\frac{1}{2}$ and 10 knots, nearer the latter. 'In the opinion of highly scientific and able nautical persons on board no other steamer could have done more than just make headway against the gale with such a sea as was running in the Channel.' The greatest speed reached was $13\frac{2}{3}$ knots from Beachy Head to Dungeness and the ship's manœuvrability at all times particularly impressed on-lookers. Of course this was the first time that a large ship had had a rudder placed immediately in the race of a propeller and the results were new. During the voyage there was a further test of steering. The ship was put full astern and reached nine or 10 knots. She was then put full ahead and to the surprise of everybody steered on the rudder while still carrying sternway. Of course the race of the propeller impinging on the rudder was known to be a powerful factor, but there was some surprise at just how great this effect proved to be, totally overcoming the motion aft through the water.[20] Only one minor incident somewhat marred the occasion. In Gravesend Reach *Great Britain* collided with a collier brig which was dragging her anchor, and carried away her bowsprit. It was the lesser of evils as otherwise the ship would have run down another vessel or put herself ashore. In the light of subsequent events under the same Captain Hosken, however, this incident may have significance.

The first voyage of the first 'modern' ship was a great success: the iron construction of the *Great Britain* bore its first trial splendidly, and we are able to assess the efficiency of the screw propeller from the data available. The manuscript lines of the *Great Britain* and sufficient drawings survive to enable us to reconstruct the screw exactly. Vickers's Experimental Tank at St Albans, under the direction of Mr David Moor, has run tests on a model of the ship to ascertain both the quality of her hull form and her efficiency of propulsion.[21] The results are most surprising (Appendix 6). Fig. 77 shows the tank test prediction for the shaft horsepower of the ship deep-loaded and (on. p. 110) the efficiency of the propeller against a power-loading coefficient compared with some modern four- and six-

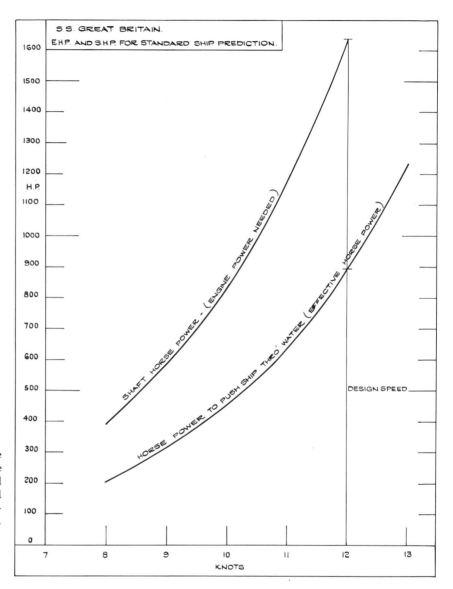

77 Horsepower curves showing the horsepower required to push the ship through the water (e.h.p.) and the horsepower the ship could develop with her propeller as designed (s.h.p.) [at a draft of 17 ft].

bladed propellers. In round terms the hull was quite good, only 30 per cent. worse than the best modern hull of the same length, fullness and general proportions. To some extent this deficiency was due to the peculiar and definitely disadvantageous midship-section shape which Brunel was forced to adopt to get the ship out of the docks. It is also partly due to the rather unfavourable shape of the waterlines at the top of the propeller aperture forced upon him by the conversion of a paddle ship to screw propulsion.

The propeller was extraordinarily efficient: as can be seen, it compares well with modern ones. Indeed, both at the horsepower loading coefficient applicable to the *Great Britain* and at the heavier ones of modern ships, there is very little to choose between this screw and modern ones. As regards overall horsepower, the tank tests indicate that at the draught intended, namely 16 ft level keel, the *Great Britain* would require about 1,430 shaft horsepower to make 12 knots, which in return would mean about 1,650 indicated horsepower. This horsepower would be available starting at a boiler pressure of 5 lb. per sq. in. and expanding down to 12 lb. per sq. in. below atmospheric. The ship would thus appear to have adequate power for just over 12 knots trial speed at a lightish draught and a service speed of, say, 11 knots, both of which were in fact achieved.

Appendix 6 summarises an analysis of the various reported speeds and revolutions of the ship during trials and her voyage to London. Results have been omitted where it is known that appreciable sail was carried or where the weather was of gale force; otherwise all spots are plotted and cover the operational range of draughts. A computer analysis has been applied to these trials to produce a mean line, and the tank test prediction is also shown. The correlation between the service figures and the Brunel prediction of $1\frac{1}{2}$ knots per engine revolution is most remarkable:

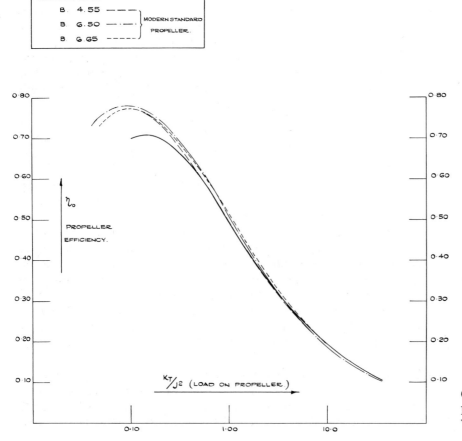

Graph: The efficiency of the propeller at various loads compared with modern propellers

CHAPTER TEN

Entry into service

The *Great Britain* stayed in the Thames for five months. In view of the economic need for her to be put into service this seems a long delay, scarcely justified by the public and royal visits which took place. On Tuesday, 23 April, Queen Victoria, Prince Albert and a retinue of six were joined by the Board of Admiralty, and the party embarked on the royal tender *Dwarf* at Greenwich Palace to visit the *Great Britain*. A state barge bearing the Lord Mayor preceded the royal yacht, and a number of river steamers packed with spectators followed.

Before boarding the *Great Britain*, Queen Victoria was given an excellent view of the ship as the royal yacht steamed right round her. The Queen them climbed a flight of carpeted stairs leading from a platform level with the deck of the tender. She was met by the chairman of the Steamship Company, Mr Busy, and other directors—Were, Miles, Pycroft Captain Claxton, Guppy—and by Brunel and Smith, the two principal technical men involved. Lieutenant Hosken, the Captain, welcomed the royal party and took them on a conducted tour. The Queen was 'quite amazed at the enormous length of the ship, one-third longer than any line of battleship in the service'.[1] She and Prince Albert, accompanied by the Captain, went right aft to stand by the wheel, and then forward into the eyes of the ship, so that from each point they could see her whole length. After inspecting the forward saloon and state-rooms, the royal party were shown a working model of the engines and screw while Isambard Brunel explained how they worked. They then went down into the engine room where they were shown round by Guppy. Here 'the immense chain which turns the screw shaft seemed particularly to engage Her Majesty's attention which was described to her to revolve at the rate of 25 miles per hour'. (This was in fact exactly twice the actual speed!)

The Queen then inspected the after quarters and was astonished at their size. At this point she was shown three models of different propellers, the first that of the six-bladed propeller actually fitted, the second the four-bladed reserve screw, and the third a model actually with only three blades.

78 Queen Victoria's visit to the *Great Britain* at Blackwall

Mr Smith was now presented to the Queen and he in turn presented her with a gold model of the propeller of the new royal yacht *Fairy*, while Claxton gave her two copies of the description of the ship. On leaving, she said to Captain Hosken, 'I am very much gratified with the sight of your magnificent ship and I wish you every possible success on your voyages across the Atlantic'. No great changes had been made to the ship for this visit, though she was, of course, dressed overall, with the band of the Lifeguards on board, all the decks cleaned and holystoned, and carpets laid in all the saloons and staircases.

The ship then entered the East India dock where she was thrown open to the public and 'in a short time was completely thronged'. There is an entertaining account of one particular visit in *Chambers' Edinburgh Journal* which graphically describes the impression created by her size.[2] These visits by the public continued throughout May; on 12 June the ship finally left for Liverpool and for work.

Again she caused great excitement. Thousands of people lined the banks at Woolwich, and the dockyard was full of naval and military officers who cheered her out of sight. She passed Gravesend at 7 p.m., steaming well on a strong tide. With 80 passengers on board she passed Cowes early the next morning and reached Plymouth at 8 p.m., having averaged 11 knots from London. All that afternoon the hills of Devon and Cornwall were studded with anxious spectators but, the weather being thick, she was only seen when within the Mewstone. Bells welcomed her and the Hoe was densely covered as she steamed into the Sound through a throng of welcoming small craft. Again, it was the way she answered her helm that caused most interest. Eventually she arrived at Liverpool, having called at Dublin on 3 July, and immediately began preparations for the historic first screw-propeller-driven crossing of the Atlantic. Dry-docked in the Queen's Graving Dock, she was again thrown open to the public. Here, perhaps because it was a shipping port, the flow of visitors was even heavier and some 2,500 people a day thronged the ship, no doubt very much hampering preparations for departure. The *Great Britain* sailed from Liverpool at 3.20 on the afternoon of 26 July 1845. She left her moorings amid the cheers of thousands of spectators who lined both banks of the Mersey, while hundreds more got a closer view from ferry boats and launches. A large party of Liverpool merchants sailed with the ship for 16 miles, as far as the Bar. The ship had a very poor passenger load, probably because of general mistrust of the new type of propulsion. Only 45 people were courageous enough to book; there were also some 360 measurement-tons of cargo on board.

The weather was not good. There were fresh westerly gales for quite a proportion of the crossing and then thick fogs at the American end. However, the voyage was a great success and $14\frac{3}{4}$ days after sailing the ship arrived at New York, having covered a total distance of 3,304 nautical miles at an average speed of 9·4 knots. This was unquestionably a brilliant achievement and one that many people had doubted possible. Perhaps the best description of the arrival is given by the *New York Herald* on 11 August:[3]

ARRIVAL OF THE MONARCH OF THE OCEAN *GREAT BRITAIN*

The *Great Britain* was telegraphed at 12 o'clock on yesterday but it was a quarter past two before she arrived off Governors Island Fort. The first indication of her approach was her salute to Fort Hamilton which was heard barely so by the spectators on the Battery. From this moment the utmost anxiety was betrayed by the masses to get the first glimpse of her and when they did it was expressed in vehement ejaculations of 'There she is', 'La Voila', etc. etc. . . . . Sailing up very slowly she at last, steering in mid-channel, came off the Battery where for the first time an impression was made worthy of her magnitude. All that has been said of her in foreign journals have not done her justice and nothing but the evidence of the senses is adequate thereto. She is truly beautiful; her vast length was strikingly exhibited in contrast of that of the *North Carolina* towards which vessel she directed her course, and turned as if on a pivot [again this emphasis on her manoeuvrability] to steer her course up the North River saluting the Fort as she passed. At each of her masts she displayed a flag and her decks seemed a miniature city. 'That is a sight', 'This ship is beautiful' was the cry on every hand.

Of course the crowd was immense and yet it would have been still greater were it not that expectation was damped a little by the diurnal reports of her arrival that had gone out for two or three days previously and which only ended in disappointment until at last she did come in all her pride and glory. On returning from the animating spectacle our reporter saw thousands rushing down in hopes of being in time but alas they had to put it off until a more convenient season. From the heights she possessed a grand and beautiful appearance. At every mast were colours streaming. At the gaff a large Union Flag of England flew gaily in the breeze. The first mast had the Austrian flag, the second the Russian, the third the Spanish, the fourth the French Tricolour, the main Union Jack, and the foremast a blended flag of England and America the Stars of this country blending with the blue, white and red of the Union of England and at the lower quartering the stripes.

The *New York Herald* went on to describe further the vast crowds and the excitement which, if anything, was even greater than in the Thames and at Liverpool. Contrary to some modern accounts of this trip, there was little or no vibration Indeed, *The Times* had this to say:

Captain Hosken informed me that nothing of any importance occurred during the voyage out. The passengers seemed all pleased with the accommodations and spoke in the very highest of terms of Captain Hosken as a gentleman and sailor. They remarked on the very slight vibratory motion in the *Great Britain* as compared with that produced by paddle wheels.

The long-suffering ship was once again thrown open to the public:

It being important to open the ship to the whole community as to make distinction without giving offence and in view of the great expense incurred by the owner in detaining her to satisfy the public curiosity it has been determined to follow the plan adopted in London, Liverpool etc. to charge a small sum for admission.

The charge was 25 cents a head, with an extra $12\frac{1}{2}$ cents for the engine room. Part of the proceeds was given to the Fire Department and the asylums for the blind, deaf and dumb. Visiting hours were from noon to five and some 21,000 visitors came.

Nineteen days later she was loaded and ready to sail. Captain Hosken and the officers gave a dinner for the merchants of the city. The toasts were 'The Merchants of Bristol, the first to risk capital in transatlantic steam navigation, and The President of the United States, The Queen of Great Britain and Ireland, Captain Hosken, The Memories of Watt and Fulton, The Pacific Influence of Steam and the Merchants of Liverpool and New York and Honourable Competition.' One wonders whether the officers were really fit to handle the ship the next day.

On 30 August the ship sailed with 53 cabin passengers, 1,200 bales of cotton and some other cargo. There was very little westerly wind during the whole passage, but the boiler gave trouble, as is evident from an otherwise congratulatory address by the passengers to the captain: 'We consider the *Great Britain* to be unrivalled. Her accommodations are commodious and airy . . . but a sufficiency of steam is not produced to work the engines with the power for which they are calculated.' A contemporary newspaper report corroborated this, stating that the engines never worked at more than 600 nominal horsepower on this trip and averaged only 13 revolutions per minute. The boilers certainly originally gave enough steam, but had perhaps by now lost some of their efficiency by becoming coated with salt deposits. It is also possible that on the long sea voyage the firemen became tired by the motion of the ship and were not able to shovel enough coal to generate the steam required. On the voyage to London Guppy did comment that 'owing to the inefficiency of the stokers the steam was not regularly or well kept up and pressure varied from 2 to 5 lb. being frequently low'. Perhaps the truth of the matter is that the vessel rolled more than most paddle steamers and insufficient provision had been made for this in the stoking arrangements.

Apart from this criticism the passengers' letter is extremely complimentary:

We . . . present to you and the company you represent our congratulations upon the successful result of this the first practical attempt to cross the Atlantic in a vessel propelled by the Archmedian screw propeller.

The considerations which especially lead us to this step are based upon the magnitude of the *Great Britain* and the nature of her material which taken in conjunction with the character of her machinery and the novelty of its application gave rise to an excited state of public opinion which attached the highest experimental importance to the successful termination of our passage.

Especially commended was the lack of vibration. The *Nautical Magazine* commented

that the vibration so generally complained of in paddle wheel steamers is scarcely felt in the *Great Britain* even in the sternmost part of the vessel. At midships and at the fore it is not at all perceptible while as a proof of the excellence of her machinery it may be mentioned that throughout the whole voyage not a screw or pin came loose.[4]

As regards the rolling already mentioned, it was said that 'when the wind keeps the sails stiff she behaves very well but when a calm prevails she rolls tremendously'. On the London voyage, three hours out of Bristol the log said, 'Ship rolling deep but easy,' and subsequently she acquired a general reputation for this. Fishbourne, writing of the *Great Britain* in the late 1840s, said: 'Very considerable speed is obtained from her although she rolls very much. It has been thought that this vessel rolled so much because she has not paddles. There is not a shadow of reason for this.'[5] He went on to claim that the main cause was the ship's 'peg top form near the waterline which occasions a continual rising and falling of her centre of gravity as she rolls each way'. The truth is that her midship-section shape, with its slack bilges and wide water-plane, was conducive to rolling, and her metacentric height or stability was excessive. Calculation shows that in average seagoing conditions at a draught of about $17\frac{1}{2}$ ft, this metacentric height would be nearly 11 ft—three times what it should have been for comfort or technical efficiency. This was the penalty of conversion from paddle propulsion after the dimensions had been fixed, but it did give a development potential that was duly exploited on the Australian route.

On the return voyage across the Atlantic the ship's main topmast snapped about half-way down, 'due to there being insufficient seamen to take in the topsail in a sudden squall of wind'. This was not a reflection of mismanagement, as a large portion of the original crew had deserted the ship at New York just when she was about to sail and the Captain had to make do with such men as he could procure. Two of the crew were seriously injured in this work—one of them had his arm amputated by the ship's surgeon—and the passengers collected £25 as compensation.

Fig. 79 shows the arrival back in the Mersey. The Customs House is

on the right and the ship is flying the flag mentioned by the *New York Herald* and *The Times* reporters but the picture is, however, fanciful because it does not show any damage to this topmast. A point of interest is the American packet on the right of the picture which may be the *Prince Albert*, a crack American packet of the day. The picture is probably symbolic, showing the return from the first screw crossing of the Atlantic and the opposition which the *Great Britain* had overcome. The daily runs of the ship on her homeward voyage are given at the end of the chapter, and particularly noticeable is the slow start made on the return voyage. Her best day's run was at exactly 12 knots. Overall the round voyage was very successful and it was clear that the ship would do much better when fully developed.

It is interesting that the *Great Britain* brought the first news of the trials of the Ericsson screw in America back to Britain. On 21 September, eight days after the ship arrived, the *Mechanics' Magazine* commented:

Official reports [of this] just brought to England—appropriately enough—by the *Great Britain* which we are happy to observe behaved as entirely to the satisfaction of all concerned on her first return voyage as during her passage outward (the only thing complained of is the deficiency of steam).[6]

Twelve days later, on 27 September, she made her third crossing of the Atlantic. The *Bristol Mirror* reported:

The steamship *Great Britain* left her moorings in the Mersey at precisely 4 o'clock this afternoon and took her departure on her third trip across the Atlantic with no less than 102 passengers, a proof that the prejudice that once existed against her is fast disappearing before the proof of her capabilities afforded by the success of her late voyage. She also carried a large amount of general merchandise. It may be interesting to mention that there was not the slightest fouling on the bottom of the *Great Britain* on her return from New York on Monday week.

This was indeed interesting, and rather surprising too.

This happy start, however, was not to last. The Captain's report for the voyage had a dismal tale to tell:

Left Liverpool 4 p.m. 27 September; the first 10 days experienced westerly winds strong gales and heavy seas at times during which the ship behaved admirably. . . . For a few hours on 2 October the wind was north-east and in a heavy squall the foremast carried away. On the 12th at noon found the ship had been set 35 miles to the northward in 24 hours and on that night found by sounding that the ship had again set to the north 30 miles from noon on the 12th to 2 a.m. on the 13th and was among the shoals of Nantucket on a thick dirty night.

It was an ordeal for the passengers. The ship was extricated from the shoals with great difficulty and although the reports are confused it seems likely that she bumped the ground. A passenger writing from the ship on the 13th, at anchor in Holmes Hole, Martha's Vineyard, had this to say:

Here we are after a voyage so far which has been tedious and not without danger. The fuel nearly exhausted although we are still 200 miles from New York. Our foremast is gone, three arms also of the propeller (as the captain so informs us) and all on one side which is scarcely credible as I have not been able to detect any irregularity in the engines. It appears that after Saturday a strong current carried us right among the breakers off Nantucket Island called the Rips.
Started with 1,050 tons of coal—coal for only 18 hrs left. Consumption $63\frac{1}{2}$ tons per 24 hrs. Condenser at $26\frac{1}{2}$ in., boiler $3\frac{1}{2}$, cut-off 13 to 16 in., $13\frac{1}{2}$ revolutions. Two inches had been riveted to each of the arms of the propeller before leaving Liverpool. It was a clumsy job and was no doubt the cause of the breakage.

This reference to blade extensions is illuminating. Repeatedly statements had been made that the propeller was not big enough; even Guppy

117

said so in his paper to the I.C.E.[7] It was simply not true. The propeller had excellent power-absorbing characteristics as has been shown by the modern tank tests, and there is no conceivable reason why the tips should have been extended. Certainly to do so would increase the stress on the blades and the vibration during riveting might well have loosened the original rivets. This meddling, plus Captain Hosken's regrettably faulty navigation off Nantucket, certainly accelerated the probably inevitable break-up of the propeller.

From 17 to 30 September only 472 nautical miles were covered. The weather began to improve—on 1 October 139 miles were covered and the next day 185. On the second the ship passed the *Great Western* going in the opposite direction. On 3 October 213 miles were covered but thereafter the weather worsened rapidly. To quote the log:

Rough gale. Sail abaft funnel came down by the run. Foremast and spanker lost in a white squall after another sail abaft the first one came down. Some hours were occupied in fishing the sails and spars out of the water but the engines only stopped about one half-hour.

Between 27 September and 13 October the ship covered 2,705 nautical miles: an average speed of under seven knots. Clearly the weather was appalling. On the 14th she left Holmes Hole at 2.30 a.m. and reached Sandy Hook at New York at about 11 p.m. There again she had to wait for the tide and finally docked in New York early on the fifteenth. On 18 October the *Great Britain* went into the sectional dry dock at New York where extensive damage to the propeller was disclosed:

Found two arms gone close to the boss and one blade. Shifted the blade of the remaining arm [on that side] to the opposite side and secured all the other blades. The rivets were nearly all loose. Came off the dock.

The ship sailed on 28 October at 2 p.m. She was in good trim—drawing 18 ft 8 in. aft and 17 ft 6 in. forward—and was on fairly low power, presumably because of misgivings over the propeller. On the 30th the log reports:

We found something wrong with the propeller striking the sternpost very hard: reversed the engines and after two or three good thumps the arm broke off.

Went on with very low steam. Cut off at 12 in. Steered by the sails. Wind north-easterly. Ship making very good way, seven to nine knots.

Friday 1st about 3 p.m. another of the arms of the propeller broke leaving only one, I think the repaired one, and the half of another with a small plate we had put on the end of it. Wind hauled to the southard and south-westerly, we made the most of her sails and very fair way just keeping the propeller from dragging. At times going 10 knots.

3 November. Wind fell to a calm in the evening of the 3rd making five knots. In the course of the night it came ahead. A moderate breeze from the east and little swell. Ship making 3½ knots against it.

5 November. Very fine weather with north-east swell.

6 November. Made use of our sails whenever there was a chance within three points of her course. She feels them directly and has I think very superior sailing qualities.

The propeller or what is left of it at this time making four knots against an easterly wind and a north-east swell rather high, Wind hauling from eastward to southward this morning and I think looks well for a south-wester very soon.

Making 8½ knots. Close as she can lay with fore and aft sails reefed, topsail and mainsail. This is good decidedly.

About a quarter past five the remaining arm of the propeller broke off leaving only a half arm and a small piece of another about 2 ft from the centre.

8 November. At 1.20 p.m. stopped the engines with half arm vertical. Moderate south-westerly winds. All sails we can carry set. Winds freshened gradually to a gale westwards. Reefed top sail and off bonnets of Spencers; sea rising fast. Increased breezes to fresh gales and hard squalls and high sea. Mainsail topsail and one spencer set. Ship scudding and steering beautifully taking spray on larboard quarter and beam occasionally but is easier than any ship I ever knew.

10 November. Passed a large ship hove to with main topsail and foresail. Dirty rainy weather. Deadlights all closed. Scuttles etc. well secured.

11 November. Wind moderating and hauling to the northward. Made all sail on her. Wind to the north-east and east. Noon saw two ships ahead and came up with them at the rate of two knots close hauled. This is wonderful with our little spread of canvas and more than I expected well as I thought of her sailing qualities.

12 November. Light breezes inclined to the north-west again. A ship in sight and we are coming with her as fast as those yesterday.

13 November. A light breeze from south-west increased to a moderate breeze. A ship ahead at daylight. Ran her out of sight by noon.

14 November. A breeze sprang up from south-west. Made all sail. At noon increased to a gale. Double reef topsail and off bonnets of Spencers. Dirty rainy weather and sea rising fast. Moderating and hauling to the west-nor'-west in the evening.

15 November. Moderate and cloudy. Made all sail at 8.30.

16 November. Daylight. Fog cleared off and saw the mizzen head. A fine breeze all day running at 10 and 11 knots.

17 November. At 1.30 passed the *Tuscar* Light off Holyhead. 1 p.m. off Port Linas. 8 p.m. got a pilot and steam tugs off north-west light vessel Liverpool.

The passage may have been the end of the first oceanic propeller but it certainly gave confidence in *Great Britain*'s sea-keeping and sailing abilities. Indeed the passengers, in an address presented to the Captain, remarked:

Far from encouraging any of the illfound prejudices against the *Great Britain*, she on this occasion strengthened our confidence and won the admiration of all on board. . . . [We] express the superiority of the *Great Britain* in a heavy gale. We take pleasure in making public the statement that we are well pleased with the *Great Britain* in every respect. For safety, speed and comfort she is unsurpassed and during this passage of unexpected length we have not suffered the slightest diminution of comfort and in particular our table has been as good and well supplied as ever.

Everybody seemed most impressed by the way the ship sailed. Indeed, she passed several packets with ease, and, run as a sailing ship on the North Atlantic, would probably have been the fastest ship in service.

Thus, after only four months, the service life of the first screw propeller ever to cross an ocean ended. Yet it had been a success. Efficient in itself, even if not too well installed, and quite correctly matched to the hull and engines, it was a brilliant achievement that deserves remembrance. To have failed because of the modern evil of metal-fatigue and because of mishandling of the ship was no disgrace; and those who smile at its short life would do well to reflect that very few real pioneers have ever done as well as Isambard Brunel and his colleagues did with this grand effort.

It was now winter and the ship was clearly in need of adjustment and overhaul.

FIRST SCREW-PROPELLED ATLANTIC CROSSING
Homeward Daily Runs

Saturday, 30 August, 4 p.m.	*Sailed from New York*
	Distance run (in miles)
Sunday, 31 August	146
Monday, 1 September	190
Tuesday, 2 September	160
Wednesday, 3 September	212
Thursday, 4 September	196
Friday, 5 September	220
Saturday, 6 September	170
Sunday, 7 September	160
Monday, 8 September	173
Tuesday, 9 September	287
Wednesday, 10 September	270
Thursday, 11 September	243
Friday, 12 September	200
Saturday morning, 13 September	Made land

A passage of $13\frac{1}{2}$ days at 9 knots.

The ship did not dock, however, for a further two days.

CHAPTER ELEVEN

The first major refit - 1846

After discharging her cargo, the *Great Britain* was laid up during the winter for extensive changes, the most important being the fitting of a new propeller, again built at the works in Bristol. This was the reserve screw mentioned by Guppy in his trials report to the directors and which Brunel had designed since the original trials. As can be seen in Fig. 50 it was four-bladed and of solid construction. Weighing 7 tons, it was heavier than the original propeller. It had the same diameter and pitch and about the same power absorption as the original, but was obviously much more robust and could be expected to last indefinitely.

Hardly less important were alterations made to increase the efficiency of the steam-raising department. A check through the machinery led to the conclusion that the air pumps were too small and that the fire flues in the boilers were inadequately designed. After alterations had been made to correct both these faults,

Her boilers gave ample steam without any difficulty, with easy firing and the consumption of coals much lessened. The alteration in the pumps, valves, etc. have answered every expectation and the screw is beyond doubt better than the old one.[1]

Trials carried out in the Irish Sea following undocking in mid-April 1846 proved very successful. The speed quoted on steam alone was 11·8 knots at 16·75 revolutions, which was appreciably better than any previous result achieved. Indicator checks of the revised engines showed that over 1,600 indicated horsepower was being developed.[2] It is in fact doubtful how substantial an improvement this was: Captain Austin, a Government surveyor, pointed out that the original indicator diagrams taken in London showed over 1,500 horsepower.

Alterations were also made to her rig. Iron wire gave way to hemp, no doubt to please Hosken and Claxton. The mast immediately abaft the funnel was removed. The fourth mast (now the third) was increased in size and re-rigged so that it resembled the original mainmast, and both it and the mainmast were fitted with topgallant masts over their topmasts. The hinges on deck were done away with and the masts taken

80 *Great Britain* in a gale of headwind in 1846 (previously unpublished painting)

through the 'tween decks. Try-sail masts were fitted abaft the two square-rigged masts. This device, which can be seen in Fig. 82, allowed the gaffs on these masts to slide up and down without fouling the hoop bands on the built masts. The original gaffs did not slide for furling sails, which were brailed. The main purpose of these rigging changes was probably to balance the rig so the ship would carry less weather helm when sailing. That sails were useful had been proved on the previous voyage and was to be proved again. However, it seems that the ship had been somewhat difficult to steer, especially with the balanced rudder and the propeller aperture before it, and this was probably the reason for the two square-rigged masts, which moved the centre of the whole sail area much further aft.

Finally, the white line on the hull was painted out and the ship assumed a handsomely sombre all-black appearance, relieved only by her gilded adornments.

The third double voyage across the Atlantic was about to begin. The *Great Britain* left Liverpool on 9 May with a dreadfully thin passenger list—28 in all; after the misfortunes of the previous voyage this was hardly surprising. Again, misfortune seemed to dog the ship. Only four days after leaving harbour, the guard of the after air pump fractured and the engines were shut down for repairs. Up to this time she had averaged $11\frac{3}{4}$ knots. The new rig now came into its own. For six days the ship simply sailed, making excellent speed: over nine knots close hauled, and nearly 12 off the wind. This was extremely good going, considering that there was a large propeller dragging through the water; however, she was probably not making good her true course, and when the repairs were completed she steamed on at reduced speed for another 10 days, arriving in New York on 29 May after a dreary 20-day voyage.

The air pump was repaired properly in New York and the *Great Britain* sailed on 8 June with rather more passengers on board: 42. This was her first really successful voyage in the new guise and she made a $13\frac{1}{2}$-day passage from dock to dock, a block average of over 230 miles a day. The *Bristol Mirror* reported:

During the passage just made by the *Great Britain* iron steamer from New York to Liverpool it was ascertained by accurate nautical observations made on Saturday, 13 June that the Leviathan propelled by her screw ran no less than 313 knots in the course of 24 hrs producing an average rate of going through the day of nearly 16 statutes miles an hr [say 13 knots], a speed never before attained and never equalled on the ocean by any paddle steamer or by any sailing vessel whatever. Such a velocity would have brought her across in $8\frac{1}{2}$ days.

This voyage was particularly gratifying as she faced headwinds for more than three-quarters of the time.

From 1838 to 1841 inclusive, the *Great Western* had averaged about $13\frac{1}{2}$ days, representing a speed of about 9·8 knots west to east. In 1842 she did better, presumably because of strong westerly winds, while in 1844 her performance fell off somewhat. The *Great Britain* had clearly to aim higher, and a target of 12 knots on average eastwards and 10 westwards did not seem unattainable. Perhaps the true measure of what

81 The fateful track on 22 September 1846

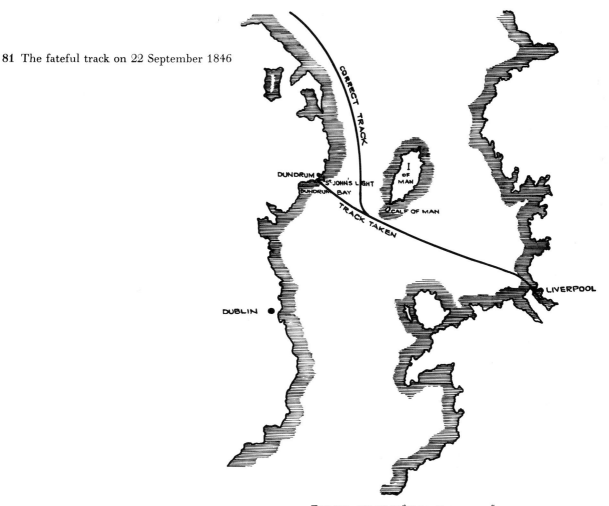

TRACK OF THE "GREAT BRITAIN"

the *Great Britain* might have done in an undisturbed career on the Atlantic was shown by the fourth double crossing which commenced on the evening of 7 July 1846. The ship carried 110 passengers, a promise of profits to come, but again suffered from what one can only conclude as faulty navigation on the part of Captain Hosken. Thick fog on the Newfoundland Banks delayed the ship and presumably was responsible for her losing her bearings and ending up scraping a bilge on Cape Broil Reef, Newfoundland. Even so she crossed at just under 10 knots in 13 days eight hrs, and would have made it in $12\frac{1}{2}$ days, stoppages apart. Despite poor weather, this was clearly better than the *Great Western* had ever done, and the return passage sailing on 1 August would have been in not much over the bare 12 days had it not been for an engine shut-down as a result of one of the driving chains breaking.

It now seemed that the ship would be able to make passages in 13 days out and 11 back when thoroughly worked up. This would have been excellent, representing a service speed of about 11 knots, very close to that intended. However, it was not to be, as disaster now struck both the ship and her owners. After dry-docking to ascertain whether the brush with the Newfoundland reef had damaged the ship (it had not), the *Great Britain* sailed from Liverpool at 11 a.m. on 22 September 1846, carrying 180 passengers and a substantial amount of cargo. The wind was favourable—easterly—and the ship set all plain sail. It was the intention to round the north of Ireland—apparently the normal course—passing the Isle of Man south of the Calf of Man, which was nearly 400 ft above the sea and marked by two lights flashing every two minutes: quite unmistakable. In the circumstances the ship could be expected to make a full 12 knots through the water, and she had nearly a knot of tide under her. Leaving the Bar Lightship at 1.20 p.m., this speed would take her past the Calf soon after 6 p.m., and if she ran on for another half-hour she would be well placed to turn north and continue on her track.[3] Inexplicably, however, she failed to do so, and at about 9.30 p.m. ran ashore in Dundrum Bay, south of the St John's light. From the Calf to Dundrum Bay is about 33 nautical miles. Allowing for some reduced speed* and adjusting the calculation, the ship would be expected to strike around the time she did. To mistake St John's light for the Calf would imply a speed made good of some eight knots; this, in the circumstances, would have been a ridiculous underestimation. Why she struck is beyond understanding. True, rain started in the latter part of the day and visibility became limited, but even relying only on dead reckoning there was an easy gap between the Isle of Man and Northern Ireland.

Captain Hosken's version of the story was outlined in a resolution of the directors of the company:

With respect to the occurrences which preceded the stranding of the unfortunate ship as explained now by Captain Hosken and by the report of Captain Claxton to the Secretary, the Directors are of the opinion that the ship was stranded in consequence of an error of judgement into which it appears her Captain was betrayed through the omission of a notice of St John's light in the chart of this year by which he was navigating, and of the want of knowledge on his part of such a light being established—it being to the directors obvious that had the light been laid Captain Hosken would have known that the judgement which led him at 8 o'clock to put his ship in the proper course of the North Channel ought not to have been persevered in.

This is an extraordinary statement, doing more credit to the directors' loyalty than to their sense.

Others were less charitable. The *Nautical Magazine* in November was cruelly blunt:

Some degree of blame was at first attached in consequence of it to the Admiralty Charts. These expressions have been zealously and very properly refuted by Mr Bate, the agent for the sale of the charts. *Great Britain* it was said ran ashore in Dundrum Bay owing to the lights on St John's Point not being inserted on the chart by which she was navigated. This proved to be *not* an Admiralty Chart but in our opinion this had little to do with it. The vessel's reckoning, allowing some little westerly set, would place here *where she is*. Had her commander who had already run beyond a discretionary distance at eight in the evening when he

* The ship turned north and shortened sail at 8 p.m. A little later she sighted the light and turned west again at much reduced speed.

shaped his course for the North Channel stopped the ship's way through the water as soon as he doubted his eyes and was at a loss to know what light it was he was looking at on his larboard bow, had he stopped his vessel's way as a seaman should have done and found out what it really was, feeling his way continually with his lead, the *Great Britain* would not have been run headlong onto the shore where she now lies. The absence of a light from a chart seen plainly and distinctly before a vessel could never occasion her loss in the hands of a careful commander in moderate weather.[4]

The December edition of the *Mechanics' Magazine* was even harsher:

When the crowning disaster of this ill-fated vessel took place we thought it due to the commander to refrain from remarking until he had given his own account and when that account was published somewhat late in the day it was such as by common consent of the world rendered all remark superfluous. The case was on his own showing and beyond all possibility of doubt the most egregious blundering.[5]

These critics cannot be refuted. Hosken had previously made this trip before the light had been installed in January 1844, but he must have known of it; he must have been aware of the speed the ship was making as he had the patent log and the ordinary one; the light was fully described in the Admiralty List of British Lighthouses—May 1846. One begins to have strong doubts as to his capabilities as a navigator. Under his captaincy the ship had drifted in among the Rips off Nantucket on the third crossing, had scraped a reef off Cape Broil on the seventh and now on the ninth had run ashore. With 180 passengers on board and success virtually achieved, there may have been a somewhat lavish send-off party, as a result of which one might surmise that neither Hosken nor his officers were paying too much attention to navigation all that day.

The passengers went through a dreadful ordeal. A Canadian on board said he was awakened by the concussion on grounding and on jumping up heard loud screams from the ladies' cabins. He ran on deck.

The night was stormy, the sea was breaking over the ship. We still continued drifting for [he thought] fully a mile. There was a light visible and Captain Hosken said that it was about a mile and a half distant and that they were near Ardglass.

This gentleman saw one of the officers examining the compass and asked the reason. The officer said that there was something the matter with it and then examined the compass in the fore part of the ship and gave the opinion that the compass was the cause of this disaster. Captain Hosken when he heard this did at least have the grace to deny that there was anything wrong with the compass. Blue lights were burnt and guns fired, and

the scene on board was most distressing. The great majority of the passengers were very ill. Several passengers who ought to have shown firmness betrayed lamentable weakness. Captain Hosken continued cool and composed and several times referred to his charts. No-one retired to rest, all were full of fears.

One robust soul, however, slept right through the whole thing. A graphic account was given by a young lady passenger in a letter to a friend:

We have indeed been in fearful peril. The ship struck the rocks at 10 o'clock.

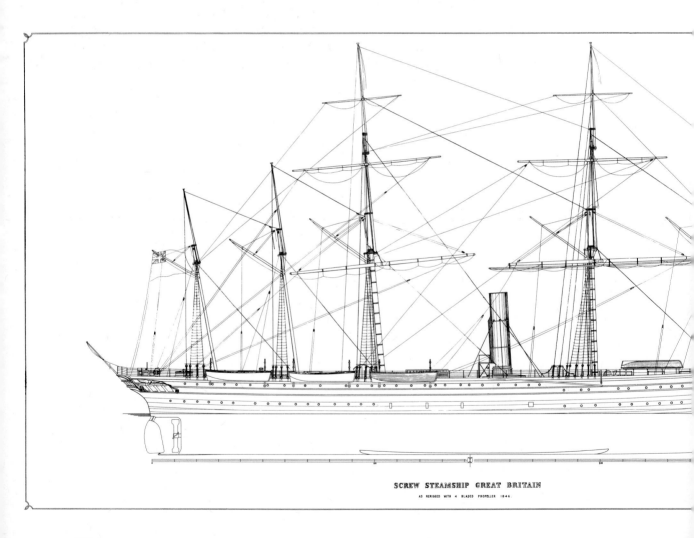

SCREW STEAMSHIP GREAT BRITAIN

AS RERIGGED WITH 4 BLADED PROPELLER 1846.

I had just gone to my stateroom and the instant I felt the shock I knew something was the matter. In a moment there was a second shock and all was confusion. Men and women rushed out, the latter from their berths, and some threw themselves into the arms of strangers. We could with difficulty stand. Oh I cannot tell you the anguish of that night. The sea broke over the ship, the waves struck her like thunderclaps, the gravel grated below. There was the throwing overboard of the coals, the cries of children, the groans of women, the blue lights, the signal guns, even the tears of men and amidst all rose the voice of prayer. The day dawned and we lay between two long ledges of rock while another stretched across our front. 500 yards to the right or left 200 yards in advance, and the ship had been dashed to pieces. . . . At dawn we were lowered over the ship's side and carried on shore in carts of seaweed manure. We walked through an Irish bog and lay down upon the floor of an Irish cabin. With much fatigue we came on to Belfast and Liverpool.[6]

This was the death of the Great Western Steamship Company. The *Great Western* had to be sold; the *Great Britain* was ashore, wrecked and perhaps never to be recovered. The company had deserved success but two men had brought it to naught—Dr Lardner with his pompous illfounded nonsense and Captain Hosken, who did not live up to his early promise and cast his great ship away. As to the *Great Britain* herself, any future she was to have would rest in the hands of the original stalwarts, Brunel, Claxton and Patterson, together with one Alexander Bremner, a salvage expert.

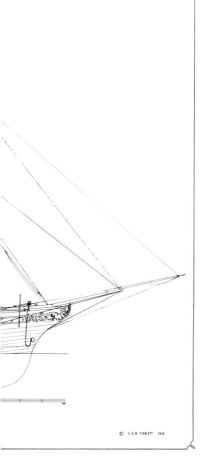

82 Outboard profile—as refitted in 1846

© E.C.B. CORLETT 1970

CHAPTER TWELVE

Salvage from Dundrum Bay

84 *Great Britain* pounded by heavy seas on Dundrum Beach

The ship was stranded on sand on the north side of Dundrum Bay. From this place two ridges of rock about 1,000 yds apart extended out into the sea for a considerable way. As the lady passenger remarked, it was by the greatest good fortune that the ship avoided both reefs and their outlying rocks. If she had not, total loss of ship and probably of life would have resulted.

Captain Claxton went at once to the ship. The ground on which she lay appeared to be sand but underneath was gravel and rock, the sand being 1–3 ft deep, the gravel below it 9–20 in. thick, and below that blue limestone rock. There were also a number of detached rocks buried in this sand and gravel. The ship had settled down on two of them but was not making very much water. James Hosken, writing from the ship on the twenty-ninth, a week after the disaster, said, 'The weather is now moderate, the ship makes very little water. Captain Claxton came yesterday.' From Hosken's comments, leaks so far must have been trivial. The next day, however, the wind increased to a gale and on 1 October blew violently from the south and south-east, producing a heavy sea. The powerful tug *Dreadnought* requested by Claxton and Hosken had to shelter and soon water was breaking right over the *Great Britain*. The ship had been moored by the stern, with a chain from an anchor running to and round the rudder post. As the seas increased, the strain on this

83 *Great Britain* soon after the stranding. Topmasts have been struck (detail from a contemporary oil painting)

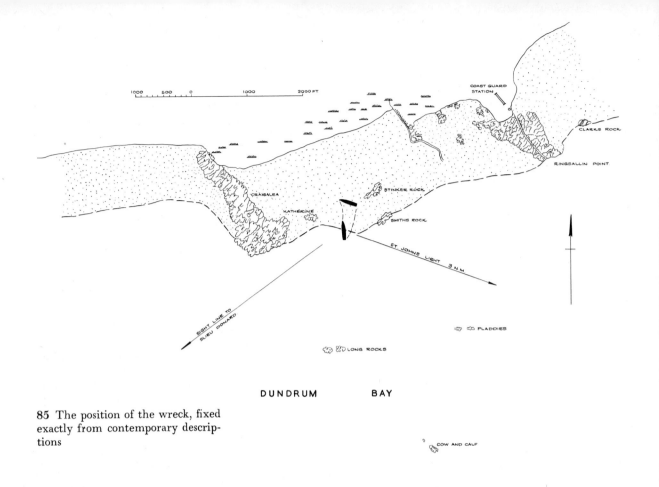

DUNDRUM BAY

85 The position of the wreck, fixed exactly from contemporary descriptions

tackle became so great that the post and some plating were carried away. This was the end of the world's first large balanced rudder. Captain Claxton, a man of action, saw that the only hope was to get the ship further in, so set sail and drove her up the beach a considerable way but in the process she turned partly broadside to it.

Plan after plan to save the ship began to pour in to the directors. An eminent engineer, Billington, made a survey in late October and remarked that most of the plans of which he had heard were ridiculous in the extreme. After describing her position he remarked that the Bay was frequently very rough and the vessel difficult to board during high tides.

On the starboard side the plates have bulged and the rivets sprung to considerable extent which admit freely the flow and ebb of the tide and several holes about 1½ in. in diameter have been drilled through the bottom to prevent her lifting or beating. At Spring Tides there are from 15 to 17 ft of water in her hold and at Low Water she is left dry with the exception of a small quantity of water left in the dock she has naturally formed for herself in the sand and gravel and about 2 ft in her bottom, she oscillates freely during high tide. She has lost her rudder, her screw propeller is slightly damaged, the cylinders, pumps and part of the turning gear are covered at high tide.

The company invited Alexander Bremner, a well known salvage expert and a most practical man, to assist immediately. By the end of the month Bremner had built a breakwater of heavy timbers nearly 18 in. thick right across the stern of the ship. However, the first heavy gale after its completion swept it away and it was obvious that there was little hope of saving the vessel from destruction by winter gales. Claxton, with great devotion to duty, repaired the breakwater only to see it swept away again.

On 8 December Isambard Brunel went to Dundrum, having been unable to do so before owing to pressure of work. He was furious.[1] He saw that the ship must be protected at all costs, and conceived the idea of a flexible breakwater made of faggots. Before leaving Dundrum he ordered Captain Hosken to start work on it, guaranteeing the cost himself if the directors would not support him. His feelings were expressed forcibly in a letter on 10 December to Claxton:

I have returned from Dundrum with very mixed feelings of satisfaction and pain almost amounting to anger, with whom I don't know. I was delighted to find our fine ship, in spite of all the discouraging accounts received even from you, almost as sound as the day she was launched. . . . I was grieved to see this fine ship lying unprotected, deserted and abandoned by all those who ought to know her value and ought to have protected her instead of being humbugged by schemers and underwriters. Don't let me be understood as wishing to read a lecture to our directors but the result . . . is that the ship is lying like a useless saucepan kicking about on the most exposed shore you can imagine with no more effort or skill applied to protect the property than the said saucepan would have received on the beach at Brighton. . . .

As to the state of the ship she is as straight and sound as she ever was as a whole. She is resting and working upon rocks which have broken in in several places and forced up perhaps 12 to 18 in. many parts of the bottom from the fore stokehole to about the centre of the engines lifting the boilers about 15 in. and the condenser of the fore engine about 6 to 8. The lifting of the fore condenser has broken that air pump, the connecting rod having been unwisely left in and the crank being at the bottom of the stroke. . . . She is beautiful to look at and really how she can be talked of in the way she has been even by you I cannot understand. It is positively cruel. It would be like talking away the character of a young woman without any grounds whatever. . . . There is some slight damage to the stern not otherwise important than as pointing out the necessity of some precautions if she is to be saved. I say 'If', for really when I saw the vessel still in perfect condition left to the tender mercies of an awfully exposed shore for weeks while a parcel of quacks are amusing you with schemes for getting her off, she in the meantime being left to go to pieces, I could hardly help feeling as if her own parents and guardians meant her to die there.

Having expressed his feelings, Isambard went on with practical suggestions: first, to disconnect the engines and airpumps and remove all the working gear so as to limit damage to the lower part. Secondly, to take all strain off the stern. (When he saw her, cables from this overhanging structure were in danger of straining it.) Thirdly, to divert all the current which was washing away the sand from around her, so that she would not break her back. (Ironically, scour in a rather similar position at Sparrow Cove 100 years later did damage her structurally.) Fourthly, to construct a breakwater of large strong faggots, ignoring solid timbering, to secure the faggots together with iron rods, weight them down with chains, and so protect her. As he said to Claxton in this letter, 'I have ordered the faggots to be begun delivering.'

Brunel followed with a formal report dated 14 December to the directors, in which he said much the same things.[2] He did point out that they must not think of her as a wooden ship where the damage she had suffered would lead to an inevitable break-up. *Great Britain* was dented and damaged on the bottom but otherwise sound. He went on to say that this was not the time for discussing the best mode of floating the vessel. The urgent thing was to protect her; a method of floating could then be devised at leisure. In any case, there was no point in floating her right in the depth of winter. His report, which is quite lengthy, went on to discuss how the breakwater should be made:

8,000 or 10,000 faggots, 300 or 400 fathoms of 1-in. or ¾-in. secondhand chain cable none of which need be lost, 300 or 400 ¾-in. rods sharpened at the end, 1,000 bags to fill with sand would suffice. . . . Can you as men of business under such circumstances waste your time at this moment in discussing what you will do in three months hence and what plan you will then adopt to take your property to market? Will you not rather first then immediately adopt decisive steps for preserving that property and then consider what you had best do with it?

Brunel urged strongly that they should not rely upon floating the vessel by camels or pontoon tanks lashed alongside. To do so would be almost impossible because of the shallow water in which the ship lay at high tide, besides which

the risk of taking such an unmanageable floating ill connected mass to sea cannot be correctly or sufficiently estimated. The certainty is of the whole going to the bottom in the event of an even very moderate gale.

In Brunel's opinion the best way would be to lift the vessel by mechanical means, lay ways under her, haul her up sufficiently far to be safe from the sea, make her watertight, launch and then tow her to Liverpool or Bristol. (In the event, this was substantially what was done.) He concluded by saying that Mr Bremner was a man of great experience and sound practical knowledge and that the Board could rely on his advice.

At Brunel's pressing request, Captain Claxton was appointed to take sole charge of the salvage operation. He had at first great difficulty in keeping the faggots down, and Brunel in typical fashion wrote,

You have failed I think in sinking and keeping down the fagots from that which causes nine-tenths of all failures in this world from not doing quite enough. . . .

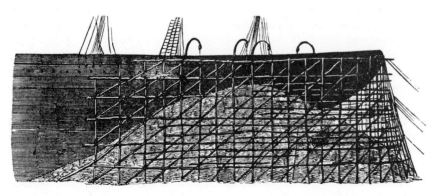

86 Claxton's flexible breakwater, built to Brunel's instructions

If a six bundle fagot won't reach out of water, try a 20 bundle one. If hundred-weights won't keep it down, try tons.

Towards the end of February, Brunel wrote a report to the Board, commenting favourably on Claxton's work:

Notwithstanding the occurrence of more than one storm at the most critical period of the work, he has, as I have fully relied upon his doing, succeeded in so far protecting the ship and she has been comparatively unaffected by violent seas. . . . We may now calculate with tolerable certainty upon preserving her without further injury until finer weather sets in . . . I had relied confidently in success when my friend Captain Claxton undertook the work and the result has fully confirmed my expectations. It is now necessary to turn our attention to the best mode of removing the ship.

Later that year Claxton made a detailed report on this breakwater to the Admiralty.[3] He started by saying that Mr Brunel's instructions to him were principally by word of mouth, the anticipated difficulty being the foundation of sand upon which to build. He exlained that the base could only be laid at low water, and that the faggots were pinned down by iron rods driven down to the rock below, loaded with stones, chain cables, air pump covers, fire bars in large bundles, the ship's guns, and so on. These faggots were about 11 ft in length and 5 ft in circumference at the butt end, and the cost was a shilling for each faggot delivered from Lord Roden's estate. Once they were down, forming a foundation, one of the ship's iron lifeboats 30 ft long, 8 ft wide and 5 ft deep was placed on them and filled with stones. This went down until only the gunwale was above the level of the sand. Claxton and his men then began to build the part intended to save the ship from the blows of the sea,

which I was instructed by Mr Brunel to bring up to a point at the ship's gun-wale in the form of a large poultice occupying the whole space under her counter and the whole of the exposed quarter [port] and inclining inwards from the outside and declining from the top to the same point forward to the after end of the bilge keel. I was to be and was as careful as I could be to secure as well as to weight down as we built . . .

A framework of beech saplings about 4–5 ft apart was then built right round the stern to about 80 ft forward of the propeller. Smaller spars from the same estate were lashed diagonally and horizontally to the verticals, and the whole was secured to anchors well out on the beach to prevent the waves moving it in. This springy breakwater, which could of course be penetrated by the sea, behaved admirably, and spars struck by violent seas at high tide

bend in the body for 3–4 ft and spring back after the blow. This I believe is the whole secret of the efficiency of the spar part of the breakwater which has stood the whole winter only one having broken.

Meanwhile the ship was being lightened (Fig. 87). Coals were taken off, furniture and fittings removed; by the beginning of May her weight

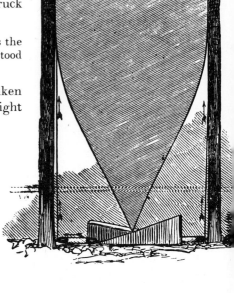

89 The adjustable keel wedges, which could be worked from the deck

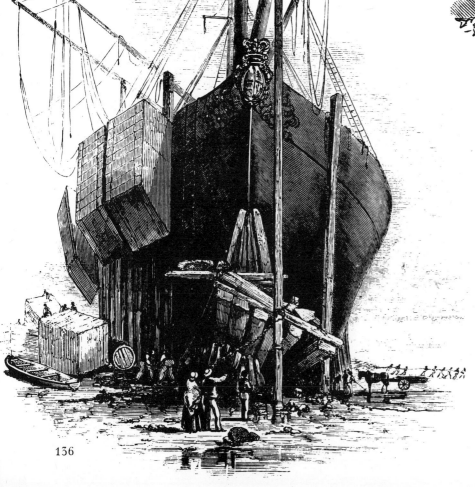

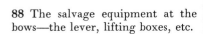

88 The salvage equipment at the bows—the lever, lifting boxes, etc.

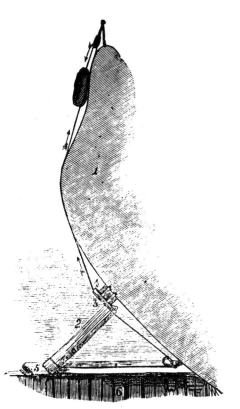

90 Bilge shores were similarly arranged to be worked from the deck

91 By an ingenious arrangement of a chute and rammer, pebbles could be pushed up underneath the hull, tending to lift the ship

was only half that when she went ashore. The weather improving, Claxton began to remove some of the breakwater, but found this very difficult. Faggots and stones were so embedded in sand

as to form a mass which is more difficult to move than granite rock would be as we cannot blast. Twenty labourers have been 21 tides at work and they have made an impression but it is not lowered over 2 ft.

Claxton also formed buoyancy compartments in the ship by making the iron cargo decks and the coal bunkers watertight, shoring them down from above to support the water pressure. He hoped by these means to take the ship off, and indeed she did rise 4 ft, was pulled over on one side and had stones packed in underneath her, but she could rise no further and the attempt failed, part of the reason being poor tides.

On 4 May 1847 Brunel recommended to the directors that suitable specialists in lifting and moving work should be called in, as the present efforts were not promising well; and that in the meantime the Dundrum Bay party should carry on increasing the buoyancy of the ship. He recommended that the directors should approach Mr James Bremner and his son Alexander. The Board agreed, and upon arrival on 22 May the Bremners devised a most elaborate scheme for lifting the ship. This consisted basically of levering up the bow with a vast lever reaching forward, at the same time lifting the forward half of the vessel by a number of great boxes hung at the ship's side on vertical piles and working on pulleys so that when filled with sand they would tend to lift the ship. Chutes were arranged so that as the ship was lifted stones could be rammed underneath to maintain her at the level reached. Arrangements were made to support her further by pulling wedges across underneath the ship on the bedrock. The whole scheme was most ingenious—almost to the point of improbability, although in fact it worked well.

The *Illustrated London News* in August 1847 gave sketches of these works. An overall picture of the operation is shown in Fig. 88. The bow lever can be seen, weighted with anchors, chains and so on. The ten pairs of wooden boxes or camels are shown and amidships can be seen the chutes for ramming stones. At the hawse-pipes were screw jacks which supplied a further lifting force of about 200 tons each. With these and the lever, some 600 tons of lift could be applied right forward. Some of the wooden boxes can also be seen. They each contained about 30 tons of sand when full and were suspended on each side by chains which went over pulleys in the upper part of the vertical timbers shown, and then passed through pulleys attached to the side of the ship, so giving a double purchase. The boxes opposite the engine room had quadruple purchases, since this part of the ship was heavier.

Fig. 89 shows the wedges under the bow. As the ship was lifted, these were pulled across and helped to keep her up. Fig. 90 shows a rather similar arrangement for the bilge wedges, while the self-adjusting shores to keep the ship at the level reached can also be seen. This ingenious device was worked automatically by the weight of large stones suspended from tackles on deck. Finally, as the ship was lifted it was the intention to ram stones underneath her by means of the chutes shown in Fig. 91. Stones could be thrown into the chute, and an iron-shod rammer, part No. 4, which was operated from the deck, pushed them right underneath.

The main leaks were sealed. The holes in the ship, varying from 2 ft × 1 ft to 6 ft × 1½ ft, were not dissimilar to the holes punched in her when she was scuttled in 1937. By all these various means, the ship's bow was raised nearly 9 ft and on the spring tide of 13 July the valves were closed and the first attempt at floating made. Willing as ever, the *Great Britain* came afloat rapidly: indeed, the valves had to be opened again to prevent her going up too much, and even so several of the boxes and the vertical timbers were damaged. Nobody had expected this or made sufficient arrangements to keep the ship at a reasonable height. We shall see that history was to repeat itself 123 years later.

On Thursday, 29 July, the ship was raised high enough to allow the boiler-makers to get at the whole of the bottom and make it watertight. After this, as the tides rose, the sand boxes were lowered and used as camels or floating buoyancy tanks, while a trench was cut from the stern of the ship out towards the sea. Fig. 92 shows the situation five or six days before the ship finally floated off the beach: men cutting the trench

92 *Great Britain* about to rise and be released. A trench was cut through the sand after she had been raised and the bottom repaired

in the sand, sand boxes being emptied and pulled into position as camels, and off to starboard the iron boat filled with the stones that had been so useful in keeping the faggots down. On 27 August a large cable was drawn round the ship just above the keel to which the floats were attached. Four cables ran from this to the anchor of the *Birkenhead* 400 yds away and to the main bower anchor of the *Great Britain* herself. Two lighters alongside supplied extra lifting power and as the tide rose the men at the capstan started to warp her off, hauling on the anchors. At 11.30 the ship moved. Captain Claxton wrote a jubilant letter to Isambard Brunel:

Huzza! Huzza! you know what that means. . . . I made up my mind to stop her at the edge of low water and then examine and secure all that might discover itself. The tide rose to 15 ft 8 in., she rose therefore easily over the rock but was clear of it by only just 5 in. which shows how near a squeak we had—it was a most anxious affair but it is over. I marked 170 yds on the sand and at

Birkenhead and the steam bomb ship *Scourge* had been sent by the Admiralty to assist and had brought a strong detachment of riggers from Portsmouth and Plymouth dockyards. In addition, they lent a considerable number of ratings from their crews to help on the *Great Britain*.

As it was clearly impossible to make for Liverpool straightaway, they struck north for Belfast Loch and it was here that the ship was finally grounded. During the night the hull was pumped out and next morning she started for Liverpool in tow by the *Birkenhead*, with 90 dockyard men, 40 of the *Birkenhead*'s crew and about 150 Irish civilian labourers on board. It was quite rough and all the landsmen were incapacitated by seasickness. Isambard's son records that the ship was only kept afloat by the exertions of Captain Claxton, the dockyard hands and ratings who had been sent to assist in navigating her across the Irish Sea.

The prize looked once more like being snatched from their grasp on the approach to the Mersey Bar, when the wind increased violently, the tow-rope snapped and the leaks began to increase with the working of the ship. However, new tow-ropes were got aboard and gaily decorated with flags, the flotilla was signalled off the Great Ormes Head at 7 a.m. on Monday, the ship having averaged six knots. The pierheads in Liverpool were thronged by thousands of people, and on reaching Liverpool at 1.30 the *Great Britain* was saluted by cannon. Finally the ship was pulled on to the gridiron in the Prince's Dock on the top of the tide; the pumps were stopped and she was allowed to sink on to it. The *Nautical Magazine* records that

the ship was thoroughly inspected with most encouraging results, safe and sound in hull and frames, not bent, shaken or strained nor indicating in the slightest degree anything that would lead to the supposition that her back had been injured while embedded in the sands of Dundrum Bay.

The Liverpool company Fawcett Preston carried out the survey and considered that it would be necessary to spend approximately £16,000 on the hull and rigging and £6,000 on the machinery in order to put the ship back into service. The survey report concluded:

We do not conceive it would have been possible under similar circumstances to stop holes of the size mentioned varying from 2 ft by 1 ft to almost 5¾ ft by 1¼ ft in the bottom of a wooden vessel, and we may further remark that the iron of which the frames and plates are made must have been of the most excellent quality.

Great Britain had been greatly under-insured at only £17,000. The directors were forced to sell the *Great Western* in April 1847 and thus had no further source of revenue. There was no hope of returning the ship to service and so the great idea of extending the Great Western Railway to New York came to an end. The depressing task of winding up the whole enterprise continued with an auction sale in Liverpool on 13 April 1848, when, amongst other articles 228 hair mattresses, 406 feather pillows, 580 blankets, 970 sheets, 1,556 towels and 781 pillow-cases were put up for sale. An auction of the ship herself was held in September 'as she lay at Coburg Dock'. Only half the reserve figure of £40,000 was bid—this for a ship which had cost nearly £120,000 only three years before.

that extent stopped her. I have no doubt that tomorrow we shall see her free.[4]

They did. The ship floated freely on the next day and moved away from the nearly fatal Dundrum Beach.

Claxton was a bluff sea-dog and believed in the proper observances. He marked the occasion by calling for three cheers each for Ireland, The Queen, Great Britain, Bremner, Mr and Mrs Montgomery who had befriended the castaway passengers, and Lord Roden whose estates had furnished the faggots that saved the ship. However, trouble was not at an end. Of the 120 Irish labourers hired to work at the pumps only 36 turned up at first, and they did not work but spent the time discussing the rate for the job. The ship was taken in tow at 4 a.m. on 28 August with 6 ft of water in the engine room, 5 ft in the forward hold and making well over a foot of water an hour. However, the iron steam frigate

CHAPTER THIRTEEN

Reconstruction

The *Great Britain* was finally sold in December 1850 to Gibbs, Bright & Co. through the agency of Patterson, who built her, for only £18,000. The original register refers to this Bill of Sale dated 2 January 1851. The new owners were George Gibbs and Robert Bright of Bristol, and Tyndal and Samuel Bright of Liverpool. Robert Bright was one of the three members of the Board who had discussed the formation of the Great Western Steamship Company with Brunel and Guppy in October 1835. He knew well the quality of the ship, and it was appropriate that these men should give her a new lease of life. The official death of the Great Western Steamship Company was delayed until February 1852 when the company was wound up.

While the *Great Britain* was lying forlornly in Coburg Dock an event took place 12,000 miles away which was to transform her life. Traces of gold were found in Victoria, Australia, in early 1850 and quantities of alluvial gold in the second half of 1851. The effect of this on the main port of Melbourne in Victoria was electric. Wages rocketed and it became impossible to find labour to work on farms or in the towns; it was even impossible to keep police and other state officials from joining in the gold rush. By the end of 1851 100,000 ounces of gold had been washed from the soil, and new fields were being discovered daily.

The shipping companies with a foot already in Australia were naturally among the first to learn of the discovery and thus had a lead over other owners to whom the news did not spread for some months. When the news reached the bulk of the population of Britain there was a rush to ship to Australia, and ship-owners and the emigration commissioners found that existing tonnage was totally insufficient to meet the demand. Blackwallers were diverted from the Indian run while Liverpool ship-owners, who took a leading part in the Gold Rush shipping, were hiring American transatlantic packets, ordering ships in America and, of course, doing their best to find shipping in Britain.

One of these owners was Gibbs, Bright & Company who ran the Eagle Line of sailing packets to Australia. Gibbs, Bright, as mentioned earlier, was a conglomeration of Bristol and Liverpool business interests. The association between the Gibbs and Bright families started in Bristol in the latter half of the eighteenth century with a friendship between George Gibbs and Richard Bright. A younger Gibbs brother, Antony, later founded the banking firm of Antony Gibbs & Sons. Both Gibbs and Bright were West India merchants, and the Brights owned large estates in Jamaica.

In 1818 George Gibbs senior and his son, George, entered into a partnership in Bristol with Robert Bright, styling it Gibbs, Son & Bright. As mentioned earlier, they played a prominent part in the formation of the Great Western Railway, George Gibbs being on the London Board and Robert on the Bristol one. In 1805 they had opened a small branch in Liverpool which was taken over by the Bristol partnership in 1818 and renamed Gibbs, Bright & Co. The firm were the loading agents in 1838 for the *Great Western* on her first voyage across the Atlantic. As the importance of Liverpool grew, the Bristol end withered and the Liverpool tail wagged the dog. In 1853 the firm opened a Melbourne branch called Bright Bros. & Company, and this had the agency for the Eagle and Blackwall Lines of sailing ships and for other packets on the same run. Finally, in 1881, Antony Gibbs & Sons of London absorbed Gibbs, Bright & Co. of Liverpool, renaming it 'Antony Gibbs, Sons & Co.,' the Australian branches being renamed Gibbs, Bright & Co.

This history forms the background to the subsequent life of the *Great Britain*; indeed, both families were connected with the ship throughout her life, from Robert Gibbs's discussion with Brunel before the Steamship Company was formed, right up to the sale of the ship to the Falkland Islands Company. One might even speculate that the family initials G.B. had some influence upon the renaming of the *Mammoth*.

Gold began to arrive in Britain from Australia in early 1852, the first ship to land it being the Aberdeen White Star sailing liner *Phoenician* which delivered £81,000 worth of gold in early February after a passage of 83 days from Sydney. The first ship to arrive in Liverpool was one of Gibbs, Bright's, the Eagle Line packet *Albatross* which in August landed £50,000 worth of gold dust. Casting around for tonnage, Gibbs, Bright, who had been the *Great Britain's* agents on the Atlantic run, thought of the ship. Here was a magnificent vessel, the largest in the world, capable of taking considerable numbers of passengers—not to mention cargo—each way, and going cheap. On 2 January 1851, not long after the news of the discovery of gold reached Britain, they bought the *Great Britain*.

A typical sailing vessel voyage to Australia is best described in the words of the great American wind expert Maury:

Australian bound vessels are advised after crossing the Equator near the meridian of 30° west, to run down through the south-east trades with topmast studding sails set if they have sea room, aiming to cross 25 or 30° south as the wind will allow which will be generally somewhere about 28 or 30° west, and soon shaping their course after they get the wind steadily from the westward more and more to the eastward, until they cross the meridian at 20° east in about latitude 45° reaching 55° south *if at all* in about 40° east. Thence the best course—if ice etc. will allow—is onwards still to the southward and east not caring to get to the northward again of your greatest southern latitude before reaching 90° east. The highest latitude should be reached between the meridians of 50° and 80° east. The course then is north-east gradually hauling up more and more to the north as you approach Van Diemens land. The highest degree of south latitude which it may be prudent to touch, depends merely on the season of the year and the winds, the state of the ship and the well being of the passengers and crew.

Around 1850 it was difficult to build a steamer which was capable of bunkering for more than 20 days on full power. The *Great Britain* as the largest ship in the world could probably exceed this but only at the expense of cargo. Before Maury's work the normal passage to Australia was 120 days but ships following his rules soon cut this to around 80. The secret was to run before the trades in the Atlantic to the coast of Brazil, then to get right down to about 55° south before turning east. This brought one into the region of heavy seas, strong westerly winds and occasional ice. It was only possible to reap the benefit of these strong following winds right round the world if a ship was large and extremely robust and weatherly. The *Great Britain* was just such a ship. However, even she could not be expected to better, say, 60 days for the passage and this would be by steaming for perhaps a half of it and sailing for the rest. The disadvantage of the sailing ship was that occasionally rogue head-winds were experienced and also that in the Doldrums there could be days on end without wind at all. If the *Great Britain* became a sailing ship with powerful steam auxiliary propulsion she would be able to overcome both these difficulties and probably cut her average voyage to not more than two-thirds that of the fastest sailing ships. This is what happened eventually, though it seems clear that Gibbs, Bright's original hope was to steer the steam-ship course, cutting down the east side of the Atlantic and bunkering at Cape Town.

The need for extensive alteration to the *Great Britain* was apparent. First, it was necessary to fit new machinery occupying less space and consuming less fuel, especially as the original machinery had been severely damaged by the stranding. Secondly, it was necessary to increase the cargo capacity which in the original ship was small and abysmally awkwardly placed. This could only be at the expense of passenger accommodation, which would have to be replaced; as the ship was over-stable in her original form, the obvious thing to do was to build this new capacity on deck. Finally, if the new machinery were to be smaller, it must be faster-running, and this necessitated a new propeller of lower pitch, together with a new rudder to replace the one destroyed at Dundrum.

Gibbs, Bright put William Patterson in charge of the whole conversion and appointed a Mr Croome, Her Majesty's Surveyor for Steamboats in Bristol, as the Inspecting Engineer on the work. The actual contracts were given out to three firms: to Thomas Vernon & Son for the iron work and the shipwrights' work around the ship, to John Penn & Co. of London for the engines, and to Mackay & Miller for the new deckhouse and accommodation.

The new machinery was quite different from the original.[1] Fig. 93 shows its detail. These were two oscillating cylinders with air pumps between them, driving upwards to a crankshaft which bore four gear-wheels 14 ft in diameter, which in turn drove four more on the propeller shaft, still with the original step-up ratio of 3:1. These engines were of 500 nominal horsepower and ran at 24 revolutions per minute. The boiler pressure was now at 10 lb. per sq. in., with a maximum of 12, and the twin cylinders were 82½ in. in diameter with the same stroke as before, 72 in. It is possible to compute the indicated horsepower of which

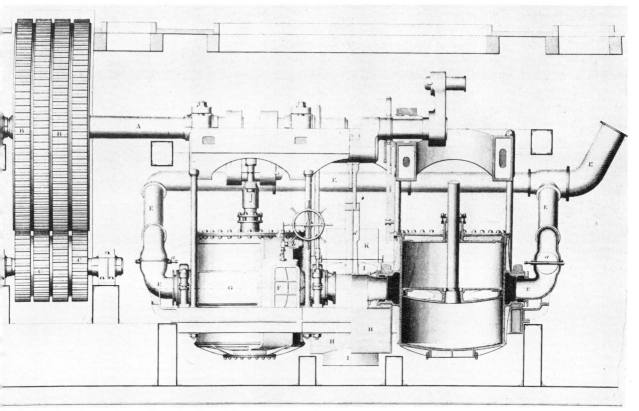

93 The longitudinal profile of the John Penn machinery, 1852

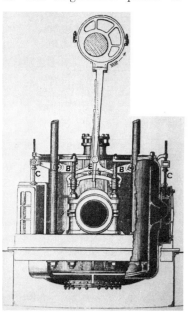

94 The valve-gear fitted to the 1852 engines

the engines should be capable; at 1,420, this is not dissimilar to that of the original machinery.

The layout of a cylinder can be seen in Fig. 94, which shows the valve eccentric arranged to work slide valves on the sides of the cylinders, with a wide belt round the cylinder for steam supply and exhaust. The two slide valves are also shown as (c), the rocking levers to them as (b). Steam came from the boiler via the stop valve, entered the belt through one trunnion and exhausted through the other. The valve gear had to operate two valves by a single eccentric without being affected by the rocking of the cylinder. To do this the rockers mentioned earlier were pivoted on the cylinders and their inboard ends worked in a transverse slot (e) on the valve rod curved concentrically with the trunnions. This slotted end of the valve rod had guides at its sides forcing it to move vertically, while the top end moved in a guide attached to the engine frame structure. Thus it moved vertically with no rotation, while the slide valves and their driving rockers oscillated with the cylinders. This improvement on the original Maudslay oscillating engines was invented by Penn himself. The valve rod was locked to the eccentric rod by means of a slotted guide in the latter into which the pin on the valve rod could be fitted in various positions as derived by a hand-locking linkage.

Positive location was ensured by a pivoting spring-loaded arm. The valve rods carried a rack, and the hand-wheel shows a pinion on the end of its shaft. By sliding this forward when the engines were stopped and the rods disengaged, the hand-wheel could be used to wind the slide valves to a new position, such as that required for going astern. Steam control was by the butterfly valves shown on the steam inlet-pipes, and expansion by a linkage from these to a stepped cam, on the crankshaft. With the engine at rest the eccentric bearing on this cam at the after end of the engine could be moved from one section of the cam to another, thus picking up a different stroke. The two valves were then linked by rods round the engine.

Fig. 93 shows a longitudinal section through the cylinder and how the steam was admitted to the double-acting piston via the slide valves which were fed from the hollow trunnions connected to a steam pipe. The air pumps were fitted between the cylinders and had crosshead guides—unlike the original ones which had a parallel motion linkage. They were 40 in. in diameter and had a stroke of 36 in., while their valves were ingeniously made from India-rubber discs on a grating; these can be seen quite clearly. The pumps were probably operated according to standard Penn practice for engine-driven pumps, with small arms on the lower outer corners of the cylinders which, by means of connecting rods, drove pistons in inverted cylinders attached to the engine entablature.

95 The air pumps of the 1852 engines

As mentioned, transmission was by four main gear-wheels 14 ft in diameter, each 13 in. broad, and staggered for quiet running—in other words, the teeth were not in line each with another but a quarter of the tooth pitch out of phase, so that cyclic errors would be minimised. The shaft wheels were 4 ft 8 in. in diameter, and a box beam was fitted on the bulkhead at the aft end of the engine-room to take the bearing for a so-called wheel shaft. The steam escaped from the cylinders through the trunnions and into the condenser labelled (h) in Fig. 93. It can be seen that this was of jet type and that the ship still worked on seawater feed.

The new propeller was a solid three-bladed casting of the same diameter as before, 15 ft 6 in. Its length of boss was 3 ft 2 in. but its pitch less than before—19 ft. The blade-area ratio (ratio of blade-area to total area of disc) was, as before, around 0·5, and the whole contraption was fitted with a sailing clutch which allowed the propeller to 'windmill' when sailing and thus supposedly cut down the drag. The sternframe was rebuilt, a new sternpost being fitted some 3 ft aft of the Brunel one. This allowed the lines to be faired out and eased. A fixed rudder post was placed aft of this; both of these posts were vertical. Behind the rudder post was an unbalanced flat plate-rudder of very conventional shape. The steering gear, however, may have been the original one.

The boilers were a great advance on the original one. There were two of them, side by side and divided into three sections athwartships. They were stoked from the sides, instead of from the ends, and this probably made it difficult for the stokers to keep their feet when the ship was rolling. Steam-smothering connections for hoses were fitted to them—it was possibly the first time that this fire-fighting device had been employed. The heating-surface totalled 875 sq. ft, with 280 brass tubes per section, and there were two funnels, placed side by side. These were frankly hideous. They had lower casings which extended right up through the deckhouse to above the hurricane deck; protruding from them, tops of smaller diameter culminated in bell mouths. It is probable that they were based upon 'Mr Taplin's Telescopic Chimneys' invented a year or two earlier. To quote a contemporary account of this device:

The manner in which chimneys on this construction act is so obvious as scarcely to need any description. The object of the plan is to enable the chimney to be shut up like a spy glass and lowered below the deck when the vessel is under sail and the chimney is consequently made in two or more lengths of different diameter so that like a spy glass they may be shut up one in another. At the top of the lowermost piece of chimney pulleys are attached over which pulley chains are passed and the ends of the chains are fixed to the bottoms of the length of chimney which has to be raised. The other ends of the chains are wound up by an appropriate mechanism. . . .[2]

To this end the steam pipes were quite separate. Finally, space was provided for about 700 tons of coal in permanent bunkers abreast of the engine-room, and about the same amount could be stowed elsewhere, some of it on deck.

Considerable modifications had to be made to the structure to accommodate this machinery. It was stated in the *Illustrated London News* that there were '10 new iron keelsons' placed in the ship, half as deep again as those formerly in her. This is an exaggeration: the keelsons which can still be seen in the ship are 4 ft deep—9 in. deeper than the originals. The same account claimed that the docking keels were removed, and Bourne's *Cyclopaedia of Machinery* told the same story, though any visitor to the ship today can see that this statement was false.

As the *Great Britain* had to work at deeper draughts on the Australian routes to carry more cargo and a great deal of fuel, eight wrought-iron beams were fitted across her at the two lower-deck levels in the engine room in order to resist the extra inward water pressure. Although a draught of 16 ft—the original lightload draught—is shown the ship normally left for Australia at a draught of about 22 ft, only 3 ft below the level of the lower deck. The timber stringers were still in place; the present box stringers in the upper 'tween decks were only installed around 1860. (The curious dip port and starboard that can be seen in these today marks where they had to be fitted under the entry doors already built in way of the chain plates of No. 3* mast). One considerable alteration was the fitting of a wood keel below the original flat plate keel. This extended the whole length of the ship and was 17 in. deep and 20 in. wide, strapped and banded to the iron plating and originally covered with zinc sheathing to protect it against worm; it still survives.

The extra cargo accommodation mentioned was provided by using all the accommodation from the lower 'tween decks or dining saloon decks. Cabins and saloons were stripped out to provide a further 57,000 cu. ft of cargo space, one-third forward and the rest aft. Access to these spaces

* 1852 numbering. See page 147.

145

left much to be desired as it was mainly through shell doors fitted in the upper 'tween decks port and starboard, abreast Nos. 1 and 3 masts in the new four-masted rig. The step was also taken out of the forward engine room bulkhead, giving another 7,000 cu. ft.

The deckhouse was a major innovation. It was 300 ft long, extending from the break of the forecastle almost right through to the stern, and 7 ft 6 in. high, giving a clearance inside it of over 6½ ft. Its inside clear width was about 31 ft. On top of the deckhouse was a hurricane deck where passengers could promenade—an excellent feature in a ship about to undertake hot-weather sailing. The great windlass forward was now buried in the deckhouse. Its arms had a span of 24 ft, so there was ample space between it and the deckhouse sides for the sailors to work. As the arms could be unshipped there was useful space around the windlass which was probably used at sea for livestock pens—hens, pigs, bullocks and so on. Wooden bulwarks were fitted right along the sides to prevent seas coming aboard; these must have made the ship somewhat claustrophobic, extending as they did to over 4 ft above deck level. They appear to have been formed by planking over the existing rails and stanchions.

The accommodation in the ship was unprecedented in the emigrant and Australian trade—the total number of passengers carried was now 730, of which 50 were in the first class. The upper 'tween decks below the main deck was given over mainly to staterooms. There were 64 aft of the engine room, with ladies' boudoirs on either side at the forward end. The extreme stern was the lounging room with transom windows right across the after end—it must have been very pleasant in the trades to take coffee sitting on the sofas with windows open and the wake bubbling away aft. From here, two staircases ascended to the after part of the deckhouse on the main deck and at the other end, close to the door of the saloon, were two more staircases. The fore saloon was right forward in the upper 'tween deck, with a number of staterooms aft of it. Above it was the dining saloon, 50 ft long by 18 ft broad. In front of this was the windlass, with stairs leading down to the lower deck at the break of the forecastle where the ice house and fruit stores were located.

The after part of the long deckhouse was occupied by the grand saloon, 75 ft long, which the *Illustrated London News* described as

tastefully decorated with paintings on glass of the armorial shields of all the nations. Two ranges of tables run the whole length. Opposite the door is the pantry and at the further end is a music room with an ornamental skylight in which the deck binnacle is placed. On either side are the Captain and Chief Officer's staterooms. Behind is the smoking room and still farther aft the wheel-house.[3]

The picture which accompanied this description is very interesting. Wine glasses and decanters can be seen in racks under the deckhead against the cabin bulkheads—the noise they made in a seaway must have been hellish! The backs of the seats could be swung over in railway-station fashion, and a lady is shown with a child sitting on one of these, facing into the cabin. The lamps are oil with glass shades and a fitted carpet covers the floor. Incidentally, two or three of the paintings on glass still

96 A long deckhouse was built above the weather deck—first-class dining saloon

survive. The area is shown in a sailing plan. This was actually drawn at a later date, after a lifting screw had been fitted, but the dining saloon had remained unchanged. When he drew the sketch the artist was standing just abreast of the two family rooms A and D, looking aft at the mast in the centre of the picture, the companionways behind it and the two mirrors on the after bulkhead. These can be seen marked on the plan.

The rig of the ship was also changed. In 1846 a topgallant mast had been added to the main or No. 2 mast, in 1852, No. 3 mast had gone, and No. 4 had been square-rigged and made similar to the original main mast. These alterations were unchanged in 1852, but No. 5 mast was totally removed: thus only Nos. 1 and 6 were left as Brunel had designed them. The sail area was now 3,000 sq. yds (27,000 sq. ft) with all plain sails set: an increase of 75 per cent. over the original sail plan. The fore and aft sails throughout on Nos. 1, 3 and 4 masts (new numbering) were given booms in place of their original loose feet. These new rigging arrangements were intended to provide a mixture of running and beating efficiency. However, when running before the wind, the sails on Nos. 1 and 4 masts would be relatively ineffective—especially on No. 1, blanketed as it was by the square-rigged mast abaft it. Moreover, the booms on the sails on these two masts would clearly be a nuisance; that of the spanker would interfere with the braces of the yards of No. 3 mast, and the staying arrangement for No. 2 would necessitate the unbending

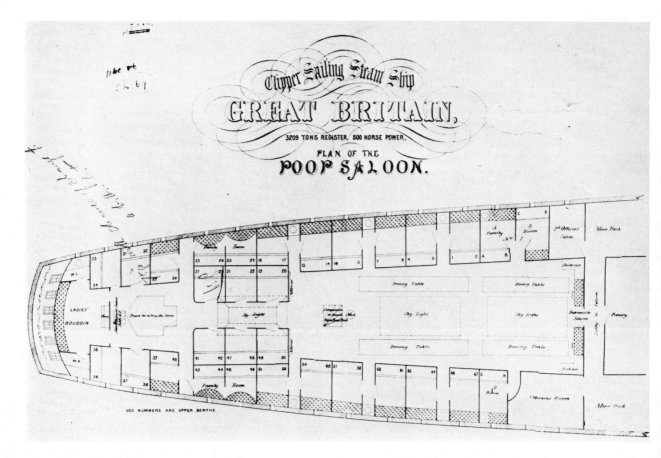

the rebending of the fore and aft sail on No. 1 every time the ship had to change tack. The square-rigged sails would lose effect when close to the wind. It was certainly not a very seamanlike rig, and one might well anticipate that it would give trouble if much reliance had to be placed upon the wind.

A charming contemporary print shows the ship sailing from Liverpool on 21 August 1852, on her first voyage to Australia. The signal flown is in the Marryat code: below the distinguishing pendant are the numbers 4, 6, 9, 1—'*Great Britain*—Liverpool—Steamer'. This picture shows clearly the wood bulwark built along the deck, and also the entry ports for cargo actually in the white band. The original Brunel bridge can be seen; the deckhouse was simply built up to and around it. The wheelhouse was right aft and all the figurehead and gingerbread work forward and aft was retained. A technical reconstruction of this form of the ship is shown in Fig. 99, page 150.

The ship was still capable of causing considerable excitement. The *Mona's Herald* published in Douglas, Isle of Man, told its readers on 14 January:

We feel a special pleasure in notifying that the owners of the mammoth steam-ship *Great Britain* have intimated their intention of supplying that vessel with Manx canvas. It must be proved satisfactory to our countrymen and to the spirited

98 Dropping the pilot, Liverpool Bar, 1852

proprietor of the sailcloth manufactory in particular, to know that the canvas manufactured at that establishment ranks so highly in the estimation of the British Mercantile Marine.

It must be recognised that the alterations did generally suit the ship for her new trade. The engines were comparatively small and efficient; the accommodation was better suited for a passage through the tropics; the extra cargo capacity and the better means of access to it would increase the ship's earning capacity; and the comparative height of the cargo would lower the ship's original excessive stability. However, the large three-bladed propeller and the hybrid rig did not promise well unless the ship could make the voyage fundamentally as a steamship without much reliance upon her sails. The transversely stoked boilers were another questionable feature.

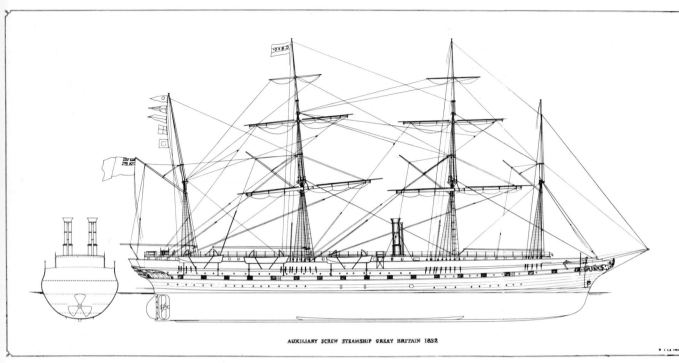

AUXILIARY SCREW STEAMSHIP GREAT BRITAIN 1852

99 1852 outboard profile

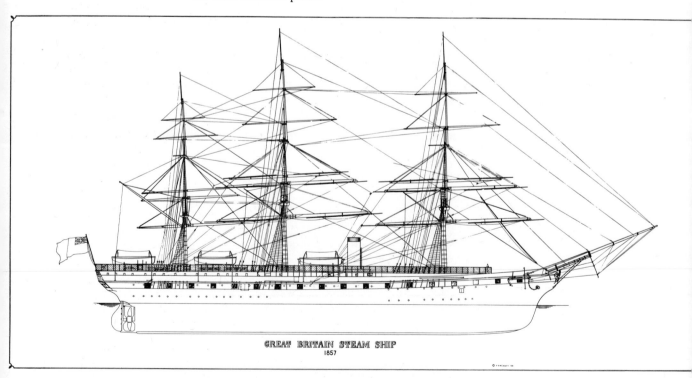

GREAT BRITAIN STEAM SHIP
1857

100 Outboard profile—1857. The final Australian ship

The Australian steamship 'Great Britain'

The ship was completed in the spring. Before they put her on the long run to Australia, Gibbs, Bright decided upon a shake-down trip across the Atlantic. Barnard Robert Matthews was appointed Captain, and before the ship sailed Francis Pettit Smith made a visit to wish her well. This occasion is recorded in a group picture which shows that Captain Matthews was a rather portly man of what was then termed a choleric cast of countenance.

The *Great Britain* sailed on 1 May 1852, with 180 passengers and some cargo. The trip to New York took 13 days 5½ hrs—an average speed of about 9·7 knots. Strong gales from the west and south were experienced for much of the time and the best day's run was 301 miles. The power of the new engines was sufficient to give a trial speed in smooth water of about 11·3 knots; for the North Atlantic service this might be expected to convert into a service speed of approximately 10·25 knots. She was slightly under half a knot worse than that, which is not unreasonable for such a heavily-rigged ship like this, as the slightest headwind would hold her back considerably.

After her return the *Great Britain* finally sailed for Australia on 21 August at 3 p.m. A new Second Officer joined the ship: John Gray, who was later to command the *Great Britain* for much of her career. The *Illustrated London News* reported:

Her passage was watched with intense interest by crowds of enthusiastic spectators on the Liverpool side. Steamboats and other craft gaily dressed with flags and streamers and filled with people were moving about in all directions, while the ferry boats were crammed with passengers. The deck of the *Great Britain* was crowded with passengers to take farewell of Old England. Several tugboats hovered around the leviathan; at intervals guns were fired from the *Great Britain* herself. . . . The *Great Britain* sped on her way with upwards of 630 passengers and a very heavy mail. [The total fares came to £23,000, an average of only £36 each.]

The *Great Britain* by the time she left the river was drawing 22 ft of water. The quantity of coal taken on board is about 1,400 tons, chiefly Welsh, there is enough to steam the whole distance without stopping. . . . It is expected that she will reach the Cape in about 25 days. After staying there two or three days she will proceed to Melbourne and Sydney and it is confidently expected that she will reach the former in 56 days from England whereas double that length of time is considered an average voyage for a sailing vessel. The *Great Britain* is fully equipped to resist any attempt to attack the vessel that might be made for she is mounted with six heavy deck guns and arms and ammunition for 100 men. The crew consist of about 130 persons.[1]

Unfortunately, this prediction of a swift voyage was grossly over-optimistic.

A young man who shipped on the *Great Britain* recorded the whole trip in a most entertaining diary.[2] He described the departure from 'a considerable altitude on the fore rigging'. They saw the land for several hours as they ran along the Welsh coast and dropped the Holyhead light at about eight o'clock. The weather was excellent. The next day the Captain held church services at 11 a.m. and 6 p.m. but had no time to give the sermon in the morning and forgot it in the evening. There were two sittings in the dining saloon but that first day many were already feeling seasick. The diary records that 'the sides of the ship are piled up with coals' and that the ship was steaming at about $9\frac{1}{2}$ knots with her sails useless through lack of wind. For the next few days they steamed steadily on, making nearly 10 knots; but with a beam sea in the Bay of Biscay the vessel was rolling a good deal and this caused a lot of seasickness. (It would appear that the centreline keel had not cured *Great Britain*'s

101 Francis Pettitt Smith with *Great Britain*'s officers

propensity for rolling.) By 26 August they were getting a little trade wind and sail was set. Speed had gone up to 10½ knots and at noon that day they passed Cape St Vincent. The writer and his friends used to sit

102 *Great Britain* arrives at Port Jackson in November 1852

on the very sternmost part of the ship below the saloon deck and then talk of our homes and those we have left behind us . . . we can look upon the waves and admire their crested tops tinged by the light of the moon.

On 27 August studding sails were set as there was a good following wind. An unforeseen accident occurred

which might have been worse. The ship came almost to a standstill. The sails on the mainmast were taken aback while those on the foremast were shivering, the voice of the second officer [a very fine fellow]* was heard above the noise of the wind to take in all sail. In an instant he seemed to possess a gift of ubiquity. His energies seemed to rouse the crew to their utmost exertions. Before his orders could be obeyed the fore studding sail boom, a spar 2 ft in circumference, snapped in two and the wreck came down on deck. Before this could be cleared away the topmast studding sail boom shared the same fate. We were all requested to assist in taking in the sail. . . . Then the ship began to be more easy but she rolled tremendously. The coal piled up in sacks round the bulwarks fell down and blocked up the road and lots of crockery was broken. The cause of all this fracas was easily accounted for, the fan or screw had been detached from her machinery by way of experiment and the vessel moving along under sail the fan gently revolved according to the speed of the vessel. In order to attach it again to the machinery [an affair of about 20 minutes] it was necessary that the fan should be stationary and not permitted to revolve. The consequence was it acted like an oar in the water to a moving boat. The ship's way was instantaneously arrested, she no longer obeyed the helm and she was for a short time at the mercy of the winds. . . .

This interesting account of the first use of the sailing clutch shows that its main advantage was to allow the rudder to steer the vessel. If locked, the disturbance of the water blanked off the rudder and the *Great Britain* came into the wind and was taken aback.

Captain Matthews was not popular. On 1 September a meeting was convened in the fore saloon in order to present him with a list of grievances. These included the badness of the provisions, the want of cleaning in parts of the ship, and the irregularity of meals. However, the diary-writer pointed out that really everything was of the best quality and nobody 'with any justice can complain'. On 2 September they were still expecting to reach Australia on schedule, and certainly the engines allowed the ship to steam through the Doldrums in grand style.

From 7 September they met apparently un-anticipated headwinds from the south-south-east as they passed 200 miles off St Helena in longitude 10° west approx. They were also meeting contrary currents. On 13 September the weather was beautiful. The diary describes

glorious sunshine, a cloudless sky and such a sky. Yet I cannot describe its peculiar shade of blue. It seems more brilliant and more transparent than our own. Everything seems clearer and brighter except our own faces which are terribly disfigured by the smuts from the chimneys or funnels.

The weather soon worsened again, with headwinds, and the contrary current increased. On the 19th, the diary recorded that there was a heavy sea with a strong headwind, and that the ship was making little way. She

* John Gray—later Captain.

was only 700 miles from the Cape of Good Hope when they decided to put back to St Helena, 1,100 miles away, to bunker. The diary remarks that upon changing course it took from 10 a.m. until 4 p.m. before all the sail could be got up on the ship. They then idled the screw and sailed under canvas at 11 knots, arriving at St Helena at midnight on 22 September.

Captain Matthews must have chosen his course from a purely steamship point of view. The wind maps show that all through this region he could expect strong south-east winds, and the Benguela current, which always runs up the west coast of Africa, was also dead against him. Matthews paid heavily for his choice of this approach, as the ship lost the chance to deliver the mails to Australia in the contracted 60 days. The direct loss to the owners was at least £3,000.

The *Great Britain* sailed again on 29 September with about 300 tons of coal on board, having bought 100 tons from ashore at £5 17s. a ton— an outrageous price in those days—and 100 tons from H.M.S. *Penelope*. This was just sufficient to reach the Cape. The Captain became more and more unpopular with the passengers, who began to cast doubts on his navigation. As there were several seamen among the passengers his whole course and plan of voyage came under criticism.

The Captain sails from Liverpool with as he supposes 1,400 tons of coal. We pass 200 miles to the east of St Helena where we could have procured coal if we needed it and when about 800 miles from the Cape we are opposed by strong south-easterly Trade winds which always blows in that direction as well as the south Atlantic current which always runs in the same direction the whole year. Our stock of coal is found to be only four days consumption instead of eight or nine, making an error of somewhere about 300 tons.

After a period of contrary winds, on 8 October the wind backed and they set sail for the Cape using every stitch of canvas. They finally arrived early in the morning of 10 October. The ship had been cleaned, boats painted; and the six eight-pounder guns all painted and so on. As the ship had gold and silver coin worth £1 million on board these weapons were probably necessary.

They sailed from the Cape on 17 October and arrived off Melbourne on 12 November. If the ship had made Cape Town without turning back, had stayed three days there as intended and had made the same speed onward, she would have reached Melbourne in exactly 60 days. As it was, the voyage lasted 83 days. On the morning of 12 November, people were hurrying from all over Melbourne on foot and horseback to vantage spots along the shores of Hobsons Bay to see the ship which had arrived under cover of darkness the previous night. She impressed everyone. After five days in Melbourne the *Great Britain* sailed on to Sydney with some 300 passengers on board, passing through Sydney Heads at 9.30 on the morning of 20 November. The shores were lined with enthusiastic crowds who cheered and hurrahed her up the harbour; and as she anchored, the *Great Britain* fired a salute in acknowledgement while the ship's band played the National Anthem. Politicians and leading citizens went on board, as did the band of the Eleventh Regiment; then the Governor and his family

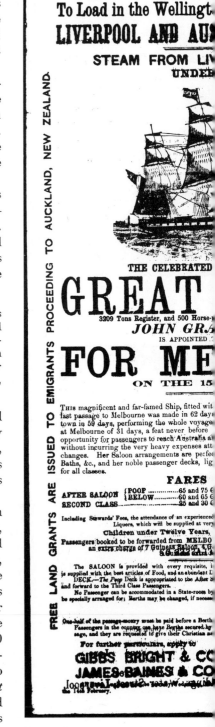

103 Sailing bill showing ship in 185

154

visited her and were greeted with a 19-gun salute. An Australian news-paper reported: 'there has been no sickness on board and only one man died—an aged Chinese taken on board at St Helena'. This was not quite true. An able seaman fell off a topsail yardarm and was lost overboard in the St Helena area.

The ship sailed from Sydney on 20 December but did not arrive in Melbourne until Christmas Day, having met heavy seas and a severe gale which forced her to shelter. Three days after Christmas a grand ball was held on board—some 400 invitations being issued to leading local citizens. An inspection of the ship was held, followed by a champagne banquet and dancing. On the 29th she was thrown open to the public and on 4 January 1853 sailed for Britain. On board were 161 passengers and over 100,000 oz. of gold. The ship steamed west, taking 33 days to Algoa Bay and calling at St Helena and Vigo, Spain, before arriving at Liverpool in April.

Overall, this was not a good voyage. The *Great Britain* was still a steamship with auxiliary sail, and the route chosen was that of a steamship. The attempt to steam into the trade winds and the Benguela current had proved the ship to be underpowered and too extravagant in coal to do this. Furthermore, the route home westwards had meant steaming against the prevailing winds much of the way to Cape Town. At least 20 days had to be cut off the running time each way and stops could not be afforded. Thus when the ship arrived home in April 1853 she was put in hand for considerable alterations and did not resume trading until the autumn of that year.

The solution to the ship's problems was forecast in an interesting paper read to the Institute of Civil Engineers in 1841 by Samuel Seaward, F.R.S., the ship- and engine-builder. He advocated:

To employ the wind as the principal moving force and to use steam power only in those cases where the failure of the wind which being contrary would cause delay on the voyage. . . . The generality of merchant vessels particularly those which trade round the Cape of Good Hope and Cape Horn, sail before the wind upon an average at 11 to 12 nautical miles an hr, in a gale this speed is increased to 13 or 14, two or three miles an hr faster than any ordinary steamer could be propelled under similar circumstances.[3]

All in all, this paper was a plea for the best of both worlds on long voyages, advocating the use of sail when the wind was free and strong and steam when the wind let one down. This still made sense in 1851, 10 years after Seaward wrote. (Ten years later still, marine engineering had progressed to the point where his conclusions were no longer valid.)

The decision was straightforward. Basically, the ship must follow the recommendations of Maury. For a big, powerful ship like the *Great Britain*, days of running before the wind at speeds of 14 to 15 or 16 knots might be anticipated—far more than she could achieve under steam and far more than compensating for the extra length of the route. Another advantage would be that the need to call at the Cape and possibly St Helena on the way home for refuelling would be avoided and a further source of delay eliminated. As a steamer she would be likely to make the voyage in the region of 70 to 80 days. As a steam auxiliary she might well count on 60 days quite regularly.

The alterations were put in hand on the return from Australia in April 1853. Her external appearance was again changed. First, the fore-and aft-rigged masts were swept away entirely. The hybrid fore and aft and square rig thus gave place to a conventional three-masted ship rig carrying top masts and topgallants on all three masts, and with a flying jib boom added to the bowsprit. The masts were not all new—the fore-mast was probably the original No. 2 from 1845, and the main mast No. 3 from 1846. In the peculiar 1852 rig she had been fitted with single lifting topsails on the second and third masts, together with single lifting top-gallants. In the new rig a royal was fitted on each of the three masts, so that on the main mast, for example, there was a course, a lifting top-sail, a lifting topgallant and a royal. A skysail was also rigged on the mainmast only. The 1852 No. 2 mast was moved forward 24 ft. The 1852 No. 3 remained in its old position, but the new mizzen mast was stepped 10 ft forward of the 1852 No. 4 mast. This gave a much more balanced rig, with the funnels almost evenly spaced between the main and fore-masts. It might be expected that the ship would be lighter on her helm, and she would certainly be better able to run her easting down in heavy weather in deep south latitudes.

The difficulties with the sailing clutch were probably a matter of seamanship more than anything else, and there seems to be a conflict of evidence as to whether the three-bladed screw was retained or whether a two-bladed screw was fitted at this stage. *The Engineer* for 6 February 1857 reported that the screw then being fitted was two-bladed like the previous one, but unlike it was of lifting type. So probably a two-bladed Griffith-type screw *was* fitted at this time. The machinery had performed well although there had been some trouble with the boilers; while the nature of this is not known, it may be that the main difficulty was in keeping up steam with transversely-fired boilers in a heavy sea. However, the boilers certainly remained transversely fired and with the original number of furnaces, so probably changes were restricted to detailed arrangements of the stoke-holes and perhaps improvements to the flues. With two natural-draught boilers, each with its own uptake, it is possible that there was some blanking effect which in a beam wind reduced the efficiency of the leeward funnel. The ship was still by clipper standards lightly rigged for her size, but she was undoubtedly much better suited to the sailing-ship route than before. Gray is known to have had a strong influence on this re-rigging and on the detailed sail arrangements.[4]

CHAPTER FIFTEEN

Australian route

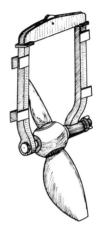

Thus altered, *Great Britain* sailed for the second time to Australia on 11 August 1853. Her sailing bill advertised fares of 'after saloon—70 guineas, Midships berths—65 guineas, Fore saloon second class—42 guineas, and a few at 25 guineas'. Before she sailed she was thrown open to the public at 1s. a head and an emigrants' home in Melbourne benefited by the takings. The scheduled time for the voyage was 65 days and the ship had to pay a penalty of 40 shillings per ton on her freight for every day over that time—a severe penalty as the standard rate for freight was £8 per ton. She sailed with 34 first-class passengers, 119 second- and 161 third-class, and in addition had 600 tons of cargo and 1,400 tons of coal on board.

The route out was via St Vincent in Portugal, and the ship arrived in Melbourne on 15 October in the good time of 65 days, thus neatly avoiding paying penalties on her freight. It is on record that 1,800 miles were covered in six consecutive days, at one point using both sails and propeller. She did even better on the way back. Sailing on 4 December she returned by Cape Horn, and in spite of sheltering off the Falkland Islands for four days owing to bad weather, arrived in Liverpool on 14 February 1854 after 72 days. This gave reason to suppose that she might well make the trip in under 60 days in favourable circumstances.

When *Great Britain* arrived in Liverpool she fired a salute from her guns which caused a Russian invasion scare, this being just before the Crimean War. As it was,

The joy was great when it was found that the invaders consisted of exactly 199 passengers and that the ship that bore them was no other than the *Great Britain* from Australia. There is a sort of national pride grown up amongst people about this ship and no wonder for her like is not to be found on the world of the waters and her late performances prove her to be by far the fleetest ship in the world.[1]

On this trip she brought back nearly 7 tons of gold and also 23 bales of cotton, the first ever to be imported from Australia. The remainder of the cargo consisted of wool and tin and some 15 tons of mail. A macabre item was the dead wife of one of the passengers, preserved in a cask of vinegar.[2]

Thus ended the first round voyage of the ship in something like her final Australian form. The conversion to a square-rigged sailing ship with auxiliary screw propulsion had been shown to be very successful, the round passage having been completed in a much shorter time than any sailing ship had ever accomplished. It was, however, Captain Matthews's last Australian voyage and he retired on reaching Liverpool. Henceforth the ship stuck to the classic sailing-ship route for all her Australian voyages, profiting from her great advantage over the pure windjammers in that the Doldrums and head winds meant little to her.

The *Great Britain* was now clearly a viable proposition on the Australian passage, and the ninth major voyage of her career, sailing from Liverpool on 13 June 1854, was the start of a long and satisfactory service on this route.

John Gray, the former First and earlier Second Mate, took command on 20 April.[3] A Shetlander, he was a forceful man as we have seen, and excelled both at getting on with passengers and at taking command in times of stress. As is often the case, much of the success of the ship in her subsequent career depended upon her master, and she was well served by John Gray.

The ship first sailed on 30 April, but this was a false start as mechanical trouble developed and they had to put back to Liverpool.[4] The first stern-tube liner fitted by Messrs Penn, which was of brass, had become worn and been replaced by one of wrought iron. This, however, welded to the shaft under friction, and May was spent replacing it with a new brass one. She finally sailed on 13 June and made a 66-day passage to Australia, arriving on 16 August, two days before the McKay-built clipper *Lightning* of the same Line left Melbourne. That ship made a splendid voyage home in 64 days, so that replies to letters sent out with the *Great Britain* reached England only 132 days later.

The *Great Britain* was indirectly involved in a sad incident on this trip. She was the first to report a vast iceberg island, extending some 60 by 50 nautical miles in 45° south, 44° west.[5] This berg was in the shape of a horseshoe and the westerly winds were driving straight into it. Some weeks later, a British ship, the *Guiding Star*, carrying 180 emigrants, was embayed and wrecked on the ice-cliffs, having missed stays in trying to beat out. The two American ships which had been accompanying her avoided the trap, and one of them, the clipper *Salem*, reported the loss of the *Guiding Star* on arrival in Australia. *Great Britain*, with her auxiliary steam propulsion, had of course been able to steam out of the trap without difficulty.

Although the ship arrived on 18 August, she had smallpox cases on board and was in quarantine until 7 September, when she steamed up the bay to Sand Ridge, now Port Melbourne; as she anchored, she fired sky rockets to celebrate release from quarantine. A number of other ships in the bay returned the salute courteously and a cry swept through Melbourne: 'The Russians have landed!' Apparently, many of the army volunteers were at a ball and, loosing their crinolined partners, rushed off to meet the foe. A number of irregular cavalry galloped along the Sand Ridge Road towards the bay, and infantry armed with sticks and pick handles as well as more formal weapons followed. The alarm spread to high quarters: The Colonial Secretary, Sir Robert Nickle, was notified; bugles called, drums beat and the General Alarm was sounded. The *Melbourne Herald*, from which much of this account is taken, concluded by saying: 'In fact Byron's description of the excitement in Brussels on the eve of Waterloo can alone give any idea of the state of Melbourne last night.' The *Great Britain* seems to have made a habit of starting such alarms. It will be remembered that there was a similar incident on the previous voyage when she returned to Liverpool.

The return voyage was fast, taking 63 days—only one day longer than the previous return journey. While on her outward voyage, on 24 July 1854, ownership had been transferred by Gibbs, Bright to their subsidiary, the Liverpool & Australian Steam Navigation Company. Obviously the ship could not be re-registered until her return, and this was done on 19 February 1855, her new home port being Liverpool. The new registry certificate, No. 76 of 1855, is curiously in error, stating that L.A.N. Co. was incorporated on 14 October 1842. The transfer, however, gives 4 October 1852 as the date of incorporation. The mistake on the registry certificate is presumably due to sloppy transcribing by clerks.

War was now to involve the ship in earnest. On her return in February she was chartered to the Government for trooping and fitted to carry 1,650 infantry and 30 horses to the Crimea. She sailed on 7 March 1855, and for the next year visited a number of ports—Gibraltar, Marseilles, Malta, Genoa, Spezia, Smyrna, Constantinople, Kertch and Balaclava. After carrying nearly 45,000 troops to the Crimea, war service concluded in June 1856 when the ship brought a load of troops home from Malta. What is known of her movements in this service is recorded in Appendix 7.

This war service, which is treated as voyage no. 12, had presumably not been unprofitable: at any rate after it the *Great Britain*'s owners were able to afford a really thorough refit incorporating all the features which, in the light of their experience over the past two or three years, they felt she needed for her future service as the consort of the new *Royal Charter*.

Only two days from sailing again under Government duty, her services were suddenly dispensed with and the ship was laid up for a short time while the owners decided upon the changes. In August Bright held a final conference on board with Captain Gray, the ship's chief engineer and John Vernon, the iron shipbuilder. Externally the *Great Britain*'s appearance was changed out of all recognition, so that little of the Brunel exterior remained. First her rig was swept away entirely. The light and by now old-fashioned square rig of 1853 gave way to an altogether heavier ship rig, more compatible with the weight and stability of the ship. In fact the masts fitted over the winter of 1856–7 stayed in her for the rest of her life, and the lower masts were only removed in 1970 when she was salvaged from Sparrow Cove. The rig carried the new type double topsails and a topgallant and a royal on all masts, with a larger bowsprit and flying jib-boom, together nearly 90 ft in length, replacing the smaller ones. The masts were new, each built from four trees, hooped with hinged iron bands fastened with taper wedges, and were as large as anything ever fitted in a sailing ship.

We have a list of the masts and spars carried by the ship on her arrival at the Falkland Islands and most of them dated from this final conversion completed in 1857, although by then double topgallants had already been fitted. The main lower mast was 95 ft from the cap to the heel and carried a main yard 106 ft long of wooden construction, later replaced by an iron yard. Above that were lower and upper topsail yards and the topgallant and royal yards. The other masts were rigged similarly, while the positions of the masts were altered from the previous ones, the main mast being moved forward 15 ft, and the mizzen 6 ft, so as to improve the steering. On all three masts was a spanker gaff, that on the mizzen being much the largest. In all, the sail-area amounted to about 33,000 sq. ft—just about double that fitted in 1845. *The Engineer* reported in February 1857,

To give the ship sailing power her masts and yards have been made larger than they were originally and to make the head sail of the ship predominate the main mast has been stepped 15 ft forward and the mizzen mast 6 ft forward of their last position.

The main mast weighs 18 tons and it is 43 in. in diameter. The size of the spars have also been increased so she will now have nearly one-fourth more sail than she formerly spread.

Sailing Ship '*GREAT BRITAIN*'
LIST OF MASTS AND SPARS ON ARRIVAL AT FALKLAND ISLANDS

	Length [Ft]	Weight [Tons]
Foremast	93	18
Foretopmast	54	1 ton 10 cwt.
Fore T'gallant and Royal Mast	54	18 cwt.
Foreyard [iron]	105	3 tons 17 cwt. 2 qr.
Fore lower topsail yard [iron]	90	2 ,, 18 cwt.
Fore upper ,, ,, ,,	76	1 ton 19 cwt. 2 qr.
,, lower T'gallant yard	65	2 tons 3 cwt.
,, upper ,, ,,	60	2 tons 3 cwt.
,, Royal	43	10 cwt.
Mainmast	95	19 tons
Main Topmast	54	1 ton 10 cwt.
,, T'gallant and Royal Mast	54	18 cwt.
Main yard [iron]	105	3 tons 17 cwt. 2 qr.
,, lower Topsail Yard [iron]	90	2 tons 18 cwt.
,, upper ,, ,, ,,	76	1 ton 19 cwt. 2 qr.
,, lower T'gallant Yard	65	2 tons 3 cwt.
,, upper ,, ,,	60	2 tons 3 cwt.
,, Royal yard	43	10 cwt.
Mizzen mast	79½	10 tons
,, topmast	54	18 cwt.
,, T'gallant mast and Royal	38	11 cwt.
Crossjack yard	73 ft 4 in.	1 ton 12 cwt.
Mizzen lower Topsail yard	68½	1 ton 2 cwt.
,, upper ,, ,,	60	19 cwt.
,, T'gallant yard	47	11 cwt.
,, Royal yard	31	8 cwt.
Bowsprit	48	
Jibboom	75	

This rig was consistent in size, weight and robustness with the driving-power of the ship's hull as a sailing ship, and would certainly be adequate for any heavy weather in deep south latitudes.

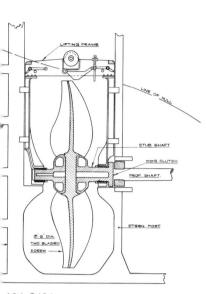

104 Lifting screw arrangement—probable details as fitted in *Great Britain* sternframe

The next stage was to arrange auxiliary screw-propulsion without interfering with sailing capabilities. As reported by *The Engineer* and *Practical Mechanics' Journal*, the newly developed lifting-screw was the answer and a new sternframe was forged by the Mersey Foundry and fitted by Thomas Vernon & Son, shipbuilders and repairers. This massive forging was the largest ever made of its kind at that date and was arranged to accommodate a lifting-screw 15 ft 3 in. in diameter, of 21 ft pitch, two bladed and of Griffiths type with a spherical boss planed off to a boss-length of 3 ft 2 in. This was carried in a lifting-frame which could be hauled up by a block and tackle into the trunk at the stern of the vessel, with the blades vertical, thus leaving the flow of water unimpeded by any propeller. A diagrammatic arrangement of this makes the principle clear. The propeller was supported on a short stub shaft rotating in two *lignum vitae* bearings in a frame which fitted inside the stern aperture. When lowered, this frame rested on shelves on the rudder and sternpost, and located the stub shaft in line with the propeller shaft. The tail shaft inside the ship could then be pushed out to engage in a square hole in the propeller stub shaft, the end of the tail-shaft itself being square. In this position, the bearings rested on the shelves and the frame itself was located on the sternpost by lugs; it could slide up and down these posts but not move sideways. Also on the posts was a series of stops so that latches on the lifting-frame could engage with the posts and prevent it dropping. These could be screwed out of the way from above. When the frame was down it was locked in position by struts fitted from above; these had to be removed, of course, before the propeller could be lifted. When it was desired to lift the screw it was necessary to take way off the ship and then rig the lifting tackle. The propeller was then set with blades vertical, and a small portable section of the shaft in the propeller shaft-line was removed, allowing the tail-shaft to be drawn.

The machinery was generally unaltered but the stoking arrangements were again improved, and a single upright oval funnel fitted on the centre-line of the ship. The boilers were altered so that the two uptakes could be trunked together into this one central funnel, and they also were rebuilt with four sections only.

Numerous other alterations were made to the ship, some minor, others more important. The original hawses were blanked off and new hawse-pipes fitted, much higher up and leading right through the upper foc'sle. The hawses interfered with the trailboards and figurehead. The former were removed and the latter re-fitted much higher up, neatly filling the gap beneath the more heavily angled bowsprit. There is some evidence that a new figurehead was carved at this time by Allan & Clothworthy, but in view of the correspondence between the remains of the figurehead and what we know of the original Brunel figurehead, this is questionable. The windlass was moved forward from its original position and fitted in the deckhouse just forward of the foremast, while at the stern the false quarter-galleries were removed, although the original decoration remained across the transom.

An important change was made to the deckhouse. At the poop it was extended right out to the stern, forming a continuation of the transom, and six windows were fitted across it. It was also extended transversely to the ship's sides and the bulwarks were built up to meet the deck above, forming a complete superstructure. Square ports gave light to this poop, while forward the deckhouse was similarly extended to the ship's side, leaving only a small portion admidships between the new forecastle and the poop as a hurricane deck. In the poop a ladies' boudoir lay across the transom, and first-class passengers were also berthed in the poop. Two bathrooms were installed, one on either side of the propeller lifting-trunk.

There were also first-class cabins in the lower saloon. The second-class passengers were berthed aft in the upper 'tween decks forward of the lower saloon, and their staterooms and saloons were forward of the engine-room. The bullion-room was right aft in the vicinity of the propeller lifting trunk. Much of the deckhouse arrangement remained unchanged, however, with the captain and the first officer berthed at the forward end of the poop house; the galleys, pantries, officers' and crew's mess-rooms were all amidships, just over the main engines. Right forward were food store-rooms, ice-houses and so on. *The Engineer* reported:

. . . A full poop has been given to the ship to berth 84 first-class passengers in the saloon . . . She will carry . . . 500 other passengers on her first line of deck below consisting of first, second and third-class passengers with room for nearly one thousand tons of coal and from 1800 to 2000 tons of cargo besides stores and water for the voyage to Australia.[6]

Little of the ship's original lightness and grace remained. Nevertheless she was undeniably impressive—heavy, powerful and reminiscent of the steam frigates of the day. Indeed, anybody might be excused for mistaking her for a warship. The modern outboard profile of the ship (*see* Fig. 100) shows well how the metamorphosis from the two-funnel, three-masted ship was achieved, while a contemporary photograph shows the appearance of the result. The inboard profile (Fig. 105) is the result of much research based upon the fragmentary evidence that remains and upon a contemporary capacity plan.

This comprehensive refit took nearly nine months, and it was not until 16 February 1857 that the ship sailed again for Melbourne. She again made a smart outward voyage in 62 days. The great McKay Clipper *Lightning* arrived at around the same time after a 70-day voyage.

Voyage 14 was spent trooping. On 8 October 1857 the ship sailed for Bombay on emergency service, carrying troops to the Indian Mutiny. She arrived on 17 December and sailed again on 20 January 1858, arriving in Liverpool on 10 April. The magnitude of the crisis facing the British Government is shown by the fact that in November 1857 the *Great Britain* was one of 68 troopships anchored in Table Bay. Interestingly, the iron screw steamship *Himalaya*, the only other ship in the world at the time to rival the *Great Britain*, was anchored near her.

For some reason the ship made her next major voyage to New York, but resumed the Australian route in November 1858, making a good passage of 64 days pilot to pilot. On 15 September 1859 Isambard Kingdom Brunel died, shortly after the explosion that occurred on the *Great*

Eastern during her trials.

Now at her best, the *Great Britain* sailed in December 1859 on a fine round passage of 55 days 16 hrs outward and 61 days home. The homeward voyage, from 8 March to 7 May, is recorded in the magazine *The Vain Effort*, published on board and printed on arrival in 1860; it shows the track of this voyage and is quaintly illustrated with little sketches of the ship under way.[7] On the outward voyage the ship left Liverpool on 11 December 1859 and crossed the Equator at longitude 20° 47′, having averaged about $9\frac{1}{2}$ knots all the way. For 18 days thereafter she averaged 11 knots, and from 16 January to 5 February, when running her easting down, her average speed was 13·6 knots. To retain this speed over 20 days shows that the ship, contrary to commonly expressed opinions today, was in fact capable of holding her own as a sailing ship with the largest and fastest clippers afloat. The *Great Britain* remained at anchor in Melbourne from 5 February to 7 March, whereupon she sailed, passing Tasmania to the east. She arrived back in Britain after a round voyage of 147 days, 31 of which were spent in Port Philip Bay, Melbourne.

The magazine is unusually comprehensive, detailing among other things the number of hours each day under sail, steam and combined sail and steam. For the homeward voyage the ship relied basically upon sail, being under canvas alone for 52·8 per cent. of the time, combined sail and steam for 31·7 per cent. and steam alone for only 15·5 per cent. The boilers were fired on 42 days, the total hours adding up to 28 full days of 24 hrs; the average daily consumption for these 28 days was 38 tons. The total quantity of fuel consumed on this voyage was 1,050 tons.

A list is given of the 504 passengers and of the cargo, consisting among other things of

592 bales of wool, 31 bales of skins, two bales of leather, one case of opossum rugs, 24 bales of old bags, 1,408 bags of copper ore, a few packages of merchandise, one trunk of effects, one case of spirit levels and one case of specimens of natural history. A total of 7,472 oz. of gold was also shipped.

A final and interesting item of cargo was 20 live snakes, one of which was specially recommended by reputation, having already caused the death of a man. The livestock shipped gives some indication of the pressure there must have been on space: 133 live sheep, 38 live pigs, two live bullocks, one milch cow, 420 live fowls, 300 live ducks, 400 live geese and 30 live turkeys. Two tons of fresh beef were also carried. The passengers had a word of advice for the agents: 'The wines and spirits placed on board were of very inferior quality, the sherry worst of all. This should be remedied in future.'

This was the fastest passage on record at that time for Australia to Britain: the ship was clearly getting into her stride. In July she sailed again for Melbourne, making a good passage of 62 days, and on 22 October sailed for Britain on a voyage which very nearly proved disastrous, being beset with incidents. On 30 October, as the screw was lowered for steaming, a fusible plug burst out of one boiler, letting out most of the water and steam and causing great consternation among the passengers.

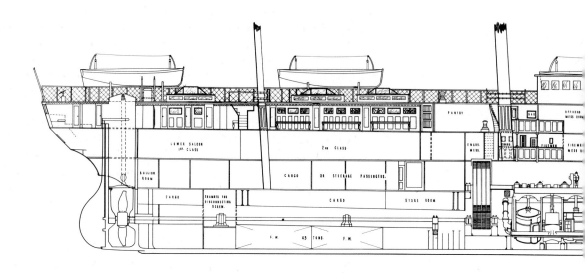

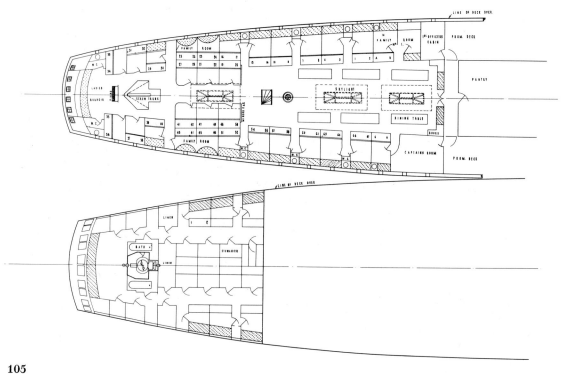

105

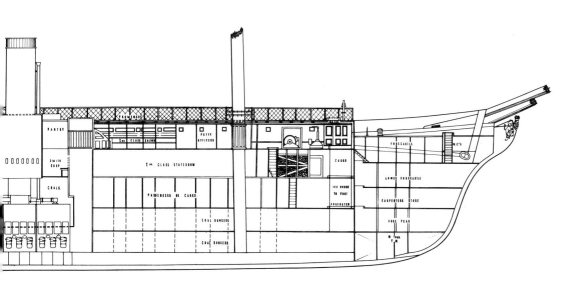

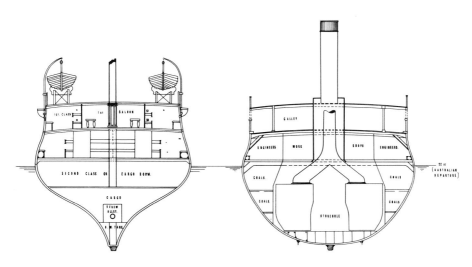

GREAT BRITAIN STEAM SHIP

1857

On 9 November the ship made 323 miles in a day. A passenger described this as follows:

Wind strong. Sailing 14 knots per hour. I had a seat on her bow and was admiring the motion of the water. I could not help thinking she was a thing of life, for one minute she would be nearly buried in the wave and her speed almost stopped, then she would make a rush as if to make up for the detention, sending the surf about 40 ft above her bows. When I went into the saloon I felt her as steady as if we were at anchor. South latitude 54.22, West longitude 128.41, miles 323.

Bearing in mind that the day was less than 24 hours, the ship was averaging well over 14 knots. That the ship could carry sail under most conditions is attested by the same passenger's comment a few days later:

Wind still strong sailing 14 knots . . . two vessels in sight ahead but we soon passed them. One a barque with the mizzen mast bare and only the main and fore topsails set closed reefed. The other a ship trimmed the same only the foresails set extra. The *Great Britain* carrying studding sails at the time but I believe the Captain is afraid to touch them for fear they should be blown off altogether. Passed another after dinner but could not manage to speak with her either. ·

This was off Cape Horn, and only a large powerful vessel such as *Great Britain* could afford to carry full sail under such conditions. It is apparent that the screw could be raised and lowered with some facility. For example, on 15 December it was lowered at 1 p.m., only to be taken up again at 6 p.m.: every advantage seems to have been taken of favourable slants of wind.

The same passenger describes a visit to the engine room:

The next thing was to go down to see the engine at work a sight that gratified me very much. The first to be seen was an indicator for telling the number of revolutions the engine was making during the voyage. The next were the two ponderous cylinders which swung from centre to centre to suit the crank. The next was a large wheel and pinion which weighed 30 tons, the pinion made three revolutions for one of the wheel. The next was the bush or block on the end of the screw shaft which bore the whole pressure required to propel the shaft. The next was a watertight compartment right in the stern of the vessel.

There was a pump fixed in readiness should anything go wrong. Lastly we had a look at the boilers. The men weighed the coals and laid them down before the different furnaces which were 18 in number. We left the price of a bottle of grog with the firemen.

Notices were put up on different parts of the ship restricting passengers to their own promenade spaces. The saloon passengers had all the quarter deck, the fore saloon the starboard side and the quarter deck to the funnel; the third class and intermediate the same on the port side; and the steerage had the deck forward from the funnel.

The meals on a voyage like this were quite good. For example: breakfast —porridge with treacle, fried salt pork, a roll, butter and coffee; dinner —Scotch broth, roast beef, boiled mutton, fresh potatoes, rice, plum pudding; tea—loaf bread and butter. Another day: breakfast—salt herring, coffee, rolls and butter, porridge with treacle; dinner—pea soup, dough pudding with salt pork, bully beef, preserved potatoes, biscuits and cheese; tea—loaf bread and butter.

The next accident occurred when two sailors were washed overboard when staging off the side of the *Great Britain*. One of them caught a rope and scrambled back over the ship but the other dropped astern. A passenger threw a lifebuoy, the ship was rapidly brought into the wind, and a lifeboat was lowered which picked the man up. Shortly after this a passenger went mad and a sailor went down with what was thought to be smallpox but luckily turned out to be something much more innocuous. However, the scare of smallpox lasted for some days and caused much alarm. Not long afterwards, one of the quartermasters nearly died and the Third Mate was involved in a violent fight with one of the passengers. It was certainly an eventful voyage.

Christmas Day was celebrated by several fights among the passengers and also among the sailors. Dinner was roast duck, pork, boiled mutton, plum pudding and tarts and a plentiful supply of port, sherry, nuts and biscuits. Three days later a full gale was blowing and the Captain held on to his canvas too long. Four sails were lost completely and many more blown into ribbons. The sea was breaking right over the ship continually and most of the passengers were sick. 'It was a fearful sight to see the *Britain* tearing through the water on her beam ends, the Captain bawling at the sailors and the wind blowing furiously.'

The final fright on this voyage occurred on its last day. On 31 December the ship had been in thick fog for some days and narrowly missed running ashore; some of the passengers said that they could have leapt on shore from the jib-boom. However, most of them were in bed and the Captain told all hands to be quiet so as not to alarm them. The ship was put astern but the helmsman pointed out that there was another rock close behind, and the engine had to be stopped. The ship drifted with the wind and tide and gradually wore round until her bows pointed out between the rocks and she was able to steam out and away from the land. No one knew where they were but later that morning the fog cleared and a number of ships were seen, outward bound but a considerable distance away. A fisherman picked up to pilot the ship said that they were 50 miles off Holyhead and steaming right for the Isle of Man. Shortly after this, at 10 p.m., the ship ran on to a sandbank and it was obvious that they still did not know where they were. Two anchors were dropped and the cannons fired together with blue lights and sky rockets. The ship began to labour heavily on the bottom but fortunately the tide was making, and at 2 a.m. she floated again, although still occasionally bumping the bottom. All hands including passengers were mustered at the windlass to raise the anchors really quickly, and they were able to steam into deep water where they anchored again for the night. In the morning, pilots were taken on board and it was found that they were 20 miles from Liverpool. The passengers were landed on the night of 4 January 1861. The ship made the round voyage in approximately five-and-a-half months.

In 1861 she made two trips to Melbourne. On the autumn one her

time outward was 64 days but her best day's run was 354 nautical miles at $14\frac{3}{4}$ knots in a day of less than 24 hours: very good going indeed. A record of this voyage survives in a well-produced ship's magazine, *The Cabinet*, published in Melbourne in 1862.[8] The ship sailed on 21 October 1861, arriving in Liverpool on 23 December. Fig. 110 shows the track of this voyage plotted along with others, e.g. the 1852 round voyage. The ship carried 691, including the crew and the All England Eleven, who had just returned from America where 'they compelled the "Twenty-Twos" of their trans-Atlantic friends to succumb to them in every match'. The feeling had arisen among the cricketing community in Australia that they would like a representative eleven to compete with them. The magazine describes the English team and concludes that they would be under a grave disadvantage in Australia owing to the hot weather there and to the fact that all that they had been able to do on the voyage was to play quoits!

An interesting breakdown is given of the crew: one captain, four mates, one surgeon, one purser, one assistant purser, two carpenters, one joiner, one sailmaker, one porter, three boatswains, four quartermasters, 38 seamen, six ordinary seamen, six apprentices, five engineers, one smith, 20 firemen, 24 stewards, one stewardess, one barman, four storekeepers, two bakers, two butchers and 10 cooks, giving a total of 140. The magazine also lists the livestock shipped: 140 sheep, 36 pigs, 528 fowl, 444 ducks, 96 geese, 48 turkeys. Considering that there were 550 passengers on board as well as the crew, the housing of this livestock must have been a problem and it was probably a great relief when much of it had been eaten.

Other magazines compiled on later voyages were *The Albatross* of 1862, *The* Great Britain *Times* of 1866, and *The* Great Britain *Chronicle* of 1868.[9] They are all interesting and readable, giving a clear picture of the 'sixties, throughout which the ship continued to sail with a regularity and reliability that endeared her to everyone. Fig. 106 shows the *Great Britain* at anchor in Australia during this period. It was an eventful decade. In 1865, Mr G. V. Brooke, a theatrical manager, and Lavinia Jones, a Victorian tragedienne, were returning to England from Melbourne, where Brooke had been running a theatre. He had absconded with about £30,000 and was hidden in a cabin cupboard by one of the ship's officers, remaining undiscovered during a police search of the ship. During the voyage, Brooke rigged a theatre in the cabin and gave Shakespearian plays to the passengers and crew. A year or so later the affair had blown over and Brooke was offered a free pardon and asked to return to Melbourne. With Miss Jones, he embarked on the *London*, a brand new ship on her maiden voyage, but in a great gale in the Bay of Biscay the ship was lost with all hands, including Brooke and Lavinia Jones. The *Great Britain* was in the Bay at the time but survived without damage.

On this voyage she made a good run to Australia, sailing on 19 February 1866, and reaching Melbourne 58 days later. The return voyage was made in the respectable time of 62 days. Captain Thomas Fish, writing in the 'twenties, described this voyage, in which he served as a deckhand:

Steam was only used in the calms and variables. She was always driven hard under canvas and the main topgallant sail was never taken off her on account of wind on the voyage either out or home.

I have seen her, when running the easting down, going 17 knots by log and in some of the black squalls which came bearing along on the starboard quarter she must have been going nearly 20 knots. She carried on the foremast, topmast and lower studding sails. . . . At the main she carried topmast and topgallant studding sails.

She was a good ship for food and we had butter the whole voyage. When we had Grog O! we all went to the forward capstan on which was a copper can holding about a gallon of rum. . . .

Another diary exists of a voyage from Liverpool to Melbourne in 1871. Sailing on 16 December, the ship arrived in Melbourne on 21 February, 67 days later. Captain Gray was still in command and seems to have become rather cautious. Shortly after sailing, he took the ship into Holyhead Harbour to shelter from a storm, and the daily runs were generally poor by comparison with previous records. The New Year was rung in on this voyage with both ship's bells (one of which is still on the ship today), and later in January the *Great Britain* made 313 miles in one day, which showed that she was still capable of achieving her old standards.

On her return in the spring of 1872 the ship was refitted and in July the owners submitted her to the examination of Lloyd's Register with a view to having her classed in the Register Book. This was a measure of the technical progress made in the regulation of ships since *Great Britain* was built. At that time there were no Lloyd's Rules for iron, but while she had been voyaging round the world a complex system of international regulations and inspection had built up. Presumably the owners felt that in the 1870s a first-class passenger ship, such as the *Great Britain* still was, required to be classed with Lloyd's. In a special report No. 23460,

107 (OVERLEAF) A fascinating painting showing two of Brunel's great ships—the *Great Britain* and the *Great Eastern*. The scene is in the River Mersey, about 1860

108 The bulwark construction —1852 to 1886

109 Taken during cleaning and restoration, this photograph shows the box stringer and bracket referred to in the 1872 Lloyd's Report

dated 19 October 1872, the Liverpool surveyors, Davey, Light and Wheeler of Lloyd's Register, reported to the local committee and to the general committee in London.[10] They pointed out that it was difficult to submit details of the ship on the formal forms, 'the peculiar construction and absence of any fixed or determinate principle in her design shutting her off from the usual method of submission'. What they meant, of course, was that she had set her own rules and did not fit theirs. The fact that she was satisfactory in service with no structural trouble spoke for itself, as they very fairly admitted. A number of interesting alterations were described in their report. For instance, they commented that the poop and foc'sle were added in 1856. (We know that this is not strictly so: the long deckhouse was in fact added in 1852 on the first conversion for the Australian route and extended to the stern and to form poop and foc'sle superstructures in 1856–7.) They said that the vessel had thick (2-in.) bulwarks with several ports therein, two for cargo and the others for freeing the wings from water. These bulwarks are shown clearly in the photographs of the ship and their construction can be seen in Fig. 108 which shows the ship at the Falkland Islands in 1886. The deckhouse had the deck over doubled in thickness in 1869, and it was claimed that the main deck had been doubled in 1858 with 4 in. of timber. From this it would appear that the decks were getting rather ripe, which was probably the reason for the refit in 1871.

The surveyors reported that the flat bottom amidships under the boilers had been renewed in 1861, and the box side stringers on the lower deck introduced in December 1866, as were the box beams to the main deck. These are a prominent feature of the ship and it is rather surprising that they should have been introduced so long after the ship went into service. However, they were all part of the box stringer structure, being 'turned down the side and connected to the box stringer by brackets'. It was also stated that

In July last (1872) the fore and aft webs on each side of the middle line which are about 40 ft in length in way of the Foremast were renewed as also the Iron Deck on them. Cement coating in way of this space was renewed and the plating and riveting there found in good order.

The report continued:

We have seen her in several sections and found her in good order. The only place where oxidation was visible was in the coal bunkers and there only slight.

The plating is well wrought and the riveting good and although the butts are single riveted only they are so close where seen by us abreast of the Fore step that they need no caulking and have never been caulked. The good riveting and very peculiar form of the vessel which prevents her carrying an ordinary amount of Cargo may account for the fact that none of the butts on the outside plating are visible on her return from her regular Australian voyages.

In other words, the curved side of the ship made her so stiff that the butts of the plating did not work in a sea-way and hence were not made visible by cracking paint and gaps, as was very often the case with riveted ships.

Generally it was felt that the structure was good:

Viewing this vessel by the present rules she appears light in her plating, the main deck beams which are principally of angle iron (the Bulb Beams being introduced at various distances) are extraordinarily trussed diagonally as will be seen from the deck plan accompanying this report. The webbing in flat of bottom with the Iron Deck across and connected to the sides well compensates for the usual cross floors.

With all the good qualities which the ship apparently possesses we feel an indisposition from her age of 30 years in submitting a recommendation making for a classification seeing that her plating is thin and that an examination has at present been made only of part of the vessel, its cargo and boiler spaces and also feeling that we ought not to judge her at her age on the condition of the whole from the inspection of a part. We respectfully submit these remarks and report as requested by the owners for the Committee's consideration, suggesting that when the Engines are removed and portions of the Passengers berths, a further survey may be made should the Committee from her construction and thickness of plating if found not less than now submitted consider her deserving of an A Classification subject to survey annually.

This was a cautious report. The ship was clearly outside the experience of the surveyors. The comments regarding the thinness of plating are unfair: as they had pointed out, there was little corrosion, and if the ship was capable of faultless service for 30 years she was certainly capable of further service. The report was accompanied by a most interesting series of notes showing thicknesses of plating taken from drillings. These may be compared with the ship as built, and it will be seen that the wastage was of the order of only 15 per cent. Details are also given of the wood keel which had been added in 1853.

The main committee in London was not favourably disposed. The minute covering its deliberations said:

We have carefully examined the two sketches of Transverse Sections and a deck plan of this vessel, the particulars given by the Liverpool surveyors and their

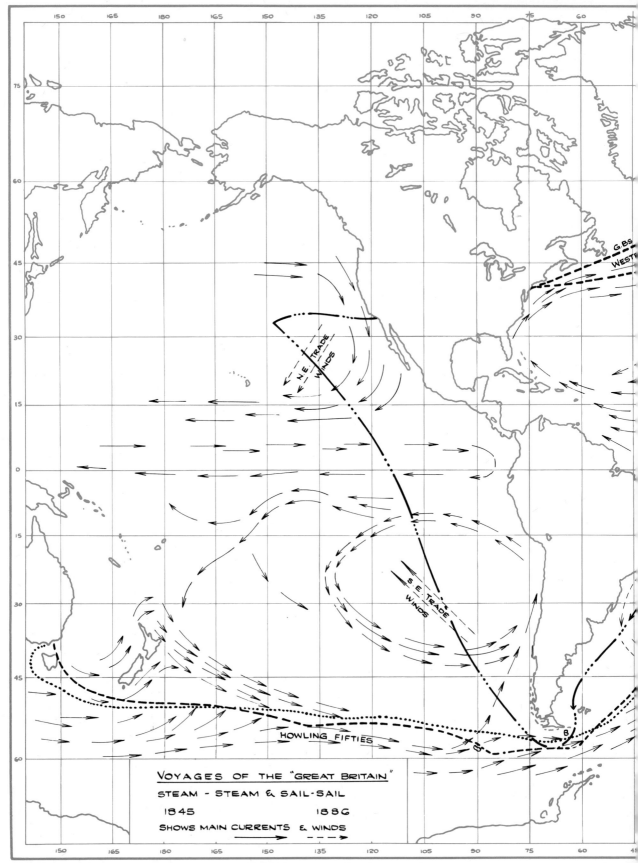

110 Some typical voyage tracks for *Great Britain* as Atlantic steamer, Australian auxiliary and pure sailing ship

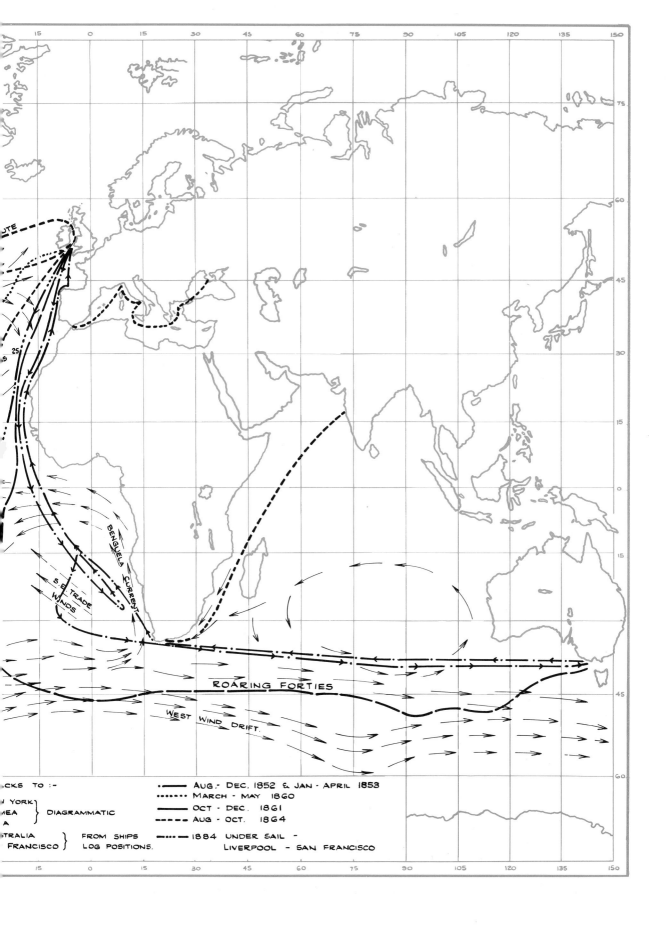

BENGUELA CURRENT

S.E. TRADE WINDS

ROARING FORTIES

WEST WIND DRIFT.

very cautious remarks with reference to 'A' Classification. Judging from the information afforded to us and bearing in mind that the parts reported upon are most likely in a better condition than those not seen from the fact that they are always being exposed to view and kept in good condition, we are of the opinion that this case is not of that description as to warrant our recommending any hope being held out by the committee that they can class this vessel 'A' in the Register Book. 23.10.72.

Considering the risks attendant upon running unclassed passenger ships and the possible difficulty of obtaining adequate insurance, the writing was probably on the wall for the old ship as from that time. However, she lived for a few years more, years which had their share of incidents and accidents. A woman died of consumption; two babies were born on one day; two days later a young seaman fell from the topgallant mizzen yard on to the deck and was killed instantly. In 1872 a dreadful event occurred which coloured the whole voyage. The ship left Liverpool on 27 July, and made her fastest ever voyage, arriving in Melbourne on 19 September, after only 54 days. Sailing on 27 October, she was only 30 days out, when Captain John Gray disappeared utterly from the ship. His servant went to call him in his room and found it empty.[11] He gave the alarm, but although the vessel was searched no trace of the Captain could be found. His cabin was at the stern and had large square transom windows, one of which was open; it was surmised that he had fallen through it, though how and why remained mysteries. Gray had commanded the ship for 18 years. He was obviously a popular and good Captain and used to climb to the three mastheads three times every week. Robertson, the First Officer, took command but Chapman, the ship's former Mate, was confirmed as Captain on the ship's return to Liverpool, in a register entry dated 20 March 1873.

The ship sailed again for Melbourne on 29 March and made the outward journey in only 56 days carrying 60 saloon passengers and 280 others. Later in the same year she again made the voyage to Melbourne in 56 days; although she was nearing the end of her career her form was evidently as good as ever, and Chapman was capable of getting the best out of her. A passenger's diary survives from the return journey of the forty-second major voyage, when the ship left Melbourne on 15 September 1874, and made the trip to Liverpool in 64 days. Little of incident occurred on this voyage but interesting relics survive from which it is apparent that even then the ship carried with her the affection and respect of the marine world. They even include a ship's biscuit!

The last Australian voyage started from London in 1875, the ship returning to Liverpool on 1 February 1876, in 66 days. The homecoming was recorded by a young cadet on the clipper *Theophane*. Sail was seen on their port bow and shortly afterwards the *Great Britain* was recognised. At noon they were abeam and they saw that she was steaming as well as sailing. *Theophane* set their topmast and lower stunsails. At 8 p.m. the *Great Britain* was out of sight astern but the day after, running up the Irish coast at 4 p.m. they saw her royals and topgallant astern. During the first watch that night *Theophane* was running about $13\frac{1}{2}$ knots with the yards just off the backstays and the leerails under, yet next morning,

111 *Great Britain* off the Skerries

with light winds off Holyhead, *Great Britain* passed them, all sails furled and under steam. When abreast:

her passengers crowded on the rails, rigging and boats and gave us a real good cheer. The good old ship got into the Mersey one tide before us and thus ended her wonderful career as a Melbourne passenger auxiliary steamer, this being her last voyage in that trade.

A photograph survives showing the old ship at Gravesend on 14 August 1875, a day or two before sailing on her last voyage.

This was the end of the ship as a steamer. The *Great Britain*'s service on the Australian route is still remembered. Hundreds of thousands of Australians must be descended from forebears carried by this old iron screw ship. However, although retired, she was not to be scrapped but was laid up to rest at Birkenhead until the next decade.

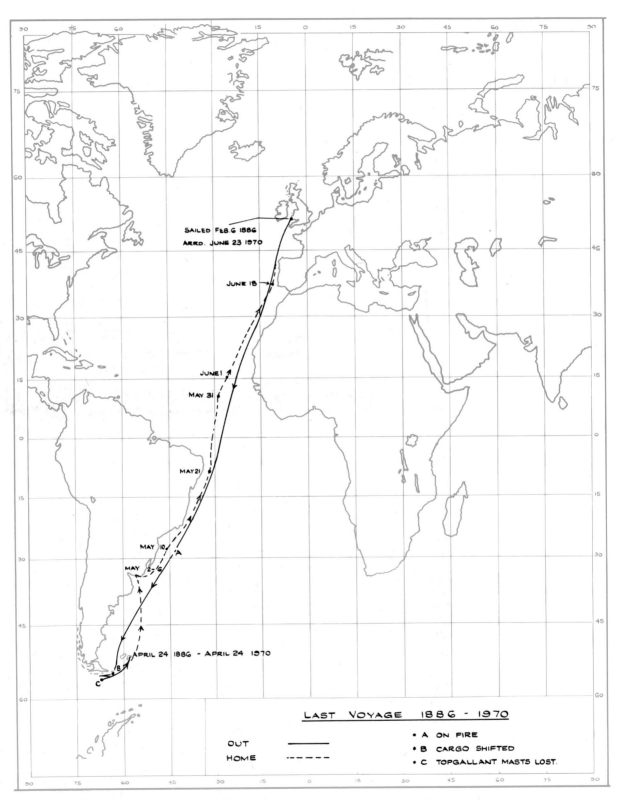

SAILED FEB.6 1886
ARRD. JUNE 23 1970

JUNE 18 →

JUNE 1 ↑

MAY 31

MAY 21

MAY 10 A

MAY 2-6

APRIL 24 1886 - APRIL 24 1970

B

C

LAST VOYAGE 1886 - 1970

OUT ————

HOME - - - - -

• A ON FIRE
• B CARGO SHIFTED
• C TOPGALLANT MASTS LOST.

112 Ship's track on her last voyage—out on her own bottom, home floating on a pontoon

CHAPTER SIXTEEN

'Great Britain': sailing ship

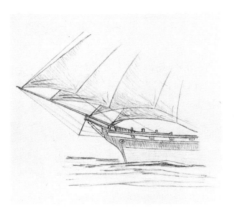

In July 1881 the *Great Britain* was put up for sale and an auction held at Birkenhead, where she lay afloat. The *Liverpool Mercury* commented:

This vessel has a history of more than ordinary interest. It was offered for sale by Messrs. Kellock & Company at their sale room . . . The event attracted a very large attendance of gentlemen who are closely identified with the shipping interests of the port. The *Great Britain* lying in the West Float, Birkenhead, was described as of 3,270 tons gross tonnage and 1,725 tons net register. Her construction is of great strength and the iron used Lowmoor of the finest quality. For the cattle trade across the Atlantic she is admirably adapted, her high 'tween decks and side ports affording grand ventilation; she can carry livestock on three decks. For a sailing ship her beautiful lines particularly adapt her and with the machinery taken out she is calculated to carry 4,000 tons deadweight. Her engines are by J. Penn & Sons of Liverpool and although this steamer has been built many years her iron is so good and strength of construction so great that with a certain outlay she could be made a most desirable merchant ship. . . . The bidding began at £2,000 and then went to £5,000, before long £6,000 was offered. There being no advance on this price Mr Kellock announced that the vessel was withdrawn.

Later that year Antony Gibbs & Sons of London absorbed Gibbs, Bright & Co. of Liverpool, renaming it Antony Gibbs, Sons & Co. Among the property they had acquired was the old ship *Great Britain*, now laid up and mouldering at Birkenhead. Antony Gibbs had extensive trading connections with the west coast of both North and South America. A busy trade in coal exports and saltpetre, nitrates or wheat imports had been built up by the larger European sailing ships. Their association with the Western Seaboard probably gave Antony Gibbs a quite different viewpoint from Gibbs, Bright, whose connections had mainly been with the Australian trade.

As the auction advertisement had remarked, the *Great Britain* was well suited to carry cargo and would have a dead weight as a sailing ship of approaching 4,000 tons, so in late 1882 the ship was transferred to the ownership of Vicary Gibbs and rebuilt by Grayson's as a sailing vessel. The main engines were removed and holes cut in the two engine-room bulkheads, commoning the cargo holds with the engine-room which in turn became a large cargo hold. Wood ceilings, some of which still exist, were fitted on the side frames throughout these spaces and all passenger accommodation was removed from the ship. The long deckhouse and superstructure were taken off and a new wood deck laid, while three hatches were fitted for the loading of cargo into the capacious holds below.

The masts remained but the main mast was moved somewhat forward in order to balance up the rig now that the funnel had gone. Other main changes were the cementing of the inside of the bottom and the wood sheathing of the hull from about 8 ft above keel to the 25-ft level. This sheathing in $3\frac{1}{2}$-in. pitch pine up to 9 or 10-in. width and in 30–40 ft. lengths was a remarkable feature and extremely expensive. It was bolted to the hull with 1-in. galvanised steel bolts, with a spunyarn and white lead grommet under the washer of each nut inside the hull. This wood was in turn sheathed with zinc on felt to above the waterline to prevent fouling and attack by worm. The exact purpose of the sheathing has never been decided. It has been suggested that it was to protect the hull from floating ice round Cape Horn, and yet the ship had sailed round Cape Horn regularly on all her voyages. May be it was to prevent her fouling at sea: although she had never suffered unduly from fouling before, she was now to lie for long periods at anchor. The Royal Navy certainly used zinc sheathing on 3/4-in. wood cladding for anti-fouling purposes at the time.[1] It should also be remembered that the ship was to some extent corroded and wasted in the bow and stern waves areas, namely forward and aft between about the 16 and 20 ft water-lines; furthermore, she might well lie at anchor in roadsteads such as Iquique and Antofagasta where loading was carried out by lighters along-side the ships and where a long, slow swell was always present. The wood would thus help both to fender and to reinforce the hull. When one considers the peculiar shape of the midship section with its bulge half-way up, it is clear that the ship would be particularly susceptible to damage by lighters alongside and that ordinary fenders would be difficult to manage. In view of Antony Gibb's Western Seaboard connections, this seems likely to have been the main reason for the sheathing.

Further work on the ship consisted mainly of alterations to accommoda-tion and equipment. The transom windows were boarded in and the officers' accommodation restricted to the area aft of the bulkhead at the forward end of the propeller-lifting trunk which, of course, remained. The trunk was plated over under the counter and, most important, the propeller aperture was plated in to improve the ship's steering. A sailing-ship rudder normally acts as a trimming flap on the end of the hull, the

113 The only known photograph of *Great Britain* as a sailing ship

whole hull being used as a lifting surface. In the case of a steamship with a screw, the wash from the propeller is the most important factor determining steering but a sailing ship cannot afford to have the aperture that a screw needs.

In this form the *Great Britain* was registered in Liverpool on 10 November 1882. Her gross tonnage was now 2,640·15, the figure that is 'carved' on the athwartships coaming on the centre hatch today, together with her registered number 25976, which of course remained the same throughout her life. At the same time she acquired a new Master—James Morris, who was registered on 13 November. Now that the ship no longer carried passengers Lloyd's relented and granted her classification in the 1882–3 Register. In that she was described as of iron, with two bulkheads, a deck and a spar deck, with wales wood-sheathed and zinced, and with a forecastle. She was granted the class A1. Fig. 113 shows her appearance in this form. As can be seen the 1852 solid bulwarks were not altered.

After loading a cargo of 3,292 tons of coal for San Francisco, she sailed in the third week of November but returned on the twenty-fourth, leaking. The wood-sheathing bolts had not been properly grommeted and therefore leaked. Captain Morris either did not like the ship or did not suit the owners because on 30 November he was replaced by Henry Stap, the ship's last registered Master. After repairs and survey the ship again set sail, on 2 December, for San Francisco. The voyage did not go well. On 30 January 1883, *Great Britain* put into Montevideo, as the crew refused to proceed unless the vessel was surveyed and lightened. A few weeks later it was reported that 200 tons of cargo had been removed completely and 500 tons taken from the lower hold and stowed in the 'tween decks to ease the ship. It may be surmised that she was unduly stable, loaded as she was, and this is not surprising in view of the broad waterline that would be immersed at a draft approaching 25 ft.

The ship arrived in San Francisco on 2 June 1883, after a dreadfully long voyage—182 days from Britain. It is true that she spent some 30 days or so in Montevideo, but nevertheless this was a far cry from round the world with passengers and mail in 140 days, as had been her wont on the Australian run. However, something of the old aura of the ship still lingered with her. The *San Francisco Alta* had this to say:

The British ship *Great Britain* docks today at Mission Street Wharf to discharge her cargo. This famous old ship is well worth a visit as she carries us back to Auld Lang Syne and shows conclusively that they put good work and good materials in vessels in early times. It is related of this vessel that during the early part of her career she was sunk in Dundrum Bay and was floated off by the novel process of filling her with bulrushes.[?] Captain Stap, her commander, is one of the best ship masters in the service and we hope his stay among us will be a pleasant one.[2]

The ship sailed for home on 28 August, carrying the very large quantity of 75,670 centals (3,390 long tons) of wheat, bound for Cork. She arrived on 1 January, 1884—154 days out from San Francisco. The sheer length of such voyages must have been very trying for the crews. The cargo was eventually discharged at Liverpool.

She sailed again on 11 May, 1884, for San Francisco, loaded with 2,870 long tons of coal. Fig. 113 shows this ship on what may well have been this voyage and is the only photograph of her in service as a sailing ship. As can be seen, the rig was with single topgallants; on her final voyage she was rigged with double topgallants and painted with false gunports. For the first six days they had strong south-west winds followed by four days of calm. The wind again set in from the south-west and little southerly progress was made: the ship did not reach the latitude of Madeira until 25 days out. With light north-east trades she crossed the Equator on 24 June and then picked up reasonable south-east trade. Light winds and fine weather were encountered until 50° south in the Atlantic where a south-westerly gale blew for five days near the Falkland Islands. On 31 July the ship was off Cape Horn in constant south-west winds, frequent squalls, a great deal of snow and hard frost. It took them 60 days to get from 50° to 50°—in other words, down from 50°, round the Horn and then back up to 50° south. In the Pacific they met mainly north-west winds, again unfavourable, and did not get the south-east trades until up in 19° south. After five days of calms before entering the trades, the ship crossed the Equator at 114° west and met the north-east trades at 16° north. They went as far as 148° west and 36° north before getting a change, and even from there to port there was very unsettled weather with gales from the north-west, south-east and north-east, and a great deal of rain and lightning. It was altogether a pretty dreadful voyage, lasting 160 days and proving a great strain on the ship and crew.

The *Great Britain* sailed again from San Francisco for Cork and Liverpool on 12 February 1885. She loaded in an even larger cargo of wheat— 3,440 long tons (76,585 centals)—and arrived in Cork on 7 July, 145 days out from San Francisco, finally docking at Liverpool on 12 July. Thus the ship completed the last full voyage she ever made on her own bottom: the next one, voyage No. 47, was her end as a sea-going ship.

She set off on this last fateful voyage on 6 February 1886, sailing from

114 Lying at anchor in Port Stanley a few days after arrival in 1886

Cardiff and carrying coal for Panama. An account taken from Captain Stap's official protest lodged when he reached the Falkland Islands gives details of what happened.[3] No trouble arose until the ship reached latitude 27° 25′ south, longitude 43° 27′ west on 25 March. They were meeting heavy weather when a small fire started. This was soon got under control, but did some damage in the ship's stores, burning sacks, ropes and general stores before it was put out. For 19 days after that all went well but on 16 April, in 54° 25′ south, 64° 28′ west—in other words, very nearly off Cape Horn—a strong south-westerly gale sprang up which increased through the night and by the following day had reached hurricane force. Seas were breaking right over the vessel and the cabin decks were leaking badly. At the start of the morning watch on 18 April the crew, beginning to get restive, came aft in a body and asked the Master to put back to the Falklands. They claimed that the ship was labouring and straining itself and that it was madness to proceed. Captain Stap refused to consider this demand and struggled on for some days more.

On 21 April, however, although the gale had moderated, the cargo of coal shifted, producing a strong list to port. A couple of days later, when the crew came to shovel the coal uphill in the 'tween decks to reduce the list, it was found to be wet. (It must be borne in mind that this ship had wood decks and was certainly not designed to carry the great weight that was in her with this coal cargo.) Captain Stap persuaded the crew to continue the fight; the coal was shovelled uphill, the ship levelled, and all was apparently well. However, on 3 May a new gale of similar intensity struck the ship and lasted for more than a week. On 10 May both the fore and main topgallant masts were lost and by the 11th a full hurricane was blowing once more. On 13 May the crew came aft for the second time to complain to the Master and this time he agreed with them, choosing to return to Port Stanley as the ship had not rounded the Horn. At 3 p.m. on 24 May the *Great Britain* arrived off Cape Pembroke (Port William). While running to the leeward of Williams Island she touched ground, but came off of her own accord after 30 minutes. She then anchored in Port William, the outer part of Stanley Harbour. Sixty fathoms of cable were paid out on the port bower anchor but the ship grounded again on 26 May and had to be helped off by a local steamer which then towed her into Port Stanley. It is not recorded where she lay when this happened but it must have been very close to the shore and the scope of cable was clearly excessive. Fig. 112 shows the ship's track on this last voyage.

First reports feared that 'her hull is a good deal strained' but Lloyd's List of 16 July 1886 put these fears at rest: 'The Liverpool Salvage Association Special Officer cables from Montevideo last night "*Great Britain*— Survey held, surveyors reporting ship quite tight".' Deck and spars repairs were, however, estimated at £5,500. The sad last registry entry for the ship is dated 18 December 1886. In this the Register is closed by being endorsed to the Constructive Loss Letter Book, with the superscription 'Registry closed 19th July 1887. Vessel converted to a hulk. Certificate not received. Advice received through Board of Trade form

70 received 20th July 1887, Certificate of registry received 5th November 1887'. On 8 November 1886, Antony Gibbs sold the *Great Britain* to the Corporation of the Falkland Islands Company. Curiously, the ship continued in the Lloyd's Register 1886–7 and it was not until the 1888 Register that she was noted as being a 'hulk-ex-steamer'.

The Falkland Islands subsist largely on wool, and there was a need at the time for a new floating wool storehouse or hulk in Port Stanley. The *Great Britain* with her commodious hull and 'tween decks was ideally suited for this purpose and was accordingly converted into a floating warehouse as she lay at anchor in the harbour. The conversion was simple: photographs taken shortly after the ship's arrival in the Falkland Islands show the essentials. The ship was stripped to her lower masts and only the main yard left. The flying jib-boom was removed but the spanker gaff, being a fixture, was left in place. The wood sheathing was stripped off the

115 Around the turn of the century. The only known photograph showing the decoration on the stern

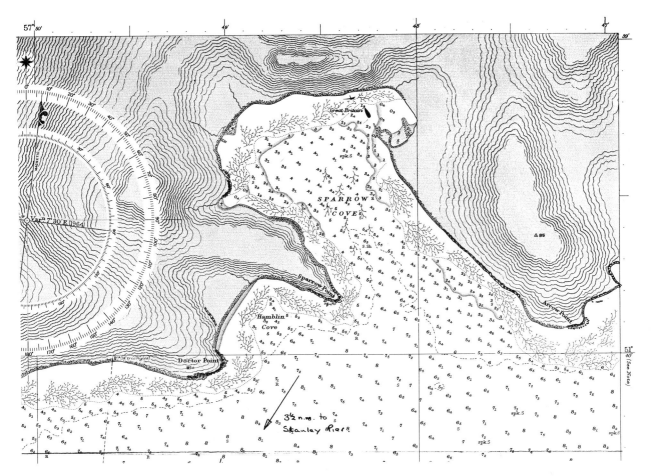

116 How *Great Britain* was scuttled across the entrance to an arm of Sparrow Cove, 13 April 1937

bulwarks; a winch-house was built just forward of the cuddy and housed a donkey engine for swaying the bales on board, the main yard being used as a derrick. One major modification was very nearly fatal. On the starboard side two cargo doors were cut in the side of the ship, one abreast of the original Brunel funnel position and one further aft, in the area of the 1852 entry port. The after one penetrated the side shell and the sheerstrake but the gunwale and the iron stringer plate on the weather deck were left intact; the forward one, however, did much more damage. Abreast of the main hatch, it completely penetrated the sheerstrake, gunwale and stringer, thus removing the top corner of the hull. The top flange of the hull girder had been severed.

From 1886 to 1936 the old ship lay at anchor in the Falklands. A photograph taken 50 years after she arrived shows her still sadly swinging to her anchor off the town jetty in Port Stanley. Even then, all of her glory had not departed. When the British Fleet under Admiral Sturdee reached the Falklands to coal before the Battle of the Falkland Islands, legend has it that the *Great Britain* helped to fuel British warships, and she lay at

anchor within sound of the gunfire that destroyed Admiral Graf von Spee's fleet. Officers from the British fleet visited the *Great Britain*; indeed, she was an object of pilgrimage to seafarers and others all through her life as a coal and wool hulk, and became something of a public monument in the eyes of the Falkland Islanders themselves.

By 1933 her days even as a hulk were past. The weather deck, new in 1882, was becoming very leaky and there was a fear that her ancient structure might give way to some strain during one of the frequent Falkland Island gales and that she might block the anchorage of Port Stanley. So the old ship was retired and replaced as a hulk by the *Fennia*, a French four-masted barque which the Falkland Islands Company had just acquired. Early in 1936 the Governor of the Colony, Sir Herber Henniker-Heston, launched a fund for the ship's preservation and restoration. The Falkland Islands Company offered to present the ship to the Government and an appeal was made in England, mainly to the citizens of Bristol and London. A preliminary survey indicated that the cost of preservation alone would be between £10,000 and £15,000 and the project was abandoned. The final suggestion was to tow the ship to sea and sink her by gunfire. The Royal Navy refused this honour, and the ship was finally taken to Sparrow Cove in Port William, some 3½ miles from Stanley, where she was run in parallel to the beach until aground, and then scuttled.

A rooted reluctance to destroy the old ship is again noticeable. The diary of the individual in charge of this operation records that she was beached on 12 April 1937, and holes driven in her with a crowbar on the following day. Fig. 116 shows the position of the ship as she lay abandoned to the elements and to the seals and penguins of the cove. A fine photograph taken by Karl Kortum in 1967 captures the desolate atmosphere: at her bow lay a bed of kelp and around her the low bare hills of East Falkland Island.

No one who saw the *Great Britain* in her grave in Sparrow Cove dreamed that she would ever have any other future; from that day for the next 30 or more years, apart from occasional visitors and the seabirds, she was left in peace—dying slowly at first but much more rapidly as time went by.

117 'A bed of kelp at her bow and the low hills all around her'

CHAPTER SEVENTEEN

Second salvage

Through the Second World War the *Great Britain* lay deserted and forgotten in Sparrow Cove, and so she continued throughout the 'forties, one hundred years after the decade in which she had made her triumphant debut. People visited her from time to time; a picture taken in 1947 shows two of them. Through the early part of the 'fifties she continued more or less forgotten, but the first stirrings of interest in her began 105 years after she had first ventured on the Australian route.

The director of the San Francisco Maritime Museum, Karl Kortum, a well-known researcher and restorer of old ships, tried to arouse interest, particularly in Britain, in the salvage and restoration of the *Great Britain*. However, there was no response—perhaps not surprisingly as the general interest in old ships was only just beginning in the 'fifties, to become a powerful movement in the next decade. Eight or nine years later Kortum did succeed in interesting an American engineer and businessman, William Swigert of San Francisco, in the whole idea, and in 1967 the two of them went to the Falkland Islands to look at the ship. They did not carry out a technical survey and the visit was really only a preliminary reconnaissance. Kortum took a number of fine photographs which played no little part later in arousing interest in the ship: for example, a fine view of the bow, and another that well illustrates the massive transverse structure in the ship's 'tween decks.

This effort was unknown to the actual salvors of the ship, whose parallel effort was quite independent. In 1952 I was presented with a copy of the lithograph showing the ship off Lundy Island in 1845—a beautiful picture—and was inspired by it to start a search through the relevant literature, especially through *Sea Breezes* which contains many references to the old ship. A picture of an utterly fascinating ship slowly built up, and in November 1967 I wrote to *The Times* suggesting that something should be done about the *Great Britain*. The response was considerable. Commander George Naish of the National Maritime Museum replied in *The Times* immediately, as did the chairman of the Falkland Islands Company. A day or two later I was asked to broadcast on the BBC programme 'Today'. Richard Goold-Adams, who later became chairman of the *Great Britain* Project, contacted me early in 1968 and by May a body of seriously interested and energetic people had banded together to form the s.s. *Great Britain* Project. The Inaugural

FIRST IRON STEAMSHI

From Mr. E. C. B. Corlett

Sir,—The first iron built ocean-go steamship and the first such ship to driven entirely by a propeller was the Gr Britain, designed and launched by Isamb Kingdom Brunel. This, the forefather all modern ships, is lying a beached h in the Falkland Islands at this momen

The Cutty Sark has rightly been p served at Greenwich and H.M.S. Vict at Portsmouth. Historically the Gr Britain has an equal claim to fame ￼ yet nothing has been done to docum the hulk, let alone recover it and prese it for record.

May I make a plea that the authori should at least document, photograph, ￼ fully record this wreck and at best something to recover the ship and pl her on display as one of the very ￼ really historic ships still in existence.

Yours faithfully,
E. C. B. CORLETT
The Coach-House, Worting Pa
Basingstoke, Hampshire, Nov. 8.

Meeting held in the City Museum, Bristol, in May 1968, was attended among others by Basil Greenhill, the director of the National Maritime Museum, Bill Swigert from the U.S.A., Robert Adley of Bristol, George Naish, and of course Richard Goold-Adams and myself.

Very little was really known as to the condition of the ship. Kortum and Swigert had only inspected the structure visually and had not taken soundings or measurements or investigated the underwater condition. Reports varied: one eminent Merchant Navy Captain had reported in *Sea Breezes* a few years before that the ship was 'open to the sea all along her port side';[1] the Captain of an exploration vessel stated that her bottom had gone completely and that the side frames and plating went straight into the sand and shingle at the bottom. Robert Adley had asked the Government of the Falkland Islands if they could give any guidance as to the condition of the ship and whether she could be made to float. The Colonial Secretary of the Falkland Islands reported early in 1968, by courtesy of the Royal Navy:

Firstly the vessel will not float independently . . . corrosion has taken place to such an extent that the fastenings are no longer capable of holding the ship together. The main strength members, i.e. transverse and longitudinal framing, deck beams, vertical keel and rider plate are also severely corroded and in some places holed therefore making it extremely doubtful of her ability to be towed with safety. . . . A great depth of water exists inside the hull at present. This report may seem unduly pessimistic but prime considerations such as expense, safety, possible disasters must be weighed against historical interest. The Writer feels that the balance must be against the success of the project.

The Colonial Secretary went on to say that the San Francisco Maritime Museum believed the only way to lift the remains would be to encase them in a metal cage and to fill the hull with polyurethane foam. As a preliminary guess, the estimate for salvage was £1 million, and a little later the Colonial Secretary wrote that further thoughts tended to suggest a much larger figure.

On the other hand, photographic evidence tended to give a more hopeful picture. I had commissioned a local photographer to take nearly 200 photographs of the structure and its detail, and close examination of these was not discouraging. With this conflict of opinion as to the condition of the ship it was clear that nothing could be done until a proper survey was carried out. In November 1968 I was offered a passage from Montevideo to the Falklands in the ice-patrol ship H.M.S. *Endurance*. This trip was financed and organised by Richard Goold-Adams, later chairman of the Project, and by me, and for five days a comprehensive survey was carried out on board the old ship. *Endurance* also carried Lord Chalfont and his colleagues on a political mission to the Falkland Islands, which fortuitously allowed a rather longer stay in Stanley than otherwise would have been the case. The Navy was most helpful. A motor whaler was available for travel to Sparrow Cove, and a number of naval volunteers worked with me throughout the survey. We had brought out a number of tools from England: an ultrasonic thickness gauge, an ultrasonic depth recorder, and as underwater survey was expected, diving-gear as well.

Lights, ladders, hammers and additional diving-gear were loaned by H.M.S. *Endurance*.

The survey was difficult. Apart from the remoteness of the ship she was covered with scale which had to be chipped off to bare metal before any thickness readings could be taken. The changeable Falkland Islands weather was a severe trial, alternating in minutes between calm sunshine and gale-force winds with rain, while the ship itself was rather frightening, full of water, often dripping with rain, her rotten wood decks a constant snare. Fig. 118 shows the after cabin during this survey. No accidents occurred and some hundreds of thickness-measurements were taken. Echo-sounder plottings were taken inside and all round outside the ship. A group from H.M.S. *Endurance* did an outline chart survey of the bed of Sparrow Cove, which later proved quite invaluable in the salvage operations, and gradually a clear picture of the ship was built up. Fortunately the wait during 1968 had allowed a number of drawings to be prepared which could be used as a basis for plotting measurements and thicknesses.

From a personal point of view the survey was fascinating. For one thing, the Falkland Islands are quite out of the ordinary. Natural marine life is abundant and rather strange to the northern eye. The survey party left *Endurance* each morning at about 8.30 a.m. and it was quite an experience to be escorted to and from the *Great Britain* by porpoises, seals and penguins, all diving in and out of the water round the whaler. One's first impressions of the ship were depressing, mainly because of the large and obvious discontinuity in her structure on the starboard side.

After the first short visit there was a general feeling of despondency, but it was recognised that this was subjective, and the quantitative and detailed survey proceeded systematically. The immediate objective was to get ultrasonic test measurements under way, and after the author had established the technique for doing this and had taken a number of them, a team from *Endurance*, headed by Shipwright Burgess, took over and the bulk of the measurements were taken by them. This freed me to make a general detailed inspection of the vessel and to take echo-sounder measurements throughout the ship and around her. It was soon apparent that she was simply sitting on the bottom, and the portable echo-sounder allowed a fairly accurate idea to be obtained of the depth of mud and water in the ship and even to probe spaces which were inaccessible, by lowering the transducer head through holes in the structure.

On the final day of the survey, the naval team assisted the author in a detailed internal and external underwater inspection of the ship. At the time she had been scuttled it had been noted that a large upwelling of water took place in the region of the mizzen mast and it was thought that she had pierced her bottom on a boulder. When the bottom was inspected from outside it was clear that she was resting on a bed of hard sand and small stones sloping athwartships with some build-up on the starboard side and some erosion to port. Fig. 119 shows the position of the ship in Stanley, with soundings taken by *Endurance* in the vicinity. A dense kelp

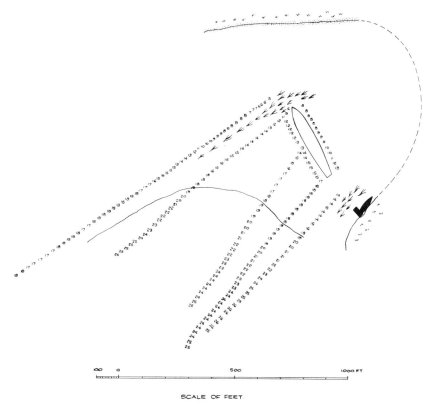

119 Soundings to seaward of *Great Britain* in Sparrow Cove, 1968

SCALE OF FEET.

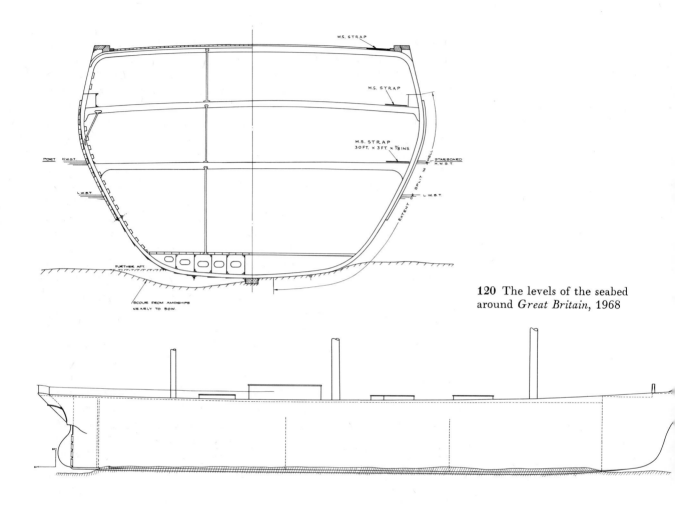

120 The levels of the seabed around *Great Britain*, 1968

bed lay round the bow but aft of that the sea bed was completely clear. Fig. 120 shows a cross-section of the vessel with the sand level around her and a longitudinal section indicating scour at the bow and stern. As *Great Britain* lay across Sparrow Cove, tidal and wind-driven currents had to find entry mainly round the stern of the ship and were thus responsible for this scour.

Diving round the ship was interesting. The sea bed was inhabited by large numbers of spider crabs which took no interest in the divers, and in places the kelp formed jungles. The outside of the ship was covered with sea squirts, mussels and weed. The bow and stern were completely unsupported for about 15–20 ft where the sand had been scoured away. On the port side amidships was a deep scour under the hull where waves impinging on the side had been deflected downwards. Naval divers and the author were able to penetrate in underneath this port side amidships right through to the wood keel and were most surprised to find that the bilge keels, which according to contemporary accounts had been removed in 1852, were in fact still in place.

By watching the tide rise inside the vessel, and by stirring up the mud inside her and then diving outside and watching it stain the clear Sparrow Cove water, a picture was built up of the holes in the ship below water level. These were much less than had been feared, although the crack was more extensive than at first was thought to be the case. When the ship was beached at Sparrow Cove and holes were driven in the stern at approximately the 16-ft water level, scour rapidly produced a severe hogging moment, and the ship split from the sill of the forward entry port right down the starboard side almost to the keel. Fortunately, the after entry port did not penetrate the gunwale and there were no ports cut in the port side of the ship, so severe damage was limited to this one split.

The seven scuttling holes ranged from 5 in. × 10 in. to 48 in. × 18 in. just forward of the stern post, between frames Nos. 6 and 9, at about the 16-ft water level. There was a small hole about 12 ft above keel level on the starboard side forward, which was probably also driven with a crowbar in order to initiate flooding. It was concluded from the survey that there were probably no other significant holes; in the event this proved to be correct. This fairly extensive investigation showed no sign whatsoever of the hole mentioned by the scuttlers in 1937. It may well be that in the diary the word 'mizzen' was used instead of 'main'; certainly, there was a loose manhole cover in the tank top abreast of the main mast, through which water did well up rapidly as the tide rose.

The thickness measurements taken during the survey showed that the bulk of the shell plating was still in the region of 0·27–0·35 in. thick, isolated readings being both below and above these levels. It was concluded that general wastage was therefore approximately 40 per cent., although of course there were unquestionably holes right through the plating, mainly in the upper levels of the ship and right forward and aft. The shell plating here was originally thinner anyway, and the particularly bad places had been covered in her early days by the trailboards and the false, wood quarter galleries. It should be borne in mind, too, that the manufacture of plate in 1840 was not quality-controlled, and local patches of inferior quality were liable to occur. There was also a tendency at that time to use higher quality materials low down and poorer higher up. Hence there could be a hole only a few inches away from $\frac{1}{2}$-in. thick solid iron. It is of interest to remember that the survey by Lloyd's in 1872 disclosed shell wastage of the order of 15–20 per cent. The transverse structure was generally in fair condition: in the upper levels the intermediate frames showed thicknesses of approximately 0·4 in., i.e. 20–25 per cent. wastage; the main web frames were virtually unwasted at 0·6 in. Lower down at about the 18-ft level the condition of the frames varied considerably. Much was sound but some patches of four to five frames were totally wasted. Generally, however, the framing was considered adequate for salvage purposes.

On the voyage back to Punta Arenas, in the Straits of Magellan, these measurements were plotted. Not long after my arrival in Britain a report was presented to the Project which was a good deal more optimistic than expected and certainly a reversal of one's first impression on boarding the old ship.[2] It was concluded, in short, that the ship could be salvaged:

[1] The *Great Britain* is in surprisingly sound overall structural condition. [2] The crack in the hull is quite serious but is capable of rectification without an undue expenditure of time and effort. [3] The transverse structure of *Great Britain* is in good shape . . . and is adequate for the provision of attachment points for the rigging of a towing bridle. [4] The hull is in a favourable position for floating off and removal . . . The masts are in good condition, will not fall in the near future, but should be lifted up and strapped down on the deck . . . The *Great Britain* is capable of salvage, the work should be within the compass of two or three months at Stanley for a salvage tug and crew and the ship is very well worth the effort. . . .

121 The crack was monitored from 1968 to the salvage: 10-in. open and 10-in. drop in 1969!

The report covered a good deal of ground. One of the conclusions was that if the ship were made watertight and pumped out she would float immediately with no further assistance. The previous comment that the side frames and shell went straight into the sea bed was explained by the fact that the iron cargo deck in No. 1 hold was unknown to the speaker and what was thought to be the sea bed was, in fact, this deck. One very important point made in the report was that the scour was increasing, that the ship was digging her own grave and that there was not a great deal of time—perhaps five years at the most—left before she would break in two. The crack was quite frankly admitted to be worse than had been expected, but the report considered that if a sagging moment (downward pressure in the middle) was applied to the ship, perhaps by making the aft end only watertight, then the crack would close, hinging about the port side. 'The writer is confident that this will be so.' The crack would then have to be strapped across with steel plates to restore continuity on the starboard side.

The first method of proposed salvage was to make the after engine-room bulkhead watertight and pump out the afterbody of the ship, first repairing the scuttling holes. Calculations showed that this would produce a sagging moment at low water of approximately 5,000 tons ft and at high water 35,000 tons ft and it was considered that this was sufficient to close the gap at the crack. At the time of the survey the crack was open 7 in. at the entry port sill level, with a vertical displacement of 5 in. due to the rotation of the afterbody about the intact port side. It was concluded that as the stern lifted it would rotate, thus closing the split in the hull longitudinally and vertically. With the after part of the ship kept afloat, the crack was to be 'planked' over with strip plates, approximately 30 ft long, 1 ft wide and $\frac{1}{2}$ in. thick. These would restore the continuity of the starboard side of the hull. A cement box placed internally would provide watertightness. The hull would then be pumped out, cleaned, filled with polyurethane foam or buoyancy bags, and towed home.

A team from a well-known towing company went out to the Falkland Islands with a view to making preparations for an expedition to tow the ship. Their report was unfavourable: the crack had opened considerably, although their measurements seemed to overestimate it; they found that some of the hull plating behind the wood sheathing could be penetrated by hammering; and they considered that the masts were completely rotten and could not be lifted out with safety. They concluded that it would be quite impossible to tow the ship home. This report naturally caused some despondency, but continuing monthly checks carried out by John Smith, a member of the Project resident in the Falkland Islands showed that, in fact, the crack was nothing like as bad as this team had stated. Further hammer tests carried out by the crew of *Endurance* during a visit showed that although it was true that in the original bow-wave area the hull could be penetrated by repeated hammering with a heavy hammer, this was localised and not by any means indicative of the general state of the ship. It was also confirmed that the masts were in fact sound, so a further attempt was made by the Project to mount a salvage effort. I remained convinced that the ship could be raised, reinforced and filled with buoyancy foam, towed home.

At this stage an alternative method of salvage was considered. The first meeting with the actual salvors who proposed it was held on 29 December 1969, when I visited them in Southampton. Risdon Beazley Ulrich Harms is an Anglo-German firm and Allan Crothall their English managing director. They proved to be extremely interested and co-operative. After careful examination of the original survey report and the hundreds of photographs which had been taken of the ship, they proposed that the vessel should be floated by the method outlined earlier and then brought over a large floating pontoon or *Mulus*, 250 ft in length and 79 ft in width, which would first be sunk on the bottom of Sparrow Cove near the *Great Britain*. After careful positioning over prepared keel blocks and cradles the ship would be lifted right out of the water by pumping air into the sunken *Mulus*. From Patterson's original lines, it was possible to anticipate accurately the shape of the blocks and cradles, and as the docking keels were known from the diving survey still to exist, side rows of blocks would be arranged on which they would rest. Two or three technical meetings followed, and a final meeting on 10 January decided upon a charter-party and settled all the details of the salvage. This was only some two weeks after the first meeting.

The finance which had been raised, mainly through the notable generosity of Jack Hayward, was still available and the scheme was out-lined to him in a transatlantic telephone call during the first week of January. It was felt strongly by me as naval architect of the Project that, although Risdon Beazley Ulrich Harms were quite confident that the ship could be salvaged, a supporting survey should be carried out and that the salvage officer designated for the work should visit the *Great Britain* immediately. Jack Hayward agreed to the whole proposal, subject to this officer's report, and Leslie O'Neill left for the Falkland Islands in the second week of January to carry out his (hopefully) con-firmatory survey. Arriving back on 28 January, he affirmed to a meeting that he estimated an 80 per cent. chance of success. This agreed exactly with my estimate given to Jack Hayward and Richard Goold-Adams. Hayward confirmed his finance; fortuitously, Richard Goold-Adams was

with him when this report came through and a cheque was handed over immediately.

The pontoon *Mulus III* had left Liverpool for West Africa with dredging equipment on 5 January 1970, in tow of the tug *Varius II*. This ship is a perfectly normal stern trawler, 200 ft long, 33 ft 9 in. beam and drawing 14 ft 9 in. when loaded. She is propelled by an 1,800 BHP diesel engine with a controllable-pitch propeller which enables her to tow with full efficiency in any conditions. The trawling winch is used for towing and the stern ramp for launching a skiff when boarding the tow at sea. Following Leslie O'Neill's report and the decision by the Project Committee to proceed, the flotilla of *Varius* and *Mulus* left West Africa early in February for Montevideo, where a sheerlegs was constructed on the bow of the pontoon, and pumps, salvage equipment, etc. which had been shipped from the United Kingdom were embarked. Meanwhile, by arrangement with the Project, a BBC film team had flown to Montevideo and embarked on the M.V. *Darwin* for Stanley to film the arrival of the flotilla. Ray Sutcliffe of BBC 'Chronicle', who had given much help to the Project with his research on the background of this ship, was in charge of this team. O'Neill and his divers and salvors also joined the *Varius* at Montevideo, together with Lord Euan Strathcona, who represented the Project. The flotilla sailed at 12.30 on Sunday, 15 March.

After a rather stormy but otherwise uneventful voyage, steaming at six knots, they arrived at Stanley ten days later and were greeted by the

122 The pontoon brought bows-on to the *Great Britain*; the sheerlegs used to lift out the masts

local Royal Naval hovercraft and a Government aircraft. To quote Lord Strathcona:

The striking thing about Stanley is the rather brilliantly painted corrugated iron roofs above the white walls which make a gay effect, but it is not a beautiful town. The setting is reminiscent of the bleaker Scottish Islands. Olive green slopes with frequent rocky outcrops running up to low scree covered peaks which remind one of Jura. The whole effect is emphasized by the pervasive smell of burning peat. The bays are littered with wrecks. It is a wonder any ship ever leaves this place. From wooden lighters to the *Lady Elizabeth*, an impressive three-masted iron clipper with the crossyards still hanging from the main mast just like the *Great Britain* herself. The old ship motif is carried on at Stanley where the jetties consist of planks laid across the yards of old ships and the 'Tee' heads of the jetties are hulks sitting on the bottom and indeed some of the warehouses, too.[3]

Work started on 26 March, the *Mulus* anchoring outside the *Great Britain*, and initially consisted of laying a temporary wood walkway on the weather deck and starting to patch the scuttling holes in the stern. Eight tons of rough timber from Montevideo were used and 120 Marine volunteers made short work of this chore. The wood weather deck, fitted in 1882, was completely rotten, and these walkways were essential. The next day was calm at dawn, as is not uncommon in the Falkland Islands, but a fresh breeze blew all day. The sheerlegs was rigged on the bow of the *Mulus* in the morning and the old galley on the *Great Britain* was patched up to make an office and store from which to work on board the ship. The steel plates to strap the crack and the patches for the scuttling holes were all got ready, and later in the day the first visible progress was made when the main yard was dropped. A marine sergeant, Tony Stott, climbed the mast and rigged the necessary tackle. The swinging chain to the yard crane was burnt through and the yard lowered without accident. Everyone was much impressed by the size of this enormous iron spar, 105 ft long, weighing nearly four tons, and which had been in position for over 110 years.

On Saturday, 28 March, the sheerlegs had been erected and the divers had fitted plywood patches on all but one of the scuttling holes. The method was to fit the plywood patch on the outside with bolts hooked over a piece of angle iron inside, straddling the hole and then to seal it from the inside with hydraulic cement. On the following day the pontoon was moved to the stern of *Great Britain* and the lifting of the mizzen mast began. This was successful, but in order to get the mast out of the mast house at deck level it was decided to cut a length off the bottom. The chain saw found the going hard, as after the first inch the wood was quite sound. The mast was then lifted well clear of the seat but the sheerlegs, pulling on it at an angle, broke it at the level of the main deck partners, and the mast toppled down quite slowly on to the top of the deckhouse, luckily causing no casualties.

By breakfast time on Monday, 30th, a full gale was blowing and it was quite impossible to work on the masts, so the strapping plates were hoisted into position on the ship and the divers went on with their patching. By day six, Tuesday, 31 March, the weather had moderated and the main mast was tackled. It had been hoped to lift out the masts in their entirety but it was found that the heel tenons were solidly rusted in, so the fore and main lower masts were cut through with a chain saw some 3 ft above weather deck level. It may be remembered that these lower masts weigh about 20 tons each and are approximately 95 ft in total length with a diameter of nearly 4 ft; they are built from four complete trees, have split mast bands and are held together by tapered wedges. A large strop was rigged to the sheerlegs block from the estimated point of balance aft of the above-deck part of the mast and a preventer down-haul was rigged round the base of the mast going down to the lower deck control base. The mast came down in one piece and the cross-section just above deck level showed that it was quite sound and would have lasted many years more in position. The foremast which was lifted out on the following day, was also fairly sound although the lead capping at its head was missing. The divers had by now come to the conclusion that it was virtually impossible to patch the after engine-room bulkhead, as it was found to be very wasted, and the large cargo door cut in it upon conversion to a sailing ship could not be patched.

A revised plan was then adopted and it was decided to strap the ship in the hogged condition at three levels: at the weather deck, upper 'tween deck and lower 'tween deck stringers. By the time of the arrival of the flotilla, the width and drop at the crack had doubled and it was clear that the conclusion reached by my survey was not pessimistic, rather the reverse. At that time it had been predicted that the ship would break completely in two well within five years. It now seemed possible that this would have occurred in the winter gales of July and August 1970 or else during those of 1971. With these plates in position the hog and twist were strapped in. The hog over the length of the ship was approximately 3 ft and the twist approximately 10 in. in way of the crack. There was also a considerable amount of mud in the double bottom. Originally it had been intended to pump this out but on reflection it was thought better to leave the contents of the ship undisturbed. The 1852 wood keel added to the draught of the ship, and the combination of hog, weight of mud and gear still in the ship, plus the wood keel, much increased the draught. The crack was made watertight with rubber matresses.

On the eleventh day, Sunday, 5th, the pumps were started around midday and the water level dropped immediately. Small holes were plugged as they appeared and working continued all through the twelfth day, Monday. At 5.30 a.m. on 7 April, the thirteenth day after the arrival of the flotilla and one day ahead of schedule, the ship rather unexpectedly came afloat. All through the morning the divers went on plugging minor leaks and finally the water level was held with only the two small pumps running. The crack was obviously closing and leaking very little. It now seemed that the main problem was the quantity of mud and silt in the bottom of the ship. There was also considerable dunnage—an anchor, a couple of old boilers, a steam engine in pieces and coils of heavy wire. At 3 p.m. the wind started to rise. The ship was afloat and immediately sheered to port, with the forward lines rigged to the shore tautening.

A critical situation now arose and finally the ship was allowed to settle on the bottom again on a smooth patch clear of her original bed. This was obviously very wise because the wind was already blowing at Beaufort Scale Force 10 and forecast to rise to Force 11. On Wednesday, 8th, the weather continued foul as it did on the fifteenth day, which incidentally was Brunel's birthday. By the evening of that day the wind was clearly moderating and it was decided to make a further attempt to float on day 16, Friday, 10 April. The pumps ran all night and the *Great Britain* came afloat quite safely in the morning. The predicted draughts assuming the ship had been cleared of mud, were 9 ft 9 in. forward and 11 ft 9 in. aft (moulded), excluding the wood keel which would add a further 17 in. When the ship came afloat her draughts were found to be 12 ft forward and 14 ft aft, and she was something like a foot over the predicted draft. This is not surprising as there must have been 200 to 300 tons of mud in the ship and she was strapped in the hogged shape.

As mentioned, the intention was to float the vessel and then bring her over the *Mulus* sunk on the bottom of Sparrow Cove. The distance between the keel of the *Great Britain* and the deck of the pontoon had to be kept as small as possible; one end of the pontoon was then to be pumped out until it broke surface, carrying the ship with it. Pumping would be continued until there was an adequate amount of the pontoon out of the water to give stability, this in the meantime being supplied by pressure of the flat stern of the pontoon on the bottom. Any rotation (turning over) would clearly tend to raise the centre of gravity of the pontoon and the ship together, thus providing a correcting effect. When sufficient of the pontoon had emerged, the after end would be pumped out and the ship lifted right out of the water.

An attempt was now made to put *Great Britain* on to the pontoon which had been submerged nearby, but she would not go on fully. This was a great worry because with the falling tide it was possible that she might break her back. Apparently, full allowance for the extra draught had not been made. The ship was moved successfully off the pontoon, which was then pumped out and moved. Before another attempt could be made the weather worsened radically, the barometer was lower than it had been for some two or three years and soon the wind was blowing at Beaufort Scale 10 and rising. This time the *Great Britain* was left afloat and rode out the storm attached by wires to the pontoon. She behaved extremely well, riding steadily and indeed steering to some extent on her rudder, which by now had been freed from its rust.

When the weather improved, pumping began again and with the *Varius* pushing at her stern the ship was finally docked on the pontoon on 11 April, after a certain amount of mud had been removed and some of the deep tanks aft pumped out. As the ship ran forward on the pontoon she overreached her correct position and a corner of the winch house on the pontoon penetrated the bow on the port side. She was left in this position, however, as it helped to anchor her on the pontoon. On 12 April pumping began and as the sagging moment produced by lifting the bow developed, the ship began to straighten herself, hinging about the port

123 The lifting sequence once the *Great Britain* was afloat

side and closing the crack. Later that day the *Great Britain*'s bows came out of the water, the first time since 1885.

By 13 April 1970 (day 19), 33 years to the day after the scuttling holes had been knocked in the ship in Sparrow Cove, she was lifted right out of the water. When finally dried out on top of the pontoon it was found that the crack had closed almost completely and furthermore that the twist had almost disappeared. Though this had been anticipated from the calculations and investigations it was gratifying and a great relief, as the possibility that the crack might have extended across the port side could not be ignored. However, the steel straps, weighing over a ton each, were severely buckled. To correct this, the distorted plates were burnt off and straightened, and lap-welded back in place on top of the existing straps. The straps could not be welded to the ship stringers because of the dissimilarity of metals. The ship was wedged firmly on her invaluable docking keels and looked immensely impressive, her yacht-like lines and bulk dominating the scene.

On 14 April the flotilla left Sparrow Cove and made the short voyage to Stanley where they received a great reception from the population. An important ceremony took place, the Government handing over formal ownership of the *Great Britain* to the Project. The ship had been a Crown wreck and it was only by detailed negotiations that Richard Goold-Adams had obtained permission to take ownership, which was to be effected only when the ship was delivered afloat to Stanley. The efforts of the Anglo-German salvage team were extremely creditable. Nobody who has not been to the Falkland Islands can appreciate the difficult and trying weather conditions for such work. The ship, too, was 127 years old and had been beached as a wreck for 33 years. These difficulties would indeed test the efficiency of any salvors, but the combined team coped magnificently with them.

The flotilla sailed on 24 April after lashing down the ship, cleaning her up and generally preparing for the voyage. They arrived in Montevideo

124 The Mulus was sunk near to *Great Britain*. The *Endurance*'s soundings helped considerably

125 In Montevideo on the way home—May 1970

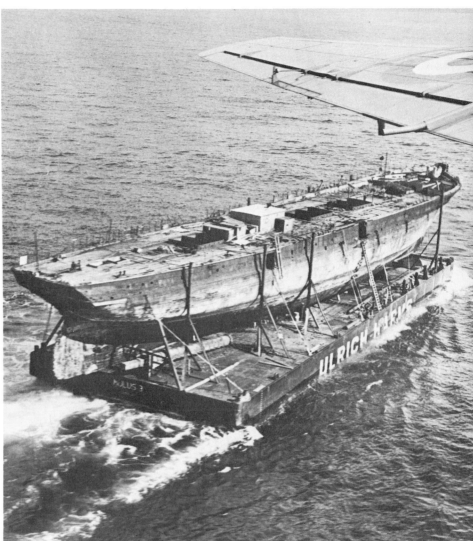

126 In northern latitudes again—*Great Britain* photographed from a reconnaissance aircraft

on 2 May and stayed four days. During the time in Montevideo some further cleaning was carried out and more cradles and lashings applied to hold the ship in position. She was held for the voyage between the six dolphins (vertical steel tubes), located by shaped steel cradles at the bilges, and strapped down with anchor cables running through holes cut in her upper 'tweens and shackled to lugs on the deck of the pontoon. The *Great Britain* had a great reception at Montevideo. Berthed as she was in a bustling port, close to the quay from which *Endurance* sailed in November 1968, she gave an overwhelming impression to those who, like myself, had seen her deserted and dreadfully lost, alone in that far-off cove.

Pressmen from all over Latin America visited her and were surprised to find that nobody felt any doubts about the remaining 6,000 nautical miles of voyage. However, as the ship had already weathered a Force 8 gale on the way up from Stanley, with virtually no shelter for over a thousand miles, the salvors and members of the Project rightly felt that the worst of the voyage was over.

On Wednesday, 6 May the flotilla sailed; by the 21st they were off Recife in Brazil and ten days later at approximately 10°N 30°W: the Atlantic had been crossed. On 18 June they were found and photographed off Finistère by R.A.F. Maritime Reconnaissance aircraft; on 23 June they arrived in Barry Roads, in sight of *Great Britain*'s point of departure on 6 February 1886—on the same voyage No. 47. This must be one of the slowest voyages on record, though perhaps that of the *Vasa* across Stockholm Harbour takes precedence. The first leg from Stanley to Montevideo had been covered at an average speed of 5·3 knots and the second leg, 6,150 nautical miles, at an average speed of 5·34 knots. Slow though this may seem, it was in fact faster than the outward part of the voyage as the *Great Britain* had sailed on 6 February 1886 and by 16 April was in 55° 15′ S, 60° 28′ W, just to the south and west of the Falkland Islands. She had thus taken 69 days to cover approximately 7,400 miles: an average speed of 4½ knots!

On 24 June the pontoon and the ship entered Avonmouth Docks to a great welcome and went thence into the Jeffries Dry Dock where the stringer straps were repaired and rebolted. A heavy ½-in. steel plate was welded between the centre and lower straps parallel to the shell, about 4 ft inboard, in order to make good the vertical strength on the starboard side. The whole crack was then locked together with steel hoops covering three frame spaces, with a light steel sheet outside and cement-boxed inside.

On 1 July, when the *Great Britain* was undocked from the pontoon, the only accident to the ship in the whole salvage occurred. The pontoon is floated by pumping air into it and sunk by opening valves on the bottom and letting air escape from the tops of the tanks. One of the valves on the top did not open, so that air could not escape and that particular compartment could not flood: the pontoon thus sank unevenly with the ship at a small angle across it. Manholes were hastily removed by divers and the pontoon sank away from the ship, which was undamaged. On 5 July the *Great Britain* left Avonmouth and floating on her own bottom was towed up the Avon to Bristol Harbour. It was felt that she could not proceed unless the weather was reasonable and a limit of around 20 knots had been set for the wind. On the evening of Saturday, 4 July, the wind was over this limit, but next morning it had dropped to just below it. The Havenmaster of Avonmouth, Captain Gibbons, the pilot and I decided that it was safe to sail, and on the flood tide the *Great Britain* left the locks at Avonmouth. Off Portishead, turning into the mouth of the Avon, one of the towing hawsers snapped, the bow tug having taken her two wires across the sharp stem of the *Great Britain*. This caused immediate anxiety, as the ship was committed to entering the river and as

127 Brunel's Clifton bridge was not there when she sailed the other way in 1845

she did so her head would have to be pulled round to clear the 'rip-rap' at the foot of the jetty. Without head hawsers this would not be possible. However, to everyone's relief, the remaining wire held and the ship was towed slowly up the Avon to Bristol Harbour.

The passage back up the Avon, mirroring her passage on 11 December 1844, was an interesting and moving occasion. On that date she had gone under the incomplete Brunel suspension bridge; now she was towed under the complete bridge. Many tens of thousands of people lined the banks, and one was reminded irresistibly of all that had happened since this great iron ship had last floated on this river. Virtually the whole history of iron shipbuilding, and all the history to date of steel ship-building and of the screw propeller had occurred since then; Britain had risen to absolute dominance as a shipbuilding nation, and in the last fifteen years Japan had achieved a similar position; Victoria, the young Queen who trod the decks of the ship in 1845, had grown old and died, and her great-great-granddaughter now reigned; the Indian Mutiny, the Boer War and the two World Wars had changed Britain out of all recognition. In the *Great Britain*'s youth even the railways were young; the whole of modern technology developed since she left the Avon. With her help the great nation of Australia had grown up during her lifetime. No other British ship except the *Victory* had been so important to her country. And now that this creation of Bristol was returning home the people of Bristol did her proud. On the morning of Sunday, 5 July 1970, the *Great Britain* floated into the Cumberland Basin and then on through the gates into the Floating Harbour. She was berthed at its head at a normal cargo berth and there prepared for her final entry into the Great Western Dock.

The draughts of the ship gave some cause for anxiety. It will be remembered that the 17-in. deep wood keel had been added in 1852. This naturally made the docking process more difficult, and on top of that the ship still had a trim of approximately 18 in. by the stern. A check through what original documentation still existed showed that the deep tanks under the propeller shaft in the after hold were subdivided into two, and it seemed probable that only the forward one had been emptied. A search was made under the wood floors laid when the ship was converted into a cargo vessel and, sure enough, the after deep tank, which was located right at the stern of the vessel, was found to contain water. It was pumped out, and the addition of a 50-ton rubber Dracone used as a portable tank right at the forward end of the No. 1 hold levelled her off at about 13 ft even keel extreme draught.

The Prince Consort had been the Guest of Honour and eventually the launcher of *Great Britain* in 1843. H.R.H. Prince Philip graciously consented to see the ship put back in the same dock, and on 9 July 1970 the ship was berthed with its royal passenger, exactly 127 years after she had been launched from the same dock. This date was auspicious but was in fact decided by technical considerations. It was necessary to flood the Floating Harbour to the 30-ft level in order to lift the ship over the sill of the dock, and the first tide after she arrived in Bristol which was of

128 The locks had been widened since she left, so there was no trouble—*Great Britain* entering the Cumberland Basin, 5 July 1970

129 The first sight of her birthplace for 125 years

sufficient height to effect this was that of 19 July. Thus the extraordinary coincidence of dates was completed: 19 July 1837—the launch of the *Great Western*; 19 July 1839—the laying of the first keel plate of the *Great Britain*; 19 July 1843—the launch of the *Great Britain*; and finally, 19 July 1970—the return of the old ship to her birthplace.

The weather was good, the tide a little better than predicted, and the ship gave no trouble whatsoever; although there was only 6 in. clearance on each side and under her keel, the whole docking went off smoothly and perfectly, a tribute to the skill of Messrs Charles Hill who were responsible. The *Great Britain* is a very tight fit in the dock and is berthed on a centre-line row of keel blocks and two side rows under her original docking keels. She is thus held in the dock exactly as she was when she was built.[4] It is to be hoped that there she will stay, to be restored and to show the people of Bristol and indeed the whole of Britain what a very early iron ship looked like and to illustrate the daring and ability of the great engineers of the Industrial Revolution and the early Victorian age. H.R.H. Prince Philip put it well: 'The *Great Britain* represents a vital stage in that revolution and is therefore of immense interest to future generations.'[5]

The iron ship has come and has gone. It is to be hoped that this ship created at the beginning of the iron shipbuilding era will remain forever as a monument to it.

> I'm Queen of the Water—each wind and wave
> Whose storm and swell I'm born to brave
> Frowned at my birth with wild despair
> And said 'We shall fail in warring there!'
> [Launch of *Great Britain*—Anon. 1843]

Postscript:— Wind and wave *did* fail in their war—but only just!

No. 1   Port of *Bristol*   dated 14 January 1845   153

Name *Great Britain*   Burthen 1016 ¹⁰⁵⁷⁄₃₅₀₀ Tons.   James Hoskin   Master.

When and where built or condemned as Prize, referring to Builder's Certificate, Judge's Certificate, or last Registry..... } Built at this Port in the year 1843, as appears by the Builders' Certificate, dated 9 March 1843.

Name and Employment of Surveying Officer   William Cripps, Tidesurveyor.

	Decks,		Masts, length	feet	inches Breadth, taken		the Main Wales,
feet	inches, Height between Decks,	feet	inches, or Depth in the Hold,		feet	inches,	Rigged with a
	Bowsprit,	sterned,	built,		Galleries,		Head,
Athwartard							

NEW FORM.

Five Decks, *Six* Masts, that her length from the inner part of the Main Stem to the fore part of the Stern aloft is 27 4 Feet _ _ _ Tenths, her Breadth in Midships is 48 Feet 2 Tenths, her Depth in hold at Midships is 31 Feet 5 Tenths, that she is propelled by Steam with an Engine Room 16 feet 8 tenths and 1919 ²²⁸⁄₉₂₄ Tons and _ _ _ _ _ *Schooner* Rigged with a *Standing* Bowsprit, *Square* Sterned Clench Built, *free* *False* Galleries, *Royal Arms* Head.

Athwartard under the Act 5 & 6 WILLIAM IV. cap. 56.

Subscribing Owners.	Shares.
~~John William Miles and Thomas Bonville Were, both of the City of Bristol, Esquires, Trustees of a Joint Stock Company, called the Great Western Steam-Ship Company,~~	~~Sixty-four.~~
Other Owners.	
John William Miles and Henry Bush, both of the City of Bristol, Esquires, Trustees of a Joint-Stock Company, called the Great-Western Steam-ship Company, — and William Wright the Younger, of the same City, Esquire, Executor of Thomas Bonville Were, late of the same City, Esquire, deceased also a Trustee of the said Company have transferred by Bill of Sale, dated 2ⁿᵈ January 1851 Sixty four shares to George Gibbs and Robert Bright, both of the said City, and Samuel Wright and Tyndall Bright both of Liverpool in the County of Lancaster, Esquires, Copartners, trading under the Firm of Gibbs, Wright and Company —	
— Produced 8 January 1851 —	

Cancelled

23

1852

CHAPTER EIGHTEEN

Reconstruction: a slow process

Since July 1970 much has happened in the Great Western Dock. The first necessity was to clean the ship of hundreds of tons of mud, scale, rotting shellfish, etc.: this alone was an enormous task. Much of the work savoured of archaeology rather than ship repair, because some of the structure was quite fragile and the mud often contained very interesting objects, among them a beautiful flowered Victorian W.C. bowl and one of the original Trotman anchors dating back to 1843.

To remove the scale and rust it was necessary either to sandblast or pressure-clean; after considerable discussion and investigation it was concluded that high pressure water cleaning was the more appropriate method. Tests were made of various systems and eventually a contract was established on favourable terms with Messrs Plant Technical Services, who had cleaned about three-quarters of the hull by the autumn of 1972. This firm uses high-pressure water jets operating at several thousand lb. per sq. in. and the treatment is most effective. Everything is removed from the metal, leaving it clean, but without damaging it. Tests have shown that because of the amount of slag included in this old iron, and the water which lodges in the pores and to some extent in the metal, it is particularly liable to breaking up if hammered or mechanically worked. The high-pressure water treatment has been shown to avoid such a risk and has the additional great advantage that the considerable quantity of very high-pressure fresh water tends to flush salt and dissolve substances out of the metal. After cleaning, the plating is thoroughly dried, using soft gas flame jets, and then, while still warm, painted with red lead. The latter was chosen after considerable investigation and it is perhaps appropriate that this supposedly old-fashioned material has shown to be so satisfactory for this purpose. The gas was donated by Shell International Chemical Co. Ltd and the red lead by International Red Hand Marine Coatings Ltd.

As the ship was cleaned it became apparent that there were many places where the shell was locally thin and even holed, and much thought was given to methods of repairing these damaged areas. The idea of replacing the plating was rejected on the grounds that it would be too expensive, that the new material would have to be iron to avoid electrolytic corrosion, and finally that the disturbance would tend to damage the remaining structure. Eventually it was decided that the best method was to laminate epoxy or polyester resin and glass fibre over the holes. Epoxy resin adheres extremely well to clean metal and the laminate is as strong as the basic iron. This method has proved extremely satisfactory and can be judged completely successful. The illustration is of the bow where the beakhead was extremely badly corroded: indeed, probably only 20 per cent. of its original structure was left after cleaning and scale removing. Work on the transom has now been carried out. The iron framework of the transom windows is intact but the thin plating round them is much corroded; this is because it was originally under wood decoration which, of course, acts as a water trap, producing highly corrosive conditions. Firms carrying out this work on favourable terms to the Project are Brensal Plastics Ltd and Cotswolds Treatments Ltd.

The woodwork in the ship varied from very good to very bad, and careful thought was given as to how to preserve and repair it. First, the wood sheathing on the shell had to be removed to restore the ship to her original condition. This entailed the cropping or undoing of thousands of nuts and the lifting off of some hundreds of tons of timber. Messrs Charles Hill & Sons Ltd who are carrying out the ship repair work on *Great Britain* have now removed all the wood sheathing and opened all the blanked-off sidelights or portholes, leaving the hull looking much more like the ship that was in the dock 130 years ago. The bolt-holes have been filled with specially made black iron bolts with simulated rivet heads which produce a very satisfactory and watertight repair. These bolts are manufactured by Messrs Guest, Keen & Nettlefold Ltd, again, as with Charles Hill, on favourable terms to the Project. Messrs Cotswolds Treatments Ltd have developed a method for repairing badly rotted wood by first digging out the rotten wood, injecting the remaining wood

131 Back on the keel-blocks on which she had been built

132 The bow after cleaning and repair, 1972

with preservatives and then filling in the cavities with vermiculite and epoxy resin. This is most successful if rather tedious, and the massive 2-ft gunwale timbers are being slowly restored in this way. The foc'sle is complete and the poop completed during 1974.

A dramatic change in the ship has been effected at each deck. At the bow the corroded and wasted beakhead has been rebuilt most successfully and the rest of the foc'sle plating has been repaired similarly. The Brunel hawse pipes have been opened following the removal of the wood sheathing; this is the first time that they have seen the light of day since 1857. At the stern, the plating fitted over the propeller aperture in 1882 has been removed, so that the ship once again looks like a steamer. The sterntube has been opened and the lifting sternframe will be carefully removed. The original Brunel sternpost is still in position, complete with all its plating, and hence it will be possible to return to the original Brunel sternframe layout. The two sternposts can be seen in Fig. 133, taken before all the 1857 sternframe was cleared away. A scuttling hole is seen just above the ladder.

A new propeller has been manufactured as a gift to the Project by Stone Manganese Marine Ltd to the drawings of Burness, Corlett & Partners, and this is now on the ship temporarily fitted in the aperture. All the original chainplates have been very carefully removed by burning out the rivets and a similar treatment has been given to all sailing-ship items such a bumpkins, lugs and eyes. These have all been stowed carefully and will be cleaned up, restored and used where appropriate in the reconstruction.

The ship is now beginning to take shape in her final form. The end of 1974 saw the new funnel erected, towering over the surrounding buildings, the

133 The Brunel sternframe was still in position just forward of the one fitted in 1857

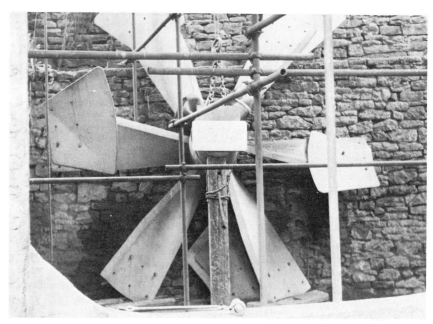

134 In 1972 the new propeller was delivered to the dock to be fitted later in the year

S.S. GREAT BRITAIN

bowsprit in place, the figurehead completed, the Brunel replica propeller in place and much of the starboard side painted in its original black, white and red. The stern windows and much of the gilded decoration across the transom are complete in their original splendour.

The policy being adopted is to restore everything in the best possible materials, envisaging a 100-year life. It is ironic to think that with this policy and in its protected environment, the *Great Britain* is likely to outlast by more than half a century all the ships afloat today. If the present rate of progress is maintained, by the end of 1976 the *Great Britain* will look substantially as she did when she left Bristol at the end of 1844.

135 A unique combination: the first 'modern ship' in the first 'modern building dock' in the first shipyard ever constructed from scratch for metal ships; a place of birth and rebirth. The state of restoration in November 1974

CHAPTER NINETEEN

Conclusion

THE PLACE OF THE *GREAT BRITAIN*

IN THE HISTORY OF THE METAL SCREW–PROPELLED SHIP

Today a vast volume of tonnage carries the commerce of the world in metal bottoms and propelled by screw propellers. The *Great Britain*, the first such large and oceangoing ship, lies in the Great Western Dock in Bristol. What was her place in the revolution that overtook the sea transport of the world, and was she really of significance? To arrive at a conclusion it helps to consider the subsequent history of iron ships following 1845.

The *Great Britain* demonstrated to the world that the large iron ship was not only practicable but desirable. Even on the delivery voyage to London her successful weathering of a very severe gale must have done much to convince the sceptics. The stranding in Dundrum Bay might well have been expected to lead to total destruction, and the successful survival of this accident probably did more than anything else to convince the shipbuilding and shipping fraternities that iron was a practicable material for large ships. To quote John Grantham:

The well known case of the *Great Britain*, for many months ashore in Dundrum Bay, exposed to a whole winter's gales, has never been equalled as a case to illustrate the strength of iron ships. . . . I surveyed the vessel for the Underwriters and therefore examined every portion most carefully. It was observed that the hull was penetrated by the rocks but that the form was preserved and that no lives were lost. Proper proportions prevented the ship from breaking up, saved the lives of those on board and I may now add the conviction that many of our modern ships with 20 per cent more iron would not have stood what she did.[1]

The hull of the *Great Britain* remained true and fair and capable of quite easy repair. Indeed, the cost was estimated at only £22,000— approximately 20 per cent. of the vessel's original cost. As the rudder and solepiece were gone and the engines not inconsiderably damaged, the actual cost of hull structural repairs could not have amounted to much.

In fairness, the case of the *Royal Charter* 13 years after the Dundrum Bay accident must be mentioned as it gave the sceptics a rod with which to beat the backs of the protagonists of iron. The *Royal Charter* was the consort of the *Great Britain*. She was launched in 1855 from the Sandycroft Iron Works of the River Dee, and Gibbs, Bright & Co., the owners of *Great Britain*, who were pressed for shipping, bought her while on the stocks. Alterations were made to suit her to the Australian run, and William Patterson, the builder of the *Great Western* and concerned with the building of the *Great Britain*, took over the completion of the ship at Sandycroft. The hull was lengthened at bow and stern to make her length seven times her breadth and she was thus slightly longer than the *Great Britain*, her length of keel being 308 ft and her overall length 336 ft. She was ship-rigged and had a very small single funnel, with a small steam engine only 40 per cent. the power of *Great Britain*'s for use when the winds were calm or contrary. On Tuesday, 25 October 1859 *Royal Charter* passed Holyhead where the *Great Eastern* was lying at anchor outside the harbour, and steamed on round Anglesey. Caught on a leeshore by a most violent storm, the ship was driven ashore straight on to the rocks in Dulas Bay, broke in two, disintegrated rapidly and drowned 454 passengers and crew.[2]

The Inquiry put the iron ship as a breed as well as the *Royal Charter* on trial. The solicitor for the Board of Trade, a Mr O'Dowd, stated that an important consideration in the Inquiry was 'this shivering to atoms of an iron vessel which seems not only to indicate a deficiency of strength but positive weakness'. The Inquiry investigated this point very thoroughly but it soon became clear that the *Royal Charter* was if anything better built than the average iron ship and definitely stronger than wooden ones. However, the sharp shelves of rock at Moelfre might almost have been designed especially to smash up a ship, and *Royal Charter* could not have been expected to survive pounding on them in a 100-mph storm. Patterson remarked that no ship was built with that object in view and that to have been more heavily built would not have saved her. 'If she had been built of 4-in. iron her own weight would only have beaten her all the more to pieces.'

The shipwright surveyor called by the Board of Trade gave his opinion that a wooden ship of the same dimensions would have gone to pieces as readily as the *Royal Charter*. Other technical witnesses testified that the plates were of high quality and well riveted. The Court in their report completely exonerated the material and workmanship. They were right. No modern ship of similar dimensions in similar circumstances would have survived although known defects in the design of the *Royal Charter* probably hastened her breaking up.

Perhaps we can let John Grantham have the last word on this point. Writing in 1858, he said: 'The *Great Britain* iron steamer built in Bristol was at the time the boldest effort in iron shipbuilding, and formed a most remarkable feature in the history of this science.'[3] The impetus this ship gave to iron and screw shipbuilding in Britain was crucial. In America, however, early efforts to compete with British screw-propelled iron ships were largely unsuccessful because the installations were in large timber-built vessels. Four or five such ships came in succession from America to Liverpool, some of them fine vessels. A good example was the wood steam auxiliary *Massachusetts*. This ship, 161 ft long and

750 tons old measurement, had a $9\frac{1}{2}$-ft-diameter Ericsson screw of wrought copper with the shaft on one side of the sternpost; thus the shaft and screw could be raised when sailing. Costing only £16,000 she carried 35 passengers ('supplied with shower 'baths'!) and made 8 knots on 8 tons of coal a day. Ericsson was responsible for the whole of the machinery. *Massachusetts* arrived in Liverpool on 10 October 1845 and was much admired, but smashed her screw only two days after setting out on the return voyage.

Not one of these ships made a second voyage. Why this should be so is clear from remarks made in 1842:[4] 'Few wooden steamers can be placed in the graving dock without first slackening the holding-down bolts of the engines to allow the vessel to spread out lest the framing should be broken.' Such a hull hardly seems a suitable environment for a long length of propeller shafting! Another disadvantage was that wood was not a homogeneous material and its density could vary within quite wide limits. One timber steamer of this type drew 2 ft 6 in. more water when her engines were put in than was contemplated, an error amounting to 200 tons difference in the total weight. Indeed, it appears that very few wooden steamers had a waterline of nearer than 6 or 12 in. to that originally intended, besides which, the tendency of the hull to soak up water resulted in steadily diminishing carrying ability.

A major factor in the choice of material—wood, iron or steel—was obviously its effect upon the basic earning ability of a ship. In capacity there was a real advantage in using metal: for instance, the *Great Britain* benefited by about 24,000 cu. ft of hull-space when iron was decided upon. In terms of weight-carrying there was an even greater advantage as iron construction was lighter than wood could ever be. Wood ships depend upon their fastenings which are never as strong as the basic material and which are largely independent of the size of ship. This disadvantage naturally increased as ships became larger under the economic pressures of development. Generally speaking, for any given size and type of vessel a wood hull weighed half as much again as an iron one. In the case of the *Great Britain* this would have meant an increase of 600 tons, requiring an increase of draught of nearly 2 ft.

As to the question of cost, it was generally believed in the early days that iron ships were cheaper to build than wood, and many shipbuilders caught a cold by working on this assumption without proper estimating. Grantham described the position in the 1840s as follows:

[1] A good serviceable iron sailing vessel not exceeding 300 tons burthen will be equal in cost to an English-built 12 years* timber-built ship of the same external dimensions without including the price of copper sheathing for the latter.

[2] Iron vessels about 300 tons are rather less expensive than wooden vessels.

[3] Very large merchant vessels and ships of war are much less expensive than wood.

[4] Iron seagoing steamers bear about the same proportion according to their different sizes.

[5] Iron vessels for rivers may be built at a light expense but as built are unfit for sea service.[5]

* Lloyd's classed vessels at that time for 12 years only in the highest class.

This seems a fair analysis. He also pointed out that the cost of repairs to iron ships was relatively much lower than for wood. Later, steel would have a similar advantage against iron, being available in larger sizes of greater uniformity, half as strong again, more ductile, and enabling ships to carry more cargo. Iron died very quickly after steel was available in quantity and at a reasonable price. Overall it can be seen that iron ships had overwhelming economic advantages over wood, and their adoption was rapid: wood construction, at any rate for steamships, died in Britain nearly as rapidly as did iron 35 to 40 years later.

It would not be difficult to follow the history of iron ships [said John Grantham in 1858]. The science which has been thus established was pursued most actively in the Clyde, the Thames, the Mersey and latterly in the Tyne* and no port of any magnitude but can claim now a share in the work. Builders can number the vessels built by them by tens of hundreds and to attempt to list the aggregate number built up to this time in the United Kingdom would be a work of no mean difficulty.

The encouragement given to iron shipbuilding in France by the admission of iron for that purpose duty free has been the means of producing a large number of very fine vessels. In the extensive yards at Toulon under the management of Messrs Taylor, I have seen as large and well built vessels as any builder in England can produce.

For some years past iron vessels have been built in ports of the Baltic and throughout the continent of Europe they are probably everywhere to be found. . . Strange as it may appear our ship owners long resisted the conviction that iron could be advantageously applied for building *sailing* ships required for long voyages. Some, however, are now yielding to the opinions that we have so long urged and many large and splendid specimens of naval architecture in the form of iron sailing ships are owned in every large port but especially at Liverpool.

Grantham's remarks about building on the Baltic are interesting as there is still in existence today a small iron steamer built only four years after he wrote. The Baumgarten and Burmeister establishment in Copenhagen which started as a steam-engine factory began building iron vessels in 1855. In 1862 they built the steamer *Hjejlen* for passenger work on the Himmelbjerg lakes in Denmark. This little ship, 80 ft in length, 12 ft in breadth and drawing only 2 ft 6 in., was undistinguished in her day, but today is still in service, propelled by her original machinery, carrying tourists along the Guden River and into the lakes.[6]

Tonnage climbed rapidly. In 1850 only 10 per cent. of the new tonnage added to the British Register was iron, in 1860 30 per cent, in 1870 60 per cent. With steamers the proportion was higher: 26 per cent. in 1850 and 80 per cent. in 1860—here perhaps we can see the real influence of the *Great Britain*. Technically, too, the pace was rapid. At the risk of overquoting from Grantham,

the climax of iron shipbuilding is reached with the *Leviathan* now building in the yard of Messrs J. S. Russell & Company, Millwall. We cannot expect for many years if ever again to have the occasion to notice a more stupendous illustration of all that can be said or argued in favour of iron as a material for shipbuilding than the *Leviathan* is likely to afford.[7]

He was correct. This enormous ship, launched in 1858 as the *Great Eastern*, over twice the length of her predecessor *Great Britain* and some

* For the record, the first iron vessel built on the Tyne was the *Prince Albert* in 1842.

136 The Danish passenger-vessel
Hjejlen in 1971

six to seven times her loaded weight, remained the largest iron ship ever built. Indeed, until the launch of the *Oceanic* in 1899 no longer ship had ever been constructed and it was not until the liners *Lusitania* and *Mauretania*—half a century after the *Great Eastern*—that anything larger in overall size was built.

The *Great Eastern* was a fantastic technical achievement and perhaps the ultimate expression of the iron shipbuilding ambitions of the engineers of early Victorian times. Overall she was 692 ft in length and 83 ft in breadth. The depth of her hull was 60 ft and the weight of iron in it 8,000 tons, or more than seven times as much as in the *Great Britain*. The extreme load draught was 30 ft, at which the displacement was around 25,000 tons. *Great Eastern* introduced almost as many new features to shipbuilding as did the *Great Britain*: sophisticated longitudinal framing was adopted, together with a complete cellular inner bottom which, extending up the sides, gave her safety undreamt of at the time. Indeed, it is reasonable to surmise that had she been substituted for the *Titanic* in 1912 she would have survived the accident. In fact she survived one of much the same nature when a considerable length of her bottom was ripped by an uncharted rock near New York. The passengers did not even know she had been holed. The inner skin remained watertight, and the outer one was repaired by a coffer dam which was sunk, placed around it and then pumped out. The ship was extremely well subdivided with 10 watertight bulkheads dividing her into compartments each 60 ft long.

Great Eastern was built mainly with standard plates whose number reached the staggering total of 10,000; approximately three million rivets being driven to hold them together. All the hull plates were $\frac{3}{4}$ in. and all the bulkheads $\frac{1}{2}$ in. in thickness. The angle irons used in her construction were standardised at $4\frac{1}{2}$ in. $\times$ $4\frac{1}{2}$ in. $\times$ $\frac{1}{2}$ in., but being longitudinally framed she did not have the conventional 'ribs' and with her cellular deck was thus of enormous longitudinal strength, probably approaching the best modern standards.[8]

This is not the place to describe the career or to analyse the design of the *Great Eastern*. Though a much denigrated ship she was in fact a brilliant technical success, and not underpowered as ships went in those days (most of her critics in this respect compared her on a crude horse power-per-ton-of-displacement basis with other much smaller ships, overlooking the crucial principle enumerated by Brunel which has been described earlier in this text). Commercially she was a failure but this was not really a conceptual fault so much as the result of two factors: first, she was never put on the service for which she was designed—non-stop, without coaling, to Australia; and secondly, when she was put on the Atlantic service her owners refused to have any truck with the only source of large numbers of passengers, namely the emigrant trade. In retrospect it is clear that the *Great Eastern* could have made much money carrying emigrants to either Australia or America. The grandeur of the ship probably frightened nearly everybody concerned with her, with the sole exception of the 'little man' himself.

To return to the developments immediately following the successful first voyage of the *Great Britain*, it must be realised that in some ways the technical position of iron shipbuilding in 1845 was still very fluid. Lloyd's Register had classed several iron ships, starting with the sailing ship *Sirius*, but the number of iron steamships was rapidly increasing, and the year before, the Committee of Lloyd's had appealed to the shipbuilders of Britain to help compile Rules for the survey and classification of iron steamers. The results were not encouraging and it was obvious that there were many parallel lines of approach, the relative merits of which had not yet been determined. Robert Napier replied to the Committee thus:

I have, like your Committee, the most earnest desire to see Iron Ships built on the strongest and most scientific principles. I am very sorry at being under the necessity of stating that I cannot see any way of filling up your Questionnaire satisfactorily as I consider the subject so involved with practical difficulties that it would be impossible to make Rules to meet the different cases honestly, and so as not to do much injury to this new and growing branch of shipbuilding and trade.

All Lloyd's could do was to ask shipbuilders to submit specifications of new ships before construction started. It is to be noted that the Building Committee of the Great Western Steamship Company did not do this. Perhaps they wished to be quite uninhibited in their approach to their great new ship. Lloyd's themselves admit that something like anarchy had developed inside the shipbuilding industry during the 1850s.[9] New ideas proliferated so widely and wildly that even different shipbuilding areas were working along different lines. In 1853 Lloyd's appointed a Subcommittee which visited the most important iron shipyards, and no doubt ships, throughout the kingdom, and in February 1854 a first set of Rules was drafted. It is in this context that the structural success of the *Great Britain* must be seen; many of her structural features, such as the flat plate keel, became standard practice years later.

These first Rules for Iron Ships, which were extended somewhat in

137 Model of the P. & O. liner *Himalaya*, the first screw-propelled ship in the fleet

1857, retained the practice used for wood ships of classifying for given terms of years—six, nine and 12—and only in 1863 were a set of revised Rules published which did away with this feature and were based solely upon the actual thickness at any time of the metal in a ship's construction. This meant that vessels could remain in Class as long as they were maintained in a state of efficiency. Furthermore, scantlings could be reduced towards the bows and sterns of iron vessels, a practice originally introduced in the *Great Britain* by Brunel. It was only in 1870 that the system of determining scantlings from the dimensions of vessels rather than from the under-deck tonnage was adopted. This, with many refinements introduced over the years, is the system used today, and the *Great Britain*'s measurements are surprisingly close to those of modern scantlings.

After the construction of the *Great Britain* the large shipping companies began, at first tentatively, to introduce iron into their programmes. The first P. & O. liner built of iron was the *Lacha*, constructed in 1842 and weighing 592 tons, in other words about the same size as the *Rainbow*. The next, slightly smaller, was the *Madrid*, built in 1845, and then the *Tiber* Class of 1846. The iron *Pottinger*, built for P. & O. in 1846, was at that time the largest vessel ever built on the Thames—1,401 register— but it was not until well into the 1850s that this great company finally abandoned wood. The *Himalaya*, built for P. & O. in 1853, was the first ship of almost the same size as the *Great Britain*. Although 55 ft longer between perpendiculars than *Great Britain* she was 5 ft narrower. Displacement on a maximum draught of 21 ft 5 in. was 4,690 tons; at 21 ft

5 in. the displacement of *Great Britain* is about 5,130. Indeed, on the Australian route *Great Britain* operated at a departure draught of 22 ft, displacing about 5,300 tons. It is on record that at Christmas in 1857 the *Himalaya* and *Great Britain*—the two largest vessels in the world and the two great forerunners of the world's screw-propelled liners—found themselves anchored alongside each other in Simonstown. *Himalaya* was also the first screw ship built for the P. & O. Company and survived until the second world war when she was sunk at Portland by German aircraft: her wreck can still be visited underwater by Scuba divers. The first P. & O. ship truly to exceed the size of the *Great Britain* was the *Khedive* of 1871, and the first Cunard vessel the *Bothnia* of 1874—both nearly at the close of the iron era.

Iron-clad ships of war had been constructed for some time, and indeed, some degree of iron armour plating was used on wooden ships even as early as the Napoleonic Wars, and notably in 1859 on the French ship *La Gloire*, but the first warship actually built as well as plated with rolled iron was *Warrior* launched in 1862. *Warrior* was of considerable size, 380 ft in length, 58 ft broad and 42 ft deep; she was armoured with iron plate $4\frac{1}{2}$ in. thick. Larger and larger sisters followed immediately.

The iron ship lasted for over thirty years after the *Great Britain* was completed, but the substitution of steel for iron was only a matter of time following the invention in 1856 by Bessemer of his air-blown converter and that in 1866 by Siemens of the regenerative process for making steel. Bessemer blew cold air through molten pig iron which not only effected the removal of the carbon and other impurities but in burning them increased the temperature of the metal to over 1,600°C. Both processes, with their high-temperature melts, facilitated the production of large ingots which could be produced as steel and which allowed much larger plates and sections to be rolled than was the case with iron. Steel had superior and more uniform properties, allowing ships to be lighter and stronger; the fact that it lacked the longevity of wrought iron was not overwhelmingly important. Above all, steel conferred crucial advantages in weightcarrying ability. When first introduced there was a tendency to use high-tensile steel, and some ships were built in material of some 50 tons per sq. in. of tensile strength.[10] With this, scantlings some 25–30 per cent. below those of iron were possible, but such steels were difficult to work and cracked easily, so shipbuilding soon settled down to the use of mild steel of around 30 tons per sq. in., Lloyd's permitting a 20 per cent. reduction in such scantlings compared with iron ones; generally, the bare hull of a steel ship weighed some 12–15 per cent. less than her iron-built counterpart.[11]

The significance of this reduction in weight in terms of carrying capacity is well illustrated by contemporary figures for a passenger and cargo liner with a load displacement of 12,500 tons.[12] In iron the hull would weigh 5,000 tons; in steel 4,300. The weight of the complete ship without cargo and coals would be 8,400 total for iron and 7,700 for steel construction. Thus the carrying capacity of cargo and coals would be 4,800 tons for the steel ship, 700 tons more than for the iron. If 2,000

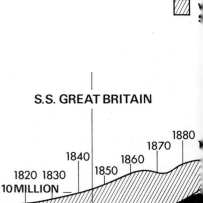

WORLD TONNA
FROM 1810

15 YEARS AFTER THE GR
WOOD TONNAGE BEGAN
5 YEARS AFTER THE FIR
IRON TONNAGE BEGAN

THE ENORMOUS PYRAM
TONNAGE PIVOTS ON T
THE FIRST OCEAN GOIN

S.S. GREAT BRITAIN

1880
1870
1840
1860
1820 1830   1850
10 MILLION

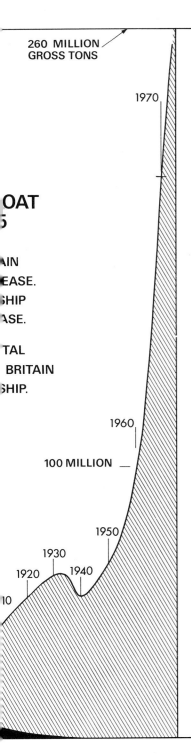

260 MILLION
GROSS TONS

1970

OAT
5

AIN
EASE.
HIP
ASE.

TAL
BRITAIN
HIP.

1960

100 MILLION —

1950

1930

1920   1940

10

Rotomahana 1879
E.C.B.C.

138 *Rotomahana*—the first seagoing steel-built vessel

tons of coal were necessary on the Atlantic service, the iron ship would only carry 2,100 tons of cargo and passengers and the steel ship 2,800 tons—a gain of one third.

Initially, steel was more expensive. In 1877, rigorously tested steel usually cost twice as much as iron, which was normally untested. However, with Admiralty vessels where iron was always tested, there was even then little difference between the two prices. By 1880 steel was only 50 per cent. more expensive than iron and was now economic as a material for construction. In 1891 it was only 10 per cent. more expensive than untested iron, the use of which had virtually ceased.[13]

The first Rules for Steel Ships produced by Lloyd's Register of Shipping appeared in November 1888; apart from allowing a reduction of 20 per cent. or so in the scantlings, they insisted upon the importance of the quality of steel to be used for ships. At this point it could be said that steel was the accepted material and iron the exception.

The length of time taken before steel ships were in service is surprising.

Probably the first steel vessel of all was the sailing ship *Formby* launched in Liverpool on 26 November 1863 by Jones, Quiggin and Co. This ship was built of high tensile steel and was 220 ft overall and 37 ft beam. She was followed the same day by the paddle blockade runner *Hope*, 281 ft by 35 ft beam and capable of 18 knots.

The first *mild** steel hull was a river boat called the *Ma Robert*, a little 73-footer built for David Livingstone and taken out to Central Africa in pieces. The first ocean-going mild steel vessel, the *Rotomahana*, was built in 1879 by Denny's at Dumbarton for the Union Steamship Company of New Zealand. This mild steel ship was also distinguished

219

by being one of the first with bilge keels, the very first of all metal ships to have them being *Great Britain*. *Rotomahana* had registered dimensions of 298 ft length, 35·2 ft breadth and 23·7 ft depth of hold. She was, therefore, considerably smaller than the *Great Britain*, but steamed at a speed of approximately 15 knots in service and, as was usual around 1880, on a boiler pressure of approximately 70 lb. per sq. in. *Rotomahana* soon demonstrated the structural advantages of steel. Shortly after entering service she touched a rock and badly set up a portion of her bottom plating. Although it was mis-shapen, no crack occurred and a formal report on the accident stated 'that the injuries were such that, had the bottom been of iron, so large a rent would have inevitably have been made as would have caused her to founder in a few minutes.'[14]

P. & O. built their first steel vessel, the *Ravenna*, in 1880 but, owing to the extreme shortage of steel even then, the next five vessels after *Ravenna* were of iron and it was not until 1882 that all new construction was of steel. The 'R' Class were 386 ft in length, 39·4 ft in breadth and 26·9 ft in depth. The two iron sisters had rather less deadweight than the steel *Ravenna* but were extremely strongly built and, as the above dimensions show, fashionably long and narrow. They were longer but narrower and shallower than the *Great Britain*, with a sea speed of 14 knots instead of her 11 to 12, and the six single-ended iron boilers working at 80 lb. per sq. in. instead of 5.

The last iron liners on the Atlantic were larger than these but nothing like the size of the *Great Eastern* and not so very much bigger than the *Great Britain*. The last iron Cunarder, *Gallia*, built by J. G. Thompson, later John Brown's, was 445 ft overall, with a breadth of 44 ft and a depth of 35 ft: again, fashionably long and narrow. Displacement at the load draught of 24 ft was about 9,000 tons, and the service speed about 15

139 The Inman liner *City of Rome*, one of the last great iron ships

knots, while pressure, as in the *Ravenna*, was 75–80 lb. per sq. in. A much more famous late iron ship was the Inman Line's *City of Rome*. This ship was intended as a Blue Riband contender and was to be of steel. An order was placed with the Barrow Shipbuilding Company for a vessel to be second in size only to the *Great Eastern*. As mentioned earlier, there was a shortage of mild steel for shipbuilding at the time, and the Inman Line eventually agreed to build the ship of iron. She was launched in 1881 and was 560 ft in length, 51 ft in breadth and 37 ft in depth. Thus she was 240 ft longer than the *Great Britain* but very little broader and not much deeper. A magnificent vessel with three funnels and four pole masts, she was not a success, mainly because her cargo capacity was lower than specified. The intention had been to provide 3,800 tons, but only 2,200 tons were in fact available in the completed ship; the difference was attributed largely to the use of iron instead of steel.

The 'iron ship' can be said to have died around 1880. Up to that time P. & O. alone had built upwards of 140 iron vessels. The material used in building iron ships was, however, quite unexpectedly durable, and even today we have a number of iron vessels floating, or capable of floating, on their own bottoms long after their builders might have expected them to return to the steelworks as scrap. One such survivor is the *Great Britain*'s naval counterpart, the *Warrior*, still afloat at Pembroke and acting as an oil jetty; there is a reasonable prospect that, like *Great Britain*, she will be preserved for posterity.

In San Diego there lies one of the oldest metal ships continually afloat: the *Star of India*, previously called the *Euterpe*. This three-masted ship was built in 1863 at Ramsey in the Isle of Man and was launched on 14 November of that year. 205 ft in length, 35 ft in breadth and $23\frac{1}{2}$ ft in depth, *Euterpe* was extremely heavily built with bottom plating $\frac{13}{16}$ in. thick and side plating $\frac{11}{16}$ in. at 18-in. frame spacing. The year after *Euterpe* went into service, Lloyd's Rules, to which she had been built, introduced notable reductions in scantlings but the old Rules plus the specified owners' extras resulted in a very heavy ship of rather full form which was slow but proved extraordinarily long-lived. *Star of India* has been restored and is in remarkably good condition. Indeed, it has been said, perhaps optimistically, that she could be put back in Class if this were so desired.[15]

As a final example, the iron monitor *Huascar* is afloat and flourishing at Talcahuano Navy Base, Chile, maintained as a shrine to the Chilean and Peruvian Navies. *Huascar* was built at Birkenhead in 1865 by Laird Bros. for the Peruvian Navy. She was one of the first ships fitted with a rotating turret as advocated by Captain Coles, the designer of the ill-fated battleship *Captain*. *Huascar* is 200 ft in length, 35 ft in breadth and 20 ft in depth, with a draught in service of 12 ft. The load displacement was 1,130 tons and the ship was fitted with Penn engines developing 1,200 horsepower on a single screw, giving 11 knots. Her main armament was a two-muzzle-loading Armstrong cannon of 10-in. calibre, firing 300-lb. projectiles. This ship, like most of the old iron ships, has had not only a long but also a romantic career. She is mainly distinguished by her

140 The iron barque *Star of India* (ex *Euterpe*) as she lies today in San Diego

141 The launch of *Euterpe* at Ramsey, Isle of Man, in 1863

142 The iron monitor *Huascar* at Talcahuano Naval Base, Chile

part in the Pacific War fought between 1879 and 1884; in particular, the action in 1879 with the *Esmeralda* of the Chilean Navy and her capture by the Chileans at the end of that year at the battle of Angamos.[16]

Technically, *Huascar* is of great interest by virtue of the indecisive action she fought with Her Britannic Majesty's Ships *Shah* and *Amethyst* in 1877. Taken over by Peruvian rebels on 29 May, she was engaged by the frigate *Shah* in the Bay of Pacocha but put herself in a position in line with the town where she could not be fired at with guns. In retaliation the British ships made the first mobile torpedo attack in history, unsuccessfully as it turned out, and in the night made a further one, again without success. *Huascar* is in good condition. She has been restored by the Chilean Navy and is a remarkable example of early iron shipbuilding. Like *Warrior*, however, she must eventually be put in a dock for final preservation.

Like many pioneer efforts *Great Britain* was perhaps commercially ahead of her time. However, if she had not been stranded in Dundrum Bay she might well have had a real, if short-lived, success on the Atlantic, unlike her successor *Great Eastern* which was simply too big and carried too many passengers for successful operation in the context of the day. Like many pioneering efforts the *Great Britain* formed a sound basis embodying many innovations from which half a century of development sprang. Indeed, in some respects her technical influence perhaps extended beyond that half-century. The successful use of iron in a comparatively large ship was obviously an unqualified success. The ship has never had any structural trouble worth mentioning, even when she was grossly overloaded beyond her original design draught. Some extra stiffening has been added to cope with this overloading—but that is all. This structural success plus her survival of the Dundrum Bay stranding undoubtedly convinced all but a few that the big iron ship was here to stay; those, such as the hitherto dominant American ship-owners, who swam against this tide of opinion soon perished commercially.

Technically, the structure of the *Great Britain* was efficient. In terms of achieved strength for weight it was equal to that of the modern ship, allowing for the use of riveted iron and not welded steel. Many of the structural arrangements, although primitive, were indicative of the lines upon which progress should be made. In particular, the use of longitudinal stiffening in the bottom led directly to the longitudinally-stiffened cellular construction of the *Great Eastern*, which was certainly the most efficient ship structure devised until the early days of the twentieth century. Many of the ideas embodied in the *Great Britain* were adopted as standard practice. Multiple bulkheads, an inner bottom which soon became watertight, and, for fast ships, hollow waterlines were all standard practice for large ships by 1850, though bilge keels had to wait 35 years before becoming generally adopted. The foundations of the design of large iron merchant ships were laid in the *Great Britain*. Upon these foundations the races of iron and steel ships were built.

Furthermore, although her first propeller was short-lived, it did prove efficient, and her successful Atlantic crossings as a full-powered screw steamship had an unquestionably profound influence on the rapid adoption of the screw propeller in the British and later the world merchant marine. In fact, the first *Great Britain* screw was probably more efficient than any paddle-wheel propeller fitted at that time, and this fact would not escape the notice of naval architects, although its practical defects, lack of strength and susceptibility to fatigue undoubtedly led to the adoption of the simpler and less efficient but stronger cast-iron 'windmill fan' type of propeller. The rudder arrangement of the *Great Britain* was a design of simplicity and originality which was not equalled for single screw ships until the turn of the century.

To a naval architect approaching the last quarter of the twentieth century the bones of a modern ship can be detected beneath the quaint and archaic skin of the *Great Britain*—the first modern ship. Allowing 20 years for each generation of ships, the place of the *Great Britain* in marine history can perhaps be described as that of the great-great-great-great grandmother of *all* today's ocean-going shipping, and surely no ship can claim a prouder place than that.

Notes

CHAPTER TWO

Page 9, n.   1   J. Fincham, *History of Naval Architecture* (1851), p. 313.

9   2   I. Brunel, *Life of Isambard Kingdom Brunel* (1870), p. 233.

10   3   The Brunel Letter Books, Wills Memorial Library, University of Bristol.

11   4   W. S. Lindsay, *History of Merchant Shipping and Ancient Commerce*, iv (1876), pp. 168–9.

12   5   C. Claxton, *Description of the* Great Britain *Steamship* (1845), pp. 6–7.

13   6   *Ibid.*, p. 7.

13   7   Brunel, *Life*, p. 247; Letter Books.

14   8   Claxton, p. 7.

15   9   Brunel, *Life*, pp. 249 ff.

16   10   *Ibid.*, p. 252.

16   11   J. Nasmyth, *Autobiography* (1883), p. 239.

19   12   T. R. Guppy, 'Description of the *Great Britain* Iron Steamship': *Minutes of Proceedings of the Institution of Civil Engineers*, iv (1845), pp. 161–2.

19   13   Brunel Letter Books.

CHAPTER THREE

21   1   C. Hood, *Iron and Steel: their Production and Manufacture* (1845), pp. 18–20.

23   2   W. Fairbairn, 'The Strength of Iron Ships': *Transactions of the Institution of Naval Architects*, i (1860), p. 81.

24   3   J. Grantham, *Iron Ship-Building* (1858), p. 6.

26   4   J. Grantham, *Iron as a Material for Ship-Building* (1842), p. 5.

28   5   Brunel, *Life*, p. 247.

27   6   Claxton, p. 22.

28   7   *Ibid.*, pp. 21–3.

28   8   The Brunel Letter Books, Wills Memorial Library, University of Bristol.

CHAPTER FOUR

29   1   E. J. Reed, *Shipbuilding in Iron and Steel* (1869), p. 182.

33   2   Grantham, *Iron as a Material*, p. 11.

35   3   Grantham, *Iron Ship-building*.

35   4   W. Fairbairn, *Treatise on Iron Ship Building* (1865), p. 14.

35   5   *Ibid.*, p. 14.

37   6   *Fairbairn, Trans. Inst. Naval Architects*, i (1860), p. 90.

37   7   Grantham, *Iron as a Material*, p. 14; Grantham, *Iron Ship-Building*, p. 43.

38   8   Grantham, *Iron Ship-Building*, p. 48.

39   9   *Ibid.*, p. 105; C. F. T. Young, *The Fouling and Corrosion of Iron Ships* (1867), p. 54; J. Fincham, *History of Naval Architecture* (1851), p. 388.

39   10   Grantham, *Iron Ship-Building*, pp. 101–2.

41   11   *Ibid.*, p. 237, 1968 Edition.

42   12   Young, *Iron Ships* 1867, p. 65.

42   13   Grantham, *Iron as a Material*, p. 58.

43   14   General References:
M. Lebech, *Hjejlen; The Golden Plover* (1961); J. Mac-Mullen, *Star of India* (1961); P. E. Ritchie, *El Monitor Huascar* (1969); J. Grantham, 'The Classification of Iron Ships': *Trans. Inst. Naval Architects*, ii (1861), pp. 128–40; G. Blake, *Lloyd's Register of Shipping*, 1760–1960 (1960).

CHAPTER FIVE

45   1   *Mins. Proc. Inst. Civil Engineers*, iv (1845), p. 154.

51   2   Brunel, *Life*, p. 259; Letter Books.

CHAPTER SIX

54   1   Fincham, p. 347.

55   2   *Mechanics' Magazine*, xxxvii (1842), p. 462.

56   3   I. K. Brunel, *Report to the Directors of the Great Western Steamship Company on Screw Propellers* (1840): Wills Memorial Library.

58   4   J. Grantham, 'Account of some Experiments on the *Liverpool Screw*': *Mins. Proc. Inst. Civil Engineers*, iii (1844), pp. 71–2.

60   5   Brunel, *Report on Screw Propellers*.

61   6   *Ibid.*

62   7   Letter Books.

62   8   Brunel, *Life*, p. 283 ff.

62   9   *Mechanics' Magazine*, xl (1844), p. 203.

63   10   *Mins. Proc. Inst. Civil Engineers*, iv (1845), p. 158.

63   11   Letter from Guppy to Great Western Steamship Co. Board, 17 Dec. 1844, quoted in Claxton, p. 8.

65   12   General References:
J. Bourne, *A Treatise on the Screw Propeller* (1867); G. Rennie, 'Observations on Screw Propellers': *Mins. Proc. Inst. Civil Engineers*, iii (1844), pp. 72–6; J. Weale, *The Great Britain Atlantic Steamship* (1847).

CHAPTER SEVEN

67   1   H. W. Dickinson, *Short History of the Steam Engine* (1939), pp. 99–104, 126–7.

70   2   Guppy in *Mins. Proc. Inst. Civil Engineers*, iv (1845), p. 160.

71   3   B. Cable, *A Hundred Year History of the P. & O.* (1937), 243, 6.

74   4   J. R. Hill, 'Description of the Steamship *Great Britain* (late *Mammoth*)': *Mechanics' Magazine*, xxxvii (1842), p. 253.

74   5   General References:
Nasmyth, *Autobiography*; T. Tredgold, *The Steam Engine* (1827); N. P. Burgh, *Modern Marine Engineering* (1855).

CHAPTER EIGHT

77	1	Claxton, p. 19.
79	2	*Ibid.*, p. 17.
84	3	*Mechanics' Magazine*, xliii (1845), p. 256.
84	4	Claxton, p. 20.
85	5	*Ibid.*, p. 20.
85	6	Hill in *Mechanics' Magazine*, xxxvii (1842), p. 257.
86	7	Grantham, *Iron as a Material* (1842), p. 62.
88	8	Weale.
88	9	Guppy in *Mins. Proc. Inst. Civil Engineers*, iv (1845), pp. 173 ff.

CHAPTER NINE

93	1	Hill in *Mechanics' Magazine*, xxxvii (1842), p. 256.
95	2	Claxton, p. 10.
95	3	*Mechanics' Magazine*, xxxvii (1842), pp. 462–3.
96	4	*Ibid.*, p. 473.
97	5	Grantham, *Iron as a Material*, pp. 47–8.
97	6	Hill in *Mechanics' Magazine*, xxxvii (1842), pp. 241–57.
102	7	*Mechanics' Magazine*, xl (1844).
102	8	*Ibid.*, p. 240.
103	9	*Ibid.*, p. 384.
103	10	*Ibid.*, p. 288.
103	11	*Ibid.*, p. 203.
103	12	Letter Books.
103	13	Letter Books.
104	14	*Mechanics' Magazine*, xli (1844), p. 423.
105	15	Letter from Guppy quoted in Claxton, pp. 7–8.
106	16	*The Times*, 10 January 1845, p. 6.
106	17	*Mechanics' Magazine*, xlii (1845), pp. 46–7.
108	18	Guppy in *Mins. Proc. Inst. Civil Engineers*, iv (1845), p. 164.
	19	*The Times*, 27 January 1845, p. 3.
109	20	M. Shuldham, 'Balanced Rudders': *Trans. Inst. Naval Architects*, v (1864), pp. 123–7; N. Barnaby, 'The Steering of Ships', *ibid.*, iv (1863), pp. 56–67; Admiral Halstead, 'Screw Ship Steerage', *ibid.*, v (1864), pp. 84–5.
110	21	Report on Resistance and Propulsion Experiments, Model Hull STA. 1622, Model Propeller STA. 557, D.Moor, Vickers Ltd., Ship Model Experimental Model Tank, St Albans.

CHAPTER TEN

111	1	*Illustrated London News*, vi (1845), p. 258.
112	2	*Chambers' Edinburgh Journal*, iv (1845), pp. 77–9.
113	3	Quoted in *Illus. Lond. News*, vii (1845), p. 157.
115	4	*Nautical Magazine*, 1845, pp. 713–14.
115	5	E. G. Fishbourne, *Lectures on Naval Architecture* (1853), pp. 109–11.
117	6	*Mechanics' Magazine*, xliii (1845), p. 256.
117	7	Guppy in *Mins. Proc. Inst. Civil Engineers*, iv (1845), p. 166.

CHAPTER ELEVEN

121	1	*Illus. Lond. News*, viii (1864), p. 317.
121	2	J. Hopkinson, *The Working of the Steam Engine explained by Use of the Indicator* (1857), pp. 111–14.
125	3	*Illus. Lond. News*, ix (1846), p. 275.

127   4   *Nautical Magazine*, 1846, p. 616.

127   5   *Mechanics' Magazine*, xlv (1846), p. 476.

128   6   *Illus. Lond. News*, ix (1846), p. 212.

CHAPTER TWELVE

133   1   Brunel, *Life*, p. 264.

133   2   *Ibid*., pp. 267–72.

134   3   *Extracts from the Letters of Capt. Claxton . . . giving a detailed Account of the Manner in which the* Great Britain *was . . . released from Dundrum Bay* (1847), pp. 60–6.

138   4   *Ibid*., p. 52.

CHAPTER THIRTEEN

142   1   J. Bourne, *The Imperial Cyclopaedia of Machinery*.

145   2   *Ibid*.

146   3   *Illus. Lond. News*, xx (1852), p. 468.

CHAPTER FOURTEEN

151   1   *Illus. Lond. News*, xxi (1852), p. 165.

152   2   Neville-Towle, *Diary of a Voyage to Australia* (1852).

155   3   Samuel Seaward, *Mins. Proc. Inst. Civil Engineers* (1841), p. 385.

156   4   G. H. Roberts, 'Capt. John Gray': *Falkland Island Journal*, 1969.

CHAPTER FIFTEEN

157   1   *Dublin Weekly Telegraph*, 18 February 1854.

157   2   *Sea Breezes*, vol. 2, p. 50.

158   3   Roberts in *Falkland Island Journal*, 1969.

158   4   *The Times*, 1 May 1854, p. 9.

158   5   *The Great Britain Times*, D. Griffith, 1866.

162   6   *The Engineer*, iii (1857), p. 113.

163   7   *The Vain Effort, S.S. Great Britain* (1860): Melbourne Public Library.

168   8   *The Cabinet, S.S. Great Britain* (1861): Melbourne Public Library.

169   9   *The Albatross, S.S. Great Britain* (1862): Melbourne Public Library. *The* Great Britain *Chronicle* (1868): Melbourne Public Library. *The Great Britain Times*, E. Griffith.

172   10   Lloyd's Special Report 23460, Liverpool. Lloyd's Register of Shipping, 1872.

174   11   *Sea Breezes*, xx (1936), p. 295.

177   12   General References:
Liverpool Mercury, 1852–76; Liverpool City Library; Passenger Ship Register, Melbourne: Melbourne Public Library.

CHAPTER SIXTEEN

180   1   Sir W. H. White, *A Manual of Naval Architecture* (1900), p. 435.

181   2   San Francisco Alta, 5 June 1883.

182   3   *Sea Breezes*, June 1948, p. 308.

CHAPTER SEVENTEEN

193	1	*Sea Breezes*, Jan. 1948, p. 60.
193	2	S.S. *Great Britain* Survey Report E. C. B. Corlett; S.S. *Great Britain* Project (1968).
197	3	Lord Strathcona, S.S. *Great Britain* Salvage Expedition Log; S.S. *Great Britain* Project (1970).
205	4	E. C. B. Corlett, 'The Steamship *Great Britain*': *Trans. Royal Inst. Naval Architects*, cxiii (1971), p. 426.
205	5	H.R.H. Prince Philip, Message to the *Great Britain* Project (1970).

CHAPTER NINETEEN

211	1	Grantham, *The Classification of Iron Ships*: Trans. Royal Inst. Naval Architects, 1861.
212	2	A. McKee, *The Golden Wreck* (1961) and *Sea Breezes*, vol. 4, 1922, p. 257.
212	3	Grantham, *Iron Ship-Building*, p. 15.
213	4	Grantham, *Iron as a Material*, p. 63.
213	5	*Ibid.*, p. 41.
214	6	M. Lebech, *Hjejlen: The Golden Plover*, p. 7.
214	7	Grantham, *Iron Ship-Building*, pp. 16–17.
215	8	R. G. Fuller, *The Great Eastern*: Trans. Inst. Mar. Engineers (Dec. 1961).
216	9	Blake, *Lloyd's Register of Shipping*, p. 42.
218	10	*Sea Breezes*, vol. 18, p. 6.
218	11	J. J. Welch, *A Textbook of Naval Architecture* (1889), p. 70.
218	12	White, *Manual of Naval Architecture*, p. 415.
219	13	*Ibid.*, p. 416.
220	14	J. J. Welch, *A Textbook of Naval Architecture* (1889), p. 72.
221	15	J. Mac Mullen, *Star of India* (1961).
221	16	Ritchie, *El Monitor*, Huascar.

List of Illustrations
and their sources

Unless otherwise stated all drawings are by the author.

Bibliography

The Steamship 'Great Britain'. Grahame Edgar Farr, Local History Pamphlet II, Bristol Historical Association, 1965

'Great Britain'. E. A. Muller, *Nautical Research Journal*, Washington, 1967

History of the Merchant Navy. Hubert Moyse Bartlett, Harrap, 1937

The 'Great Eastern'. R. G. Fuller, Trans. I.M.E., Canadian Division, 1961

The Big Ship: Brunel's Great Eastern. Patrick Beaver, Evelyn, 1969

The Western Ocean Packets. A. B. Lubbock, Brown, Son & Ferguson, 1956

The China Clippers. B. Lubbock, Brown, Son & Ferguson, 1946

Ships and Men. W. J. Bassett-Lowke and G. F. G. Holland, Harrap, 1946

Isambard Kingdom Brunel. L. T. C. Rolt, Longmans, 1957

Appendix 1

Length on keel	289 ft
Length overall	322 ft
Breadth extreme	50 ft 6 in.
Depth to Upper Deck	32 ft
Length between Perpendiculars	285 ft
Design Draught	17 ft
Load Draught	18 ft
Displacement at Load Draught	3,675 tons overshell
Block Coefficient at Load Draught	0·505 on LBP
Prismatic Coefficient at Load Draught	0·638
Midship Section Coefficient	0·792
Tons per inch	26·6
Waterplane Coefficient	0·790
Transverse Inertia Coefficient	0·646
Longitudinal Centre of Buoyancy	0·02% aft
LCF	2·03% aft
KM	27·75 ft
Half angle of entrance	24·7°
Iron Weight	1,040 tons
Wood and Outfit Weight	370 tons
Engines & Boiler Weight (dry)	520 tons
Lightship Weight	1,930 tons
Wetted Surface at 17·75 ft draught	15,626 sq. ft
Cabins	26 single berth
	113 two berth
Fares	35, 28, 25, 22 and 20 guineas
Crew and Firemen	130

TONNAGE

Measurement Rule	Year of measurement					
	1845	1852	1853	1855	1882	1886
Old Builders Rule of 1773	3443	—	—	—	—	—
Act of 1835	1016 $\frac{1888}{3500}$	1460 $\frac{48}{100}$	1460 $\frac{48}{100}$			
Act of 1855 (Moorsom)	—	—	—	1733 $\frac{69}{100}$ After 1857 alterations: 1794 $\frac{57}{100}$	2640 $\frac{15}{100}$	2640 $\frac{15}{100}$
Register Certificate No.	10/1845	23/1852	66/1853	76/1855	186/1882	130/1886
Registered No.	25967	25967	25967	25967	25967	25967
Place	Bristol	Bristol	Bristol	Liverpool	(Liverpool)	London

Appendix 2

BRUNEL AND GUPPY'S SCREW EXPERIMENTS ON
ARCHIMEDES

(Addendom in 1971)
Rating of screws

Number of experiment	Strokes of engines per minute	Horse-power by indicator	Speed of vessel in knots	Speed of screw in knots	Ratio of speed of vessel to that of screw		Diameter of screw		Pitch			Relative order of merit of propellers	Actual revolutions per minute of propellers
							ft in.		ft in.				
1	25·41	67·1	8·375	10·646	0·787	Smith's two half threads made of wrought iron	5	9	8	0		86	135
2	20·75	53·7	8·16	10·88	0·75	,, ,, ,, ,,	5	9	10	0		100	110
3	26·25	63·59	7·55	8·23	0·917	Smith's two half threads made of cast iron	7	0	6	0		68	139
4	20·5	57·13	7·42	8·52	0·87	,, ,, ,, ,,	7	0	8	0		71	108
5	20·0	57·3	18·75	8·0	1·02	Woodcrofts increasing pitch 3-blades made of cast iron, as first made	7	0	7	7⅞		93	106
6	21·5	62·6	8·1	8·1	1·0	The same with 3 in. cut off the termination of the blades	7	0	7	2⅛		85	114
7	22·5	62·12	8·2	8·73	0·94	The same with 4 in. cut off the entering edge of the blades	7	0	7	5		88	118
8	20·5	51·4	7·49	8·566	0·87	4 wrought iron arms with blades each 2 ft 9 in. long by 1 ft broad	7	0	8	0		81	108

Appendix 3

Original Propeller—1845

Diameter	15·50 ft
Mean face pitch	25·00 ft
Mean face pitch ratio	1·613
Number of blades	6—left hand
Developed area ratio	0·527
Rake	Zero
Skewback	Zero
Distance forward of after perpendicular	9·5 ft
Height above moulded base	8·00 ft
Material	Wrought iron. Arms fire-welded to forged boss. Palms riveted to arms.

Clearances

	Forward at 0·7 radius	above 16% below 16%
	Aft	Minimum above 46% Minimum below 23%
	Tips	Minimum above 1% Minimum below 2%
Weight	77 cwt	

Rudder

Chord at shaft centre	7·624 ft
Thickness/chord ratio	0·103

Replacement Propeller—1846

Type	Solid—4 bladed
Weight	7 tons
Diameter	15 ft 6 in.
Pitch	25 ft
Blade area ratio	0·5 approx.
Sections	Semi-round back with flat trailing edge

1st Australian Service Propeller—1852

Type	Solid—3 bladed
Weight	Unknown
Diameter	15 ft 6 in.
Pitch	19 ft
Blade area ratio	0·50
Length of propeller	3 ft 2 in.
Fitted with sailing clutch	

2nd Australian Service Propeller—1853

Type	2 bladed Griffith non-lifting (other details unknown)

3rd Australian Service Propeller—1857

Type	Built—2 bladed Griffith/Penn lifting with trunk above aperture
Diameter	Believed to be 15 ft 6 in.
Pitch	Unknown
Length of boss	3 ft 2 in.
Carried in a lifting frame located by stern and rudder posts	

Appendix 4

DETAILS OF MAIN ENGINES, SHAFTING AND BOILER

Main Engines—1845

Type: Inverted V, two pairs of cylinders, 60° included angle
Maker: Great Western Steamship Co.

Diameter of cylinders	88 in. 4 in number
Stroke	72 in.
Valves	20 in diameter, Piston type
Cut-off	at 1/6th stroke (design)
Throttle	Butterfly valve
Stroke of Air Pumps	72 in.
Diameter	45½ in.
Crankshaft	17 ft long, 28 in. diameter, 24 in. diameter in bearings. Water cooled
Engine shaft	28 ft 2 in. long, 16 in. diameter
Intermediate Shaft	61 ft 8 in. long 30 in. diameter (internal) ¾ in. shell thickness Torque tube type
Tailshaft	25 ft 6 in. long, 17 in. diameter in stern tube
Design rpm	18 engine, 53 shaft
Design hp	1,000 nominal 1,800 ihp (approx.)
Piston rings	Metallic Split
Valve Piston Rings	Metallic Split
Chain Drive	4 chains. Each set 3 links and 2 links alternately, 24 sq. in. cross sectional area. Primary chain wheel—18 ft dia. × 38 in. wide Secondary chain wheel—6 ft dia. Gear Ratio—2·95 : 1

Boiler

Type:	Rectangular, 34 ft long, 31 ft wide, 21 ft 8 in. deep, sub-divided into three bays, with screw-down wedge shut-off valves Furnaces—12 each end, grate area—360 sq. ft Furnace surface—1,248 sq. ft Normal pressure—5 lb. psi gauge
Feed	Sea water, pre-heated by jacket heater on funnel
Circulating Pumps	190 tons per hour capacity, fitted with suctions to all bilges
Bunker Capacity	About 1,100 tons

Main Engines—1852

Type: Twin Cylinder Oscillating
Maker: John Penn

Diameter of cylinders	82½ in. 2 in number
Stroke	72 in.
Valves	Slide by eccentric
Throttle	Butterfly valve
Stroke of air pumps	36 in. 2 in number
Diameter	40 in.
Air pump valves	India rubber discs on grating
Crankshaft	18 in. diameter, 11 in. crank pins
Engine shaft	13 in diameter
Design rpm	about 24
Design hp	500 nominal
Transmission	Step-up gear. Crankshaft wheels 14 ft diameter. Machined gear wheels—4 in number abreast, each 13 in. broad. Wheels staggered for quiet running. Shaft wheels—4·66 ft diameter, 4 in number. Gear ratio 3 : 1

Boiler

6 independent bays
Heating surface 875 sq. ft
Working pressure 10 psi

Funnels

Twin, side by side, possibly telescopic

Bunker Capacity

700 tons in way of engine room
500 tons stowed elsewhere

Appendix 5

DIMENSIONS OF 1845 MASTS AND SPARS

	Length	Maximum diameter	Type (all wood)
	ft	in.	
Bowsprit	41	19	Spike
No. 1 lower mast	68	19	Hinged at deck. Hinge borne by stub mast
No. 1 gaff	31	8	
No. 1 top mast	54	11	
No. 2 lower mast	103 to keel	34	Stepped on keel. Hooped
No. 2 top mast	55	18	
No. 2 main yard	83	21	Carried studding sail booms
No. 2 topsail yard	66	17	
No. 3 lower mast	70	20	Hinged at deck
No. 3 gaff	32	8	
No. 3 top mast	48	10	
No. 4 lower mast	68	20	Hinged at deck
No. 4 gaff	32	8	
No. 4 top mast	43	9	
No. 5 lower mast	64	15	Hinged at deck
No. 5 gaff	28	7	
No. 5 top mast	40	8	
No. 6 lower mast	57	15	Hinged at deck
No. 6 gaff	23	6	
No. 6 top mast	33	7	

Appendix 6

POWERING REQUIRED TO PROPEL *GREAT BRITAIN*

The model of *Great Britain* tested was 16 ft long and eventually fitted with working propeller and dummy rudder. The materials were hard wax, as is usual, for the hull and hard brass for the propeller.

In such tests first the bare hull is towed to find its resistance at differing speeds, the propeller is tested without the hull to find its detailed characteristics such as thrust developed, power absorbed, etc. at varying revolutions and speeds forward; and finally the model is in effect propelled by the propeller and various characteristics measured.

From all this it is possible to predict accurately the horsepower required to propel the ship over her speed range. The whole procedure was originally developed by William Froude, a contemporary and acquaintance of Brunel's. However, Froude's work took place long after the building of the *Great Britain* or indeed the *Great Eastern*.

For the trials analysis, reported logged speeds and revolutions have been plotted together with Brunel's prediction of 1 knot of speed for every $1\frac{1}{2}$ revolutions of the main engines. However, if sails were set or gales blowing the relevant report was omitted because its inclusion would be misleading. A computer analysis produced an accurate mean line and as can be seen the accuracy of Brunel's prediction is remarkable.

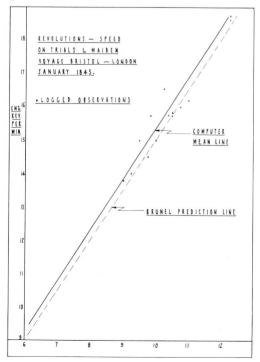

Appendix 7

Omissions in these tables occur where the relevant information was not available at the time this book was printed.

THE VOYAGES OF S.S. *GREAT BRITAIN*

DATES

Year	Month	
1838	Spring	*Great Western* makes first crossing of Atlantic with fuel reserves under power
1838	Spring	Brunel starts designing a bigger wood paddler—GB(1)
1838	Autumn	Brunel, Guppy, Claxton start thinking of iron. *Rainbow* visits Bristol
1839	July	Fabrication starts GB(5)—iron paddler
1839	December	Keel laid
1840	Spring	*Archimedes* visits Bristol—chartered by Great Western Steamship Company
1840	November	Paddle engines cancelled—GB(6)
1843	July	Naming and floating of GB(6)
1844	April	Started to move
1844	December	Finally got clear of docks

Year	Month	Voyage No.	
1845	January	1	Trials and voyage to London
1845	June	2	Sailed for Liverpool
1845	July	3	Maiden voyage to New York (first screw-propelled crossing of Atlantic)
1845	August	3	Maiden voyage New York–Liverpool

Year	Date	Voyage No.	From	To	Time	Crew	Pass.	Captain
1845	26. 7.45	3	Liv.	N.Y.	14 d. 21 h.	130	45	Hosken
1845	30. 8.45	3	N.Y.	Liv.	15 d. 12 h.	130	53	,,
1845	27. 9.45	4	Liv.	N.Y.	18 d.	130	102	,,
1845	28.10.45	4	N.Y.	Liv.	20 d.	130	?	,,
1845	Winter		Laid up and overhauled with modifications—GB(7)					
1846	9. 5.46	5	Liv.	N.Y.	20 d.	130	28	,,
1846	8. 6.46	5	N.Y.	Liv.	13 d. 12 h.	130	42	,,
1846	7. 7.46	6	Liv.	N.Y.	13 d. 12 h.	130	110	,,
1846	1. 8.46	6	N.Y.	Liv.	13 d. 6 h.	?	?	,,
1846	22. 9.46	7	Liv.	N.Y.	Stranded Dundrum	130	180	,,

1847	27. 8.47		*Great Britain* refloated, arrived Birkenhead 3 days later
1850	December		Bought by Gibbs Bright

1851 and 1852—Rebuilt as GB(8) with 2 funnels and 4 masts and 3-bladed screw

Year	Date	Voyage No.	From	To	Time	Crew	Pass.	Captain
1852	1. 5.52	8	Liv.	N.Y.	13 d. 7 h.		160	Matthews
1852	1. 6.52	8	N.Y.	Liv.				,,
1852	21. 8.52	9	Liv.	Mel. and Syd.	81 d.	142	630	,,
1853	4. 1.53	9	Mel.	Liv.			161	,,

Rebuilt as GB(9) with 2 funnels and 3 masts

Year	Date	Voyage No.	From	To	Time	Crew	Pass.	Captain
1853	11. 8.53	10	Liv.	Mel.	65 d.	141	319	Matthews
	arr. 16.10.53							
1853	4.12.53	10	Mel.	Liv.	72 d.	141	199	,,
	arr. 14. 2.54							

(Sailed April but stern tube failed on 31.4.54)   Gray

Year	Date	Voyage No.	From	To	Time	Crew	Pass.	Captain
1854	13. 6.54	11	Liv.	Mel.	66 d.			,,
	arr. 18. 8.54							
1854	22.11.54	11	Mel.	Liv.	63 d.			,,
	arr. 24. 1.55							
1855	7. 3.55	12	Crimean trooping					,,
	14. 6.56 (see detail sheet)		Completed trooping at Liverpool					

CRIMEA TROOPING

Year	Date	Voyage No. (all coded voyage 12)	From	To	Time	Captain
						Gray
1855	7. 3.55	12a.	Liverpool	Queenstown		
	13. 3.55		Queenstown	Malta	6 d.	
	24. 3.55		Malta	Portsmouth	11 d.*	
	14. 4.55	12b.	Portsmouth	Malta	10 d.	
	13. 5.55		Arrived Marseilles from Malta			
	24. 6.55		Arrived Constantinople			
	16. 8.55		Arrived Liverpool			
	4. 9.55	12c.	Liverpool	Gibraltar	6 d.	
	11. 9.55		Gibraltar	Malta	4 d.	
	25.10.55		Malta	Portsmouth	13 d.	
	17.11.55	12d.	Portsmouth	Gibraltar	6 d.	
	17.11.55		,,	Smyrna	16 d.	
	6.12.55		Smyrna	Constantinople		
	16.12.55		Arrived Malta from Scutari			
	18.12.55		Malta	Portsmouth		
1856	2. 1.56	12c.	Portsmouth	Liverpool	1 d.	Gray
	10. 2.56		Liverpool	Queenstown	1 d.	
	15. 2.56		Queenstown	Gibraltar	5 d.	
	,,		,,	Malta	9 d.	
	15. 3.56		Arrived Genoa			
	24. 3.56		Arrived Malta			
	28. 3.56		Arrived Genoa			
	8. 4.56		Arrived Malta			
	13. 4.56		Malta	Constantinople	8 d.	
	28. 4.56		Arrived Spezia			
	10. 5.56		Arrived Malta			
	12. 5.56		Malta	Constantinople		
	28. 5.56		Arrived Malta			
	29. 5.56		Malta	Liverpool	16 d.	

* 30th March—Dep. Gibraltar with H.M.S. *Vengeance* in tow.

Rebuilt as GB(10) with 1 funnel, 3 new masts, lifting screw and superstructures

Year	Date	Voyage No.	From	To	Time	Crew	Pass.	Captain
1857	16. 2.57	13	Liv.	Mel.	62 d.	136		Gray
arr.	19. 4.67							
1857	20. 5.57	13	Mel.	Liv.	93 d.			,,
arr.	22. 8.57							
1857	24. 9.57	14	Cork	Bombay (Trooping Indian Mutiny)				,,
arr.	17.12.57							
1858	20. 1.58	14	Bombay	Liv.				,,
arr.	10. 4.58							
1858	28. 7.58	15	Liv.	N.Y.	14 d.			,,
arr.	11. 8.58							
1858	25. 8.58	15	N.Y.	Liv.	13 d.			,,
arr.	7. 9.58							
1858	21.11.58	16	Liv.	Mel.	86 d.			,:
arr.	24. 1.59							
1859	3. 3.59	16	Mel.	Liv.	63 d.			,,
arr.	8. 5.59							
1859	1. 7.59	17	Liv.	N.Y.	14 d.			,,
arr.	15. 7.59							
1859	?. 7.59	17	N.Y.	Liv.				,,
arr.	10. 8.59							
1859	11.12.59	18	Liv.	Mel.	55 d. 16 h.	120		,,
arr.	4. 2.60							
1860	8. 3.60	18	Mel.	Liv.	61 d.		504	,,
arr.	7. 5.60							
1860	20. 7.60	19	Liv.	Mel.	62 d.	130	404	,,
arr.	22. 9.60							
1860	24.10.60	19	Mel.	Liv.	69 d.			,,
arr.	1. 1.61							
1861	17. 2.61	20	Liv.	Mel.	75 d.	129		,,
arr.	3. 5.61							
1861	?. ?.61	20	Mel.	Liv.				,,
arr.	4. 8.61							
1861	20.10.61	21	Liv.	Mel.	64 d.	140	551	,,
arr.	23.12.61							
1862	13. 2.62	21	Mel.	Liv.	54 d.			,,
arr.	8. 4.62							
1862	15. 6.62	22	Liv.	Mel.	60 d.	140	501	,,
arr.	14. 8.62							
1862	15. 9.62	22	Mel.	Liv.	66 d.			,,
arr.	20.11.62							
1863	25. 1.63	23	Liv.	Mel.		134	526½	,,
arr.	4. 4.63							
1863	. .63	23	Mel.	Liv.				,,
arr.	3. 7.63							
1863	15.10.63	24	Liv.	Mel.	63 d.	138	589	,,
arr.	17.12.63							
1864	28. 1.64	24	Mel.	Liv.	68 d.	134	536½	,,
arr.	6. 4.64							
1864	26. 5.64	25	Liv.	Mel.	60 d.	137	451	,,
arr.	25. 7.64							

* The ½s in the Passenger Lists refer to children.

Year	Date	Voyage No.	From	To	Time	Crew	Pass.	Captain
1864	27. 8.64	25	Mel.	Liv.	54 d.			Gray
	arr. 28.10.64							
1864	17.12.64	26	Liv.	Mel.	62 d.	137	478	,,
	arr. 17. 2.65							
1865	15. 3.65	26	Mel.	Liv.	66 d.			,,
	arr. 20. 5.65							
1865	25. 7.65	27	Liv.	Mel.	56 d.	137	504	,,
	arr. 21. 9.65							
1865	21.10.65	27	Mel.	Liv.	62 d.			,,
	arr. 22.12.65							
1866	18. 2.66	28	Liv.	Mel.	58 d.	136	409½	,,
	arr. 17. 4.66							
1866	15. 5.66	28	Mel.	Liv.	62 d.			,,
	arr. 20. 7.66							
1866	27.10.66	29	Liv.	Mel.	59 d.	120	329½	,,
	arr. 25.12.66							
1867	24. 1.67	29	Mel.	Liv.	57 d.			,,
	arr. 29. 3.67							
1867	19. 5.67	30	Liv.	Mel.	59 d.	139	528	,,
	arr. 17. 7.67							
1867	22. 8.67	30	Mel.	Liv.	58 d.			,,
	arr. 19.10.67							
1867	15.12.67	31	Liv.	Mel.	57 d.			,,
	arr. 11. 2.68							
1868	10. 3.68	31	Mel.	Liv.	74 d.			,,
	arr. 23. 5.68							
1868	9. 7.68	32	Liv.	Mel.	58 d.			,,
	arr. 3. 9.68							
1868	7.10.68	32	Mel.	Liv.	58 d.			,,
	arr. 7.12.68							
1869	3. 2.69	33	Liv.	Mel.	59 d.		561	,,
	arr. 8. 4.69							
1869	5. 5.69	33	Mel.	Liv.	65 d.			,,
	arr. 9. 7.69							
1869	12. 8.69	34	Liv.	Mel.	62 d.			,,
	arr. 13.10.69							
1869	22.11.69	34	Mel.	Liv.	75 d.		177	,,
	arr. 4. 2.70							
1870	19. 3.70	35	Liv.	Mel.	57 d.			,,
	arr. 15. 5.70							
1870	15. 6.70	35	Mel.	Liv.	69 d.		422	,,
	arr. 23. 8.70							
1870	6.10.70	36	Liv.	Mel.	59 d.			,,
	arr. 4.12.70							
1871	12. 1.71	36	Mel.	Liv.	69 d.		238	,,
	arr. 22. 3.71							
1871	24. 5.71	37	Liv.	Mel.	64 d.	140	346½	,,
	arr. 28. 7.71							
1871	30. 8.71	37	Mel.	Liv.	61 d.		212	,,
	arr. 8.11.71							

Year	Date	Voyage No.	From	To	Time	Crew	Pass.	Captain
1871	17.12.71	38	Liv.	Mel.	66 d.	132	388½	Gray
	arr. 21. 2.72							
1872	20. 3.72	38	Mel.	Liv.	69 d.		389	,,
	arr. 28. 5.72							
1872	27. 7.72	39	Liv.	Mel.	54 d.	132	337	,,
	arr. 21. 9.72							
1872	23.10.72	39	Mel.	Liv.	63 d.		133	Gray/
	arr. 25.12.72							Robertson
1873	30. 3.73	40	Liv.	Mel.	57 d.	134	340½	Chapman
	arr. 26. 5.73							
1873	2. 7.73	40	Mel.	Liv.	64 d.		339	,,
	arr. 3. 9.73							
1873	27.10.73	41	Liv.	Mel.	56 d.	133	591½	,,
	arr. 21.12.73		(and on to Brisbane)					
1874	7. 2.74	41	Mel.	Liv.	69 d.		439	,,
	arr. 17. 4.74							
1874	4. 6.74	42	Liv.	Mel.	56 d.	137	369½	,,
	arr. 30. 7.74							
1874	4. 9.74	42	Mel.	Liv.	75 d.		205	,,
	arr. 18.11.74							
1875	11. 1.75	43	Liv.	Mel.	67 d.	134	343½	Robertson
	arr. 19. 3.75							
1875	7. 5.75	43	Mel.	Liv.	64 d.		313	,,
	arr. 10. 7.75							
1875	26. 8.75	44	London	Mel.	54 d.	137	355	,,
	arr. 19.10.75							
1875	27.11.75	44	Mel.	Liv.	65 d.		154	,,
	arr. 30. 1.76							

1876   LAID UP AT BIRKENHEAD.

1882   *Bought by Antony Gibbs and converted to sail—GB(11)*

Year	Date	Voyage No.	From	To	Time	Crew	Pass.	Captain
1882	2.11.82	45	Liv.	San Fr.	183 d.			Stap
	arr. 2. 6.83							
1883	30. 8.83	45	San Fr.	Liv.	155 d.			,,
	arr. 1. 2.84							
1884	11. 5.84	46	Liv.	San Fr.	160 d.			,,
	arr. 19.10.84							
1885	12. 2.85	46	San Fr.	Liv.	145 d.			,,
	arr. 8. 7.85							
1886	6. 2.86	47	Penarth	San Fr.				,,
	24. 5.86		Arrived Falkland Islands and hulked					
1933			Retired from hulking					
1937	13. 4.37		Scuttled Sparrow Cove					
1968	November/ December		Surveyed Sparrow Cove					
1970	7. 4.70		Refloated					
1970	13. 4.70		Lifted out of water					
1970	21. 6.70		Arrived Penarth Roads					
1970	5. 7.70		Entered Bristol Docks					
1970	19. 7.70	47	Back in Great Western Dock, Bristol!					

KNOWN ACCIDENT LOG

Date	Name of other vessel	Description
23. 1.45	*Norah Creina*	*Great Britain*'s anchor fouled wreckage of this schooner which had been run down and sunk some weeks before
24. 1.45		Off Lundy Island at 3.20 p.m. was struck by a very heavy sea and slightly damaged
26. 1.45	A collier brig	Collided with *Great Britain* in Thames. Collier lost her bowsprit. No damage to *Great Britain*
10. 9.45		Lost maintopmast on return leg of first screw crossing of the Atlantic
3.10.45		Foremast and spanker lost in white squall
13.10.45		On Nantucket shoals. Lost 2 arms of one blade of propeller
30. 9.45		Lost another arm of the propeller
1.10.45		Lost rest of propeller
13. 5.46		Broke swinging link on after air pump
20. 7.46		Scraped Cape Broil reef, Newfoundland
22. 8.46		Wrecked in Dundrum Bay
31. 4.54		Sterntube liner seized on sailing from Liverpool and ship put back
2. 1.56	*Habana*	Collision sailing from Portsmouth. *Great Britain* lost bowsprit and figurehead. *Habana* had port quarter damaged
6.12.59	*Celestia*	Collided with *Celestia* off Madeira.
21. 9.60	*Oscar*	Collided between Cape Otway and Port Phillip Heads. (See complete inquiry report.)* *Minutes of Evidence taken before the Board of Enquiry 27 September 1860. Slight damage to *Great Britain*'s cutwater.
31.12.60		*Great Britain* narrowly missed stranding on Isle of Man, and was then stranded on a sandbank in Liverpool Bay. No damage.
14. 1.63		Fire when in Bramley dock, Liverpool. 'Trivial damage'
4. 3.68		Arrived at Melbourne with burst steampipe
3. 9.70	*Monckton* (Schooner)	Got athwart hawse of *Great Britain* at anchor in Mersey. *Monckton* beached at New Ferry
26.11.72		Captain Gray disappeared overboard
20.11.74	*Mysore*	*Great Britain* from Melbourne and *Mysore* for Calcutta in collision in the Sloyne. *Great Britain* lost anchor and received damage to hull. *Mysore* drifted ashore but was refloated
25. 3.86		Small fire in ship's stores.
10. 5.86		Lost fore and main topgallant masts off Cape Horn
24. 5.86		Grounded Port William, Stanley. No damage
13. 4.1937		Scuttled Sparrow Cove

Appendix 8

MACHINERY USED IN THE CONSTRUCTION OF THE *GREAT BRITAIN* AND HER CONTEMPORARIES

At the time the *Great Britain* was built, all significant development in iron shipbuilding was taking place in Britain and, of course, the bulk of production as well. Monsieur Dupuy de Lôme, *Sous-Ingénieur de la Marine* of the French Navy, was sent over to carry out a survey of methods of construction and machinery used in up-to-date British shipbuilding practice. In December 1842 he reported at length to his superiors and appended to his report an 'atlas' containing drawings showing constructional methods of the ships he saw—including the *Great Britain*—and details of the machinery used in the shipyards.* It is of interest that M. de Lôme later became Chief Constructor of the French Navy and was responsible for the design of the first French ironclad with an iron hull— *Napoleon*, which followed some time after the British ship *Warrior*.

De Lôme's illustrations of shipyard machinery are of great interest, as it is quite likely they are of the actual machinery used in the construction of the *Great Britain*. The Great Western Shipyard was built from scratch to construct the ship and Napier supplied new machinery for that purpose—for example, the plate rolls were delivered to the yard in July 1839. All this machinery was sold in November 1850 on the liquidation of the Great Western Steamship Company.

* They are reproduced here by courtesy of D. I. Moor of Vickers, St Albans from an original copy (now in the National Maritime Museum).

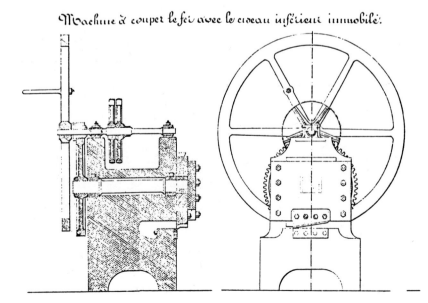

Machine à couper le fer avec le ciseau inférieur immobile.

1 De Lôme shows various types of shears and piercing machines. First there is a fixed, hand- or belt-driven set of shears where the moving cutter is uppermost. This machine is virtually identical to those used ever since in shipyards, the main difference being that it can be hand-powered, having a heavy flywheel geared to an eccentric which moves the jaw.

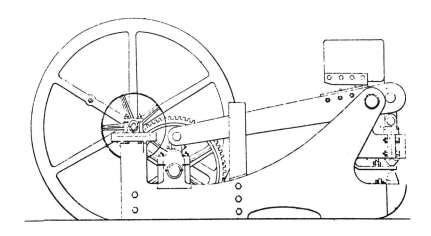

Machine à percer et à couper, locomobile.

2 The second type of machine, however, is quite remarkable in that, while again hand- or belt-powered, it is a combined piercing and shearing machine with a movable lower jaw. For cutting plate or strip this would be a very difficult machine to use, as the work would move with the lower jaw, and it must be assumed that this use was incidental to the main one, namely piercing for rivets. Here a conventional punch is employed: one similar to those in use throughout the age of riveted shipbuilding. The machine, though heavy, can be hand-powered. There is a mobile version which, as can be seen, is identical except that it is smaller and has a pair of wheels under the working end and a transverse wheel under the other end. (**3**)

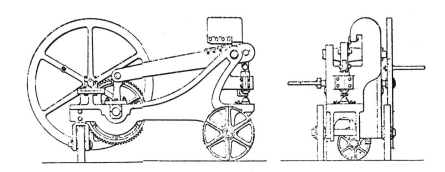

Machine à rouler les tôles

4. A set of hand rolls might well be the type installed in the yard in July 1839. There is no difference in principle between these rolls and those used even today, except that latter-day rolls are much larger and are, of course, mechanically driven, and the adjustments of the rolls are also powered. In this case the rolls were adjusted by hand toggle screws. We still have examples of exactly this type of machine taken from old shipyards.

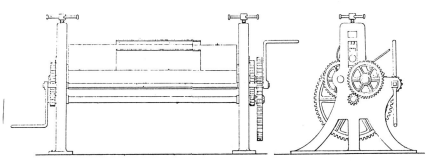

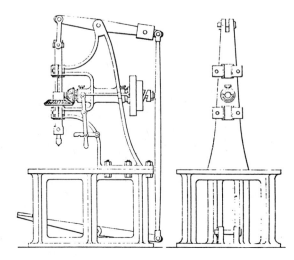

Machine à fraiser et à percer à la mèche.

5. A radial drill which was belt-driven. This type of machine remained unchanged right up to the introduction of electrical integrally powered drills in this century.

All these machines were quite sizable. For example, the fixed combined shears and punch was approximately 12 ft in length, and the mobile version 8 ft, while the rolls could admit plates up to about 5 ft 6 in. in width although the thickness that they could handle would be quite limited, probably no more than $\frac{3}{8}$ in., and that on narrow widths.

Presse pour saisir les tôles des pièces de quille pendant qu'on en plie les rebords.

6. The *Great Britain* had a flat plate-keel, but towards the ends of the ship this became a trough plate to which the shell and then the stem and sternpost respectively were attached. This illustration shows a press for holding plates while they are bent into this form of trough, and it is likely that it was the actual machine used for bending the *Great Britain*'s trough plates.

Foret à rochet pour percer et fraiser sur place.

(Échelle d' ¹⁄₁₀.)

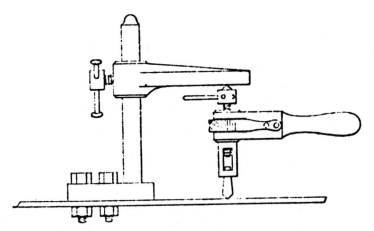

Marteau riveur.

(Échelle de ¹⁄₁₀.)

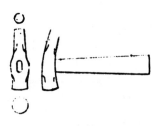

Port de Toulon 1854.

7. A hand ratchet-drill which would have been used for reaming out rivet-holes and for drilling holes in place. The principle is obvious; the type, and indeed the detail, is identical to tools used today.

8. A hand riveting hammer.

Index